CGP is the solution to Maths revision!

There's no doubting it, SQA Higher Maths can be hard as nails. But don't worry — this superb CGP Revision Guide hammers home everything you need to know.

Each topic is explained clearly and simply with exam-style questions to test your skills. There are even some jokes along the way to keep you sane. What more could you want?

How to access your free Online Edition

You can read this entire book on your PC, Mac or tablet, with handy links to all the online audio files. Just go to **cgpbooks.co.uk/extras** and enter this code:

0371 1352 1402 8046

By the way, this code only works for one person. If somebody else has used this book before you, they might have already claimed the Online Edition.

CGP — still the best! ☺

Our sole aim here at CGP is to produce the highest quality books — carefully written, immaculately presented and dangerously close to being funny.

Then we work our socks off to get them out to you — at the cheapest possible prices.

Published by CGP

Editors:
Michael Bushell, Sarah George, Shaun Harrogate, Tom Miles, Caley Simpson, Michael Weynberg

ISBN: 978 1 78294 960 2

With thanks to Barbara Nicol, Garry Simpson and Ruth Wilbourne for the proofreading.
With thanks to Jan Greenway for the copyright research.

Clipart from Corel®
Printed by Elanders Ltd, Newcastle upon Tyne.

Based on the classic CGP style created by Richard Parsons.

Contents

Section One — Algebraic Skills

Section Two — Trigonometric Skills

Section Three — Geometry Skills

Section Four — Calculus Skills

Section Five — Reasoning Skills

Quadratic Equations

You've probably been solving quadratic equations since before you could walk, so lots of this should be familiar.

Solve quadratic equations by Factorising

Factorising is probably the quickest way to solve a quadratic equation — if it looks fairly **simple**, try to factorise it.

EXAMPLE: Solve $x^2 - 8 = 2x$ by factorising.

This is just a reminder — you should have done this at National 5.

Put into $ax^2 + bx + c$ form: $x^2 - 8 = 2x \Rightarrow x^2 - 2x - 8 = 0$

Solve the equation by **factorising**: $(x + 2)(x - 4) = 0 \Rightarrow x + 2 = 0$ or $x - 4 = 0 \Rightarrow \mathbf{x = -2}$ or $\mathbf{x = 4}$

Completing the Square puts any old quadratic in a Special Form

Completing the square means writing a quadratic expression $\mathbf{ax^2 + bx + c}$ in the form $\mathbf{a(x + \text{something})^2 + d}$.

You start with something like this... ...sort the x-coefficients... ...and end up with something like this.

$2x^2 + 8x - 5$ → $2(x + 2)^2 + ?$ → $2(x + 2)^2 - 13$

The method below can be used to complete the square of a quadratic expression:

Completing the Square of $ax^2 + bx + c$

① Take a **factor of a** out of the x^2 and x terms: $a\left(x^2 + \frac{b}{a}x\right) + c$.

② Rewrite the bit in the bracket as **one bracket squared.** The number in the brackets is always $\frac{b}{2a}$, so the bracket is $a\left(x + \frac{b}{2a}\right)^2$.

③ **Add d** to the bracket to complete the square and **find d** by setting the new and original expressions **equal** to each other:

$$a\left(x + \frac{b}{2a}\right)^2 + d = ax^2 + bx + c$$

Expanding the LHS gives: $\cancel{ax^2} + \cancel{bx} + \frac{b^2}{4a} + d = \cancel{ax^2} + \cancel{bx} + c$. Then cancel and rearrange to get d.

④ **Solving** this equation always gives $d = \left(c - \frac{b^2}{4a}\right)$, so:

$$a\left(x + \frac{b}{2a}\right)^2 + \left(c - \frac{b^2}{4a}\right) = ax^2 + bx + c$$

Complete the square to find Exact Solutions

If you're asked to find an **exact solution**, complete the square — usually this means **surds** will be involved.

EXAMPLE: a) Write $2x^2 - 8x + 3$ in the form $p(x + q)^2 + r$.

1) Take a **factor of 2** out of the x^2 and x terms: $2(x^2 - 4x) + 3$
2) Rewrite the bracket as **one bracket squared:** $b = -8$, so $\frac{b}{2a} = \frac{-8}{2 \times 2} = -2$, so the bracket is $2(x - 2)^2$
3) **Add d** to the bracket. $2(x - 2)^2 + d$
4) Find d by setting the new and original equations **equal** to each other:
$2(x - 2)^2 + d = 2x^2 - 8x + 3$
$2x^2 - 8x + 8 + d = 2x^2 - 8x + 3$
$8 + d = 3 \Rightarrow d = -5$,
so the completed square is $\mathbf{2(x - 2)^2 - 5}$

Using $d = c - \frac{b^2}{4a}$ also gives $d = 3 - \frac{(-8)^2}{4 \times 2} = 3 - 8 = -5$.

b) Hence find exact solutions to $2x^2 - 8x + 3 = 0$.

1) Set your answer from part a) **equal to 0** and **solve** to find x: $2(x - 2)^2 - 5 = 0 \Rightarrow (x - 2)^2 = \frac{5}{2}$
2) There's a **positive** and **negative** square root: $\Rightarrow x - 2 = \pm\sqrt{\frac{5}{2}} = \pm\frac{\sqrt{10}}{2}$
3) You're asked for the **exact solutions** so leave your answer in **surd form:** $\mathbf{x = 2 + \frac{\sqrt{10}}{2}}$ or $\mathbf{x = 2 - \frac{\sqrt{10}}{2}}$

Rationalise the denominator: $\sqrt{\frac{5}{2}} = \frac{\sqrt{5}}{\sqrt{2}} = \frac{\sqrt{5}\sqrt{2}}{\sqrt{2}\sqrt{2}} = \frac{\sqrt{10}}{2}$

Quadratic Equations

Completing the square can be **Helpful** when sketching **Graphs**

Once you've completed the square, you can very quickly say **loads** about a quadratic function. And it all relies on the fact that a squared number can **never** be less than zero... **ever**.

EXAMPLE: Sketch the curve of $f(x) = 3x^2 - 6x - 7$.

Complete the square of $f(x)$:

$$f(x) = 3x^2 - 6x - 7 = 3(x - 1)^2 - 10$$

Find where $y = f(x)$ **crosses the axes**:

When $x = 0$, $y = -7$, so the curve crosses the y-axis at -7.

When $y = 0$, $3(x - 1)^2 - 10 = 0$

$$\Rightarrow \quad (x - 1)^2 = \frac{10}{3}$$

$$\Rightarrow \quad x - 1 = \pm\sqrt{\frac{10}{3}}$$

$$\Rightarrow \quad x = 1 \pm \frac{\sqrt{30}}{3}$$

Rationalise the denominator.

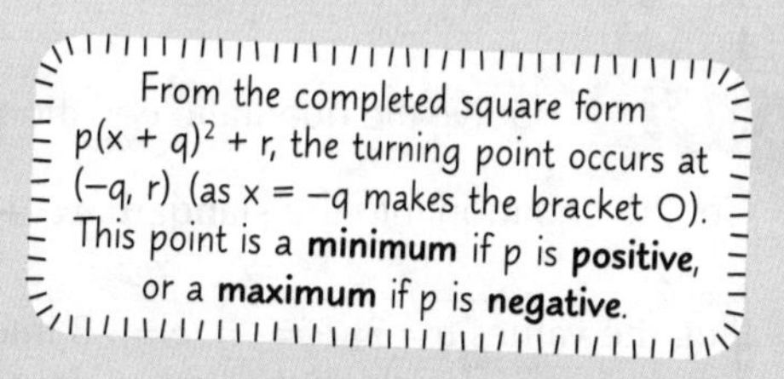

So the curve crosses the x-axis at:

$$x = 1 + \frac{\sqrt{30}}{3} \text{ and } x = 1 - \frac{\sqrt{30}}{3}$$

$(x - 1)^2 \geq 0$, so the smallest value occurs when $(x - 1) = 0$, i.e. when $x = 1$.

Find the **minimum** by substituting $x = 1$ into $f(x)$:

$f(x) = 3(x - 1)^2 - 10$, so $f(1) = 3(1 - 1)^2 - 10 = -10$

So the minimum is at **(1, –10)**.

Now you can use this information to **sketch the graph** (the coefficient of x^2 is **positive**, so it's a **u-shaped** graph).

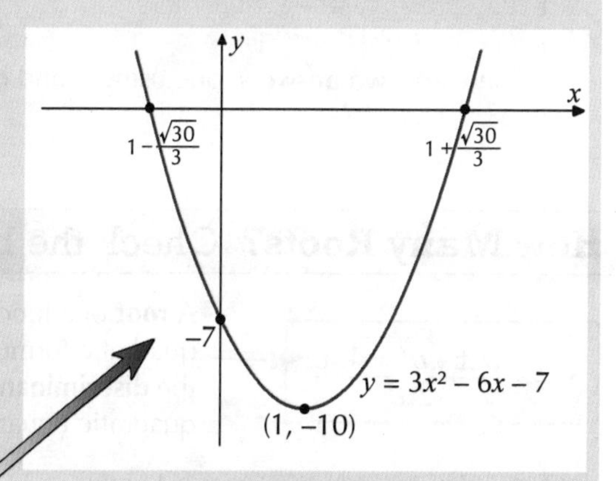

If the coefficient of x^2 is negative, the graph is n-shaped.

Warm-Up Questions

Q1 Complete the square for each of the following quadratic expressions:
a) $x^2 - 6x + 5$ b) $x^2 + 4x - 6$ c) $2x^2 - 6x - 5$ d) $3x^2 - 7x + 3$

Q2 Solve the equation $5x^2 - x - 7 = x^2 - 3x$.

Q3 Sketch each of the following curves, labelling the maximum/minimum and the points where it crosses the axes.
a) $y = x^2 + 4x - 5$ b) $y = 2x^2 - 7x + 6$ c) $y = 25 - 4x^2$ d) $y = 11x - 10 - 3x^2$

Exam Questions

Q1 a) Write $3x^2 + 2x - 2$ in the form $p(x + q)^2 + r$. [3 marks]
b) Hence, or otherwise, find the coordinates of the turning point of $3x^2 + 2x - 2$. [1 mark]

Q2 Find the exact solutions of the equation $6x^2 = 1 - 3x$, by completing the square. [4 marks]

Q3 a) $f(x) = x^2 - 14x + k$, where k is a constant. Given that one of the solutions of $f(x) = 0$ is $x = 7 + 2\sqrt{6}$, find the value of k, and hence verify that the other solution is $x = 7 - 2\sqrt{6}$. [4 marks]
b) Sketch the curve of $y = f(x)$. Label the minimum and the points of intersection with the axes. [3 marks]

Q4 a) Rewrite $x^2 - 12x + 15$ in the form $(x - a)^2 + b$, for integers a and b. [2 marks]
b) Find the minimum value of $x^2 - 12x + 15$ and state the value of x at which this minimum occurs. [2 marks]

I'm popular with squares — they always tell me how I complete them...

By writing in the form $p(x + q)^2 + r$, you can quickly tell if the graph of a quadratic function ever crosses the x-axis. If the minimum point $(-q, r)$ for a positive (u-shaped) quadratic lies above the x-axis (i.e. $r > 0$), then the function never crosses the x-axis and so has no real roots (see next page). The reverse applies to a negative (n-shaped) quadratic — if the maximum point $(-q, r)$ lies below the x-axis (i.e. $r < 0$), then the function never crosses the x-axis and has no real roots.

The Quadratic Formula

You might remember the quadratic formula from National 5 — and unlike factorising, it works every time...

I shall teach you the ways of the **Formula**

If you want to solve a quadratic equation $ax^2 + bx + c = 0$, then the answers are given by the **quadratic formula**:

$$x = \frac{-b \pm \sqrt{b^2 - 4ac}}{2a}$$

You need to learn this formula — it's not given in the exam.

EXAMPLE: Solve the quadratic equation $3x^2 - 4x = 8$, leaving your answer in surd form.

Get the equation into the **standard $ax^2 + bx + c = 0$ form**: $3x^2 - 4x - 8 = 0$

Plug the values $a = 3$, $b = -4$, $c = -8$ into the **formula** (be very careful with all the minus signs):

$$x = \frac{-(-4) \pm \sqrt{(-4)^2 - 4 \times 3 \times (-8)}}{2 \times 3}$$

$$= \frac{4 \pm \sqrt{112}}{6} = \frac{2 \pm 2\sqrt{7}}{3}$$

$112 = 16 \times 7$

There are **two answers** (one using + and one using –): $x = \frac{2 + 2\sqrt{7}}{3}$ or $x = \frac{2 - 2\sqrt{7}}{3}$

How Many Roots? Check the b² – 4ac bit...

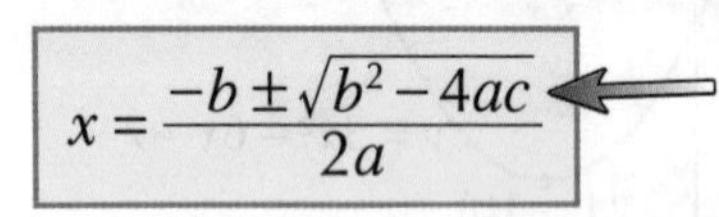

A **root** of a function f(x) is a **solution** to the equation **f(x) = 0**. In the quadratic formula, the $b^2 - 4ac$ bit (under the square root sign) is called the **discriminant** — it can be positive, zero, or negative, and it tells you if the quadratic equation has **two real roots**, **one repeated real root**, or **no real roots**.

It's good to be able to picture what the graphs will look like in these different cases:

$b^2 - 4ac > 0$
Two distinct real roots

The graph crosses the x-axis twice and these values are the roots:

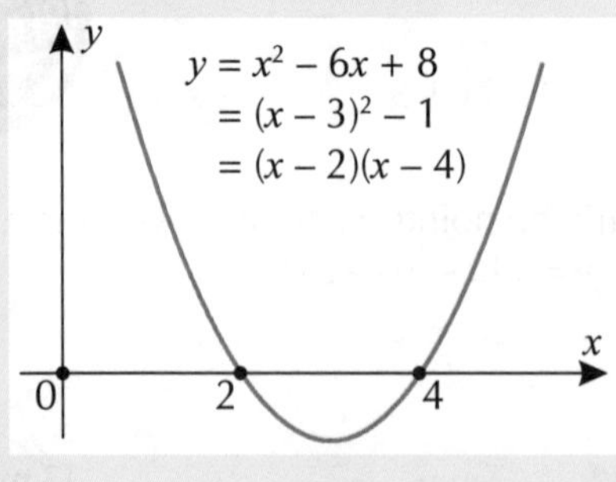

$b^2 - 4ac = 0$
One real root

The graph only touches the x-axis once — i.e. the x-axis is a tangent to the curve.

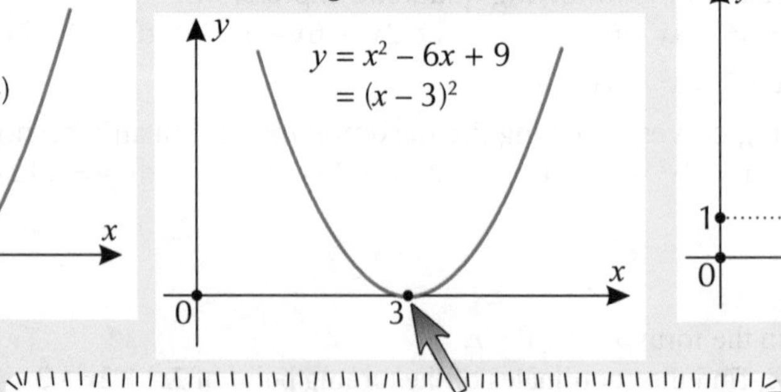

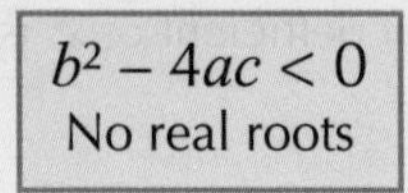

The graph doesn't touch the x-axis at all.

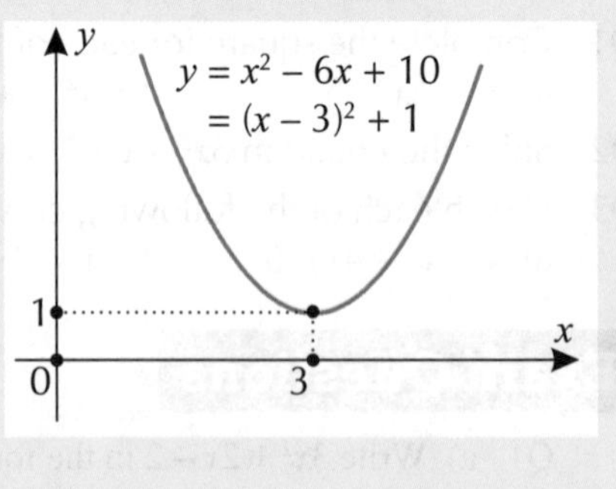

You might also see the terms 'repeated root' or 'equal roots'. A repeated root is a **stationary point** of the curve — see p.57.

Identify a, b and c to find the **Discriminant**

Make sure you get them the **right way round** — it's easy to get mixed up if the quadratic is in a **different order**.

EXAMPLE: Find the discriminant of $15 - x - 2x^2$. How many real roots does $15 - x - 2x^2 = 0$ have?

First identify a, b and c: $a = -2$, $b = -1$ and $c = 15$ (NOT $a = 15$, $b = -1$ and $c = -2$)

Work out the **discriminant**: $b^2 - 4ac = (-1)^2 - (4 \times (-2) \times 15) = 1 + 120 = \mathbf{121}$.

The discriminant is > 0: So $15 - x - 2x^2 = 0$ has **two real and distinct roots.**

The Quadratic Formula

a, b or c might be Unknown

In exam questions, you might be given a **quadratic** where one or more of a, b and c are given in terms of an **unknown**. This means that you'll end up with an **equation** or **inequality** for the discriminant **in terms of the unknown** — you might have to **solve** it to find the **value** or **range of values** of the unknown.

EXAMPLE: If $f(x) = 3x^2 + 2x + k$, find the range of values of k for which:
a) $f(x)$ has 2 distinct real roots, b) $f(x)$ has equal roots, c) $f(x)$ has no real roots.

Using $a = 3$, $b = 2$ and $c = k$, work out what the **discriminant** is:

$b^2 - 4ac = 2^2 - 4 \times 3 \times k = \mathbf{4 - 12k}$

The only difference is the (in)equality symbol.

a) **Two distinct real roots** means:

$b^2 - 4ac > 0 \Rightarrow 4 - 12k > 0$
$\Rightarrow 4 > 12k$
$\Rightarrow k < \frac{1}{3}$

b) **Equal roots** means:

$b^2 - 4ac = 0 \Rightarrow 4 - 12k = 0$
$\Rightarrow 4 = 12k$
$\Rightarrow k = \frac{1}{3}$

c) **No real roots** means:

$b^2 - 4ac < 0 \Rightarrow 4 - 12k < 0$
$\Rightarrow 4 < 12k$
$\Rightarrow k > \frac{1}{3}$

You might have to Solve a Quadratic Inequality to find k

When you put your values of a, b and c into the formula for the **discriminant**, you might end up with a **quadratic inequality** in terms of k. You'll have to solve this to find the **range** of values of k — there's more on this on p.6.

The equation $kx^2 + (k + 3)x + 4 = 0$ has two real and distinct solutions.
Show that $k^2 - 10k + 9 > 0$, and find the set of values of k which satisfy this inequality.

Using $a = k$, $b = (k + 3)$ and $c = 4$, work out what the **discriminant** is:

$$b^2 - 4ac = (k + 3)^2 - (4 \times k \times 4) = k^2 + 6k + 9 - 16k = k^2 - 10k + 9$$

The equation has **two real and distinct** solutions, so the discriminant must be > 0:

$k^2 - 10k + 9 > 0$

Now, to find the set of values for k, it's easiest to **factorise** the quadratic:

$k^2 - 10k + 9 = (k - 1)(k - 9)$

This expression is 0 when $k = 1$ and $k = 9$.
From the graph, you can see that this quadratic is > 0 when:

$k < 1$ or when $k > 9$

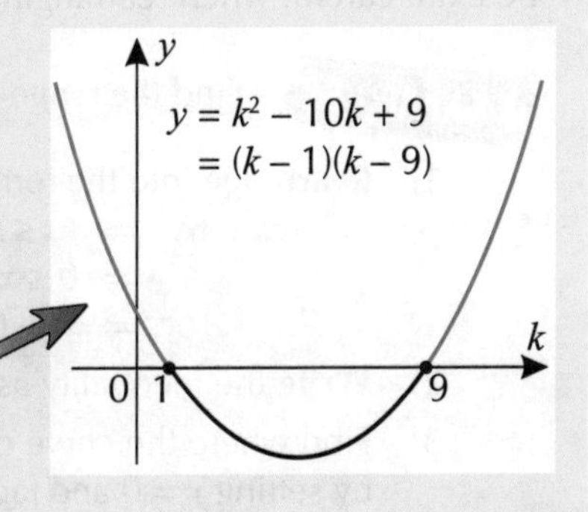

Warm-Up Questions

PRACTICE QUESTIONS

Q1 For each of the following:
(i) Find the discriminant and state the number of real roots of the quadratic.
(ii) Find the exact values of its real roots, if it has any.
a) $4x^2 + 28x + 49 = 0$ b) $3x^2 + 3x + 1 = 0$ c) $9x^2 - 6\sqrt{2}x + 2 = 0$

Q2 Given that p is a real number, show that the roots of the equation $px^2 + 3x + 3 = p$ are always real numbers.

Exam Questions

Q1 The equation $x^2 + 2kx + 4k = 0$, where k is a non-zero integer, has equal roots. Find the value of k. [3 marks]

Q2 The equation $(p + 1)x^2 + (p + 1)x + 1 = 0$ has two real and distinct solutions for x (p is a constant).
a) Show that $p^2 - 2p - 3 > 0$. [3 marks]
b) Hence find the range of possible values for p. [3 marks]

All the best mathematicians are raised on quadratic formula...

Although it might be tempting to hide under your exam desk and hope a discriminant question doesn't find you, there's no escaping these questions — so get practising until you can recite the quadratic formula in your sleep.

Quadratic Inequalities

Solving quadratic inequalities is very similar to solving quadratic equations. You just have to be really careful that you keep the inequality sign pointing the right way.

There are Rules for Simple Quadratic Inequalities

1) **Simple** quadratic inequalities, like $x^2 > a$ and $x^2 < a$, can be solved easily — there are two **rules** to follow:

If $x^2 > a^2$, then $x > a$ or $x < -a$	If $x^2 < a^2$, then $-a < x < a$

The same rules apply for ≥ and ≤ as well.

2) For **>** or **≥**, the solution is in **two parts**, and for **<** or **≤**, the solution is just **one bit**.
3) If a quadratic inequality contains no bx **term**, then you can **rearrange** it and use the rules above. Be careful — you can **add or subtract** terms from both sides, and **multiply or divide** by a **positive** number. But **multiplying** or **dividing** by a **negative** number **changes the direction** of the inequality sign.

EXAMPLE: Find the range of values of x that satisfy: a) $x^2 \geq 25$ b) $3x^2 + 10 < 37$

a) If $x^2 = 25$, then $x = \pm5$. $x^2 \geq 25$ so:

$x \geq 5$ **or** $x \leq -5$

If you're not sure about your answer, you can check it with a sketch — see below.

b) **Rearrange** the inequality to get it in the form $x^2 < a$:

$3x^2 + 10 < 37 \Rightarrow 3x^2 < 27 \Rightarrow x^2 < 9$

If $x^2 = 9$, then $x = \pm3$. $x^2 < 9$ so:

$-3 < x < 3$

Sketch a Graph to solve Harder Quadratic inequalities

With quadratic inequalities that have all three terms, you're best off sketching the **graph** and taking it from there. Be extra careful when rearranging these — never divide by x, because it could be negative (or worse, zero).

EXAMPLE: Find the range of values of x that satisfies $36x \leq 6x^2$.

1) **Rearrange** into the form $f(x) \geq 0$:

$36x \leq 6x^2 \Rightarrow 6x \leq x^2$ ← Start by dividing by 6...

$\Rightarrow 0 \leq x^2 - 6x$ ← ...take 6x from both sides...

$\Rightarrow x^2 - 6x \geq 0$ ← ...and rearrange.

2) **Write** the inequality as an **equation**: $y = x^2 - 6x$.
3) Find where the curve **crosses** the x**-axis** by setting $y = 0$ and factorising:

   $x^2 - 6x = 0 \Rightarrow x(x - 6) = 0$

   So $x = 0$ and $x = 6$.
4) Use a **sketch** to find where $x^2 - 6x \geq 0$.
5) The graph is **non-negative** to the **left** of $x = 0$ and to the **right** of $x = 6$ (inclusive). So the solution is $x \leq 0$ **or** $x \geq 6$.

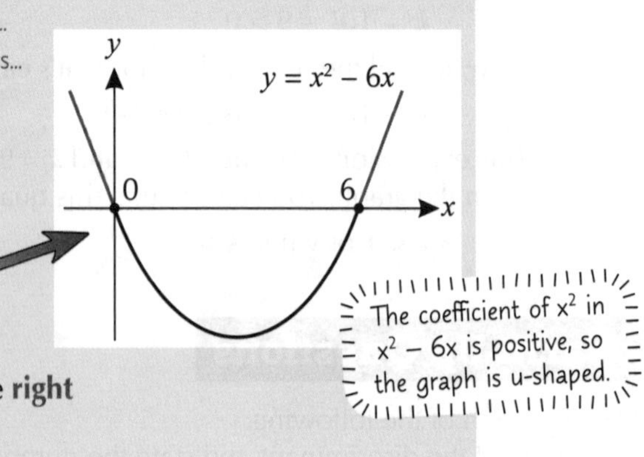

The coefficient of x^2 in $x^2 - 6x$ is positive, so the graph is u-shaped.

Solutions to Inequalities can be given in Set Notation

A **set** is just a collection of numbers, e.g. the range of solutions to a quadratic inequality. You might see **set notation** in your exam — so make sure you understand it. Here are some things you'll need to know...

You don't need to use set notation in your answers.

Set Notation

- Set notation uses **curly brackets** — e.g. $\{x: x < a\}$ means 'the set of values of x such that x is less than a'.
- The numbers in a set are known as its **elements** (or **members**). The symbol $\in$ means that a number is an element of a set and the symbol $\notin$ means that it's not — e.g. $5 \in \{x: x \leq 5\}$ but $5 \notin \{x: x < 5\}$.
- The symbol $\varnothing$ (or empty brackets {}) indicates an **empty set** — e.g. the real roots of a quadratic with negative discriminant = $\varnothing$.
- A **subset** is just a set contained within a larger set — e.g. $\{x: x > 3\}$ is a subset of $\{x: x \geq 0\}$.

There are some examples of common sets on p.21.

Quadratic Inequalities

Quadratic Inequalities can be hidden in Geometric Problems

Sometimes a problem will contain a quadratic inequality in **disguise** — don't let it fool you, just find the inequality and solve like you did on the previous page.

EXAMPLE: A triangle has height $2x$ cm and base length $(x - 4)$ cm. If the area of the triangle is less than 32 cm², find the range of possible values of x.

Find an expression for the **area** of the triangle:

$\frac{1}{2} \times (x - 4) \times 2x = x^2 - 4x$

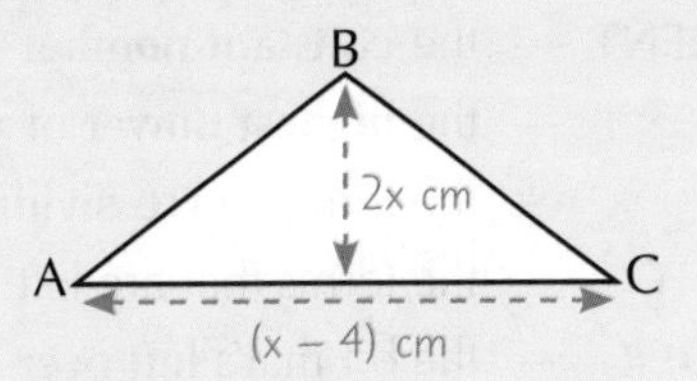

You know that the area is **less than** 32: $x^2 - 4x < 32$

Rearrange to get it in the standard form: $x^2 - 4x - 32 < 0$

Now solve the **quadratic inequality** — you'll need to sketch the graph of $y = x^2 - 4x - 32$.

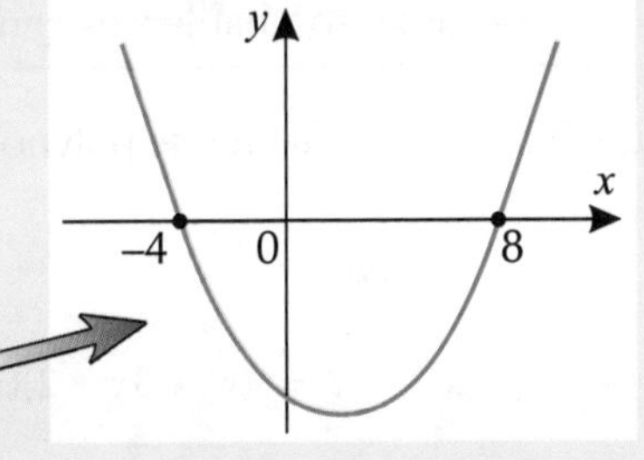

First **factorise** the quadratic expression:

$x^2 - 4x - 32 = (x + 4)(x - 8)$

So the curve **crosses** the **x-axis** at:

$x = -4$ and $x = 8$

You're looking for where the curve is **below** the x-axis — as the curve is u-shaped, x must lie in the range:

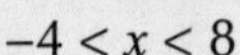

$-4 < x < 8$

But remember, $2x$ and $x - 4$ both measure a **length** which must be **positive**, so not all values in this range are **possible**. x must be bigger than 4 (otherwise $x - 4$ would be ≤ 0), so the range of possible values of x is:

4 cm < x < 8 cm

Always think about your solutions in the context of the question — some answers might be impossible.

Warm-Up Questions

Q1 Find the ranges of x that satisfy these inequalities:
a) $x^2 < 100$ b) $4x^2 - 8 > 0$ c) $7 - x^2 \leq -18$

Q2 Find the ranges of x that satisfy the following inequalities:
a) $3x^2 - 5x - 2 \leq 0$ b) $6 - x - 2x^2 < 0$ c) $3x^2 + 7x + 4 \geq 2(x^2 + x - 1)$

Q3 Find the ranges of x that satisfy these jokers.
a) $x^2 + 3x - 1 \geq x + 2$ b) $2x^2 > x + 1$ c) $3x^2 - 12 < x^2 - 2x$

Exam Questions

Q1 Find the set of values for x that satisfy the inequalities below.
a) $2x^2 + 2 \leq x^2 + 18$ [1 mark]
b) $20 - x - x^2 > 0$ [2 marks]
c) both $2x^2 + 2 \leq x^2 + 18$ and $20 - x - x^2 > 0$ [1 mark]

Q2 A rectangular shed with a width of $(x - 3)$ m and a length of x m is being built. It needs to have a total floor area of at least 10 m². What is the possible range of values for x? [3 marks]

Q3 A parallelogram has base $(4x + 1)$ m and height $2x$ m. If the area of the parallelogram is less than 1 m², find the range of possible values of x. [4 marks]

Inequalities > vectors > biology...

For inequality questions involving quadratic equations, it really helps to sketch a graph — find where the curve intersects the x-axis, then check the inequality sign to see which range of values you want. Be careful when multiplying and dividing by negative numbers — if you forget to flip the sign, you'll get the wrong answer.

Factorising Polynomials

Now you're an expert at factorising quadratics, I'm going to spoil you with three methods for factorising higher order polynomials like cubics and quartics. But before you get stuck in, you need to get to know the Factor Theorem.

There are some **Terms** you need to **Know**

1) POLYNOMIAL — an **algebraic expression** made up of a **sum** of **constant terms** and **variables** raised to **positive integer powers** (e.g. $2x^3 - 4x + 1$ is a polynomial, but $x^2 + \frac{1}{x} + 2$ isn't).
2) COEFFICIENT — the **constant number** in an algebraic term, e.g. **5** is the coefficient in the term $5x^3$.
3) DEGREE — the **highest power** of x in the polynomial (e.g. the degree of $4x^5 + 6x^2 - 3x - 1$ is **5**).
4) DIVISOR — the thing you're **dividing by** (e.g. if you divide $x^2 + 4x - 3$ by $x + 2$, the divisor is $x + 2$).
5) QUOTIENT — the terms that are left when you **divide** by the divisor (not including the remainder).
6) REMAINDER — the bit that's **left over** after dividing.
7) FACTOR — a divisor that leaves **zero remainder** — it goes into the polynomial **exactly**.

Don't worry, you'll learn how to **factorise** polynomials shortly — for now, just learn what each **term** means.

$x^3 - 7x$ has **degree** 3 — $x - 3$ is the **divisor**

$$x^3 - 7x = (x^2 + 3x + 2)(x - 3) + 6$$

6 is the **remainder**

$x^2 + 3x + 2$ is the **quotient**

Since the remainder is 6 (and $6 \neq 0$), the divisor $x - 3$ is **not a factor** of $x^3 - 7x$.

The **Factor Theorem** links **Roots** and **Factors**

Forgive me — there's another theorem to learn first:

The Remainder Theorem — When you **divide** a polynomial f(x) by ($x - a$), the **remainder** is **f(a)**.

When f(x) = $x^3 - 7x$ is **divided** by $x - 3$ the **remainder** is **f(3)** = $3^3 - 7 \times 3 = 27 - 21 =$ **6.**

If you get a **remainder of zero** when you divide f(x) by ($x - a$), then ($x - a$) must be a **factor** of f(x) — and that's the **Factor Theorem**:

The Factor Theorem — If f(x) is a polynomial and **f(a) = 0**, then ($x - a$) is a **factor** of f(x).

In other words, if you know the **roots**, you also know the **factors** — and vice versa.

EXAMPLE: The quartic polynomial $g(x) = x^4 - 8x^3 - 87x^2 + 342x + 1512$ has roots at $x = 12, 6, -3$ and -7. Fully factorise g(x).

If a is a **root** of g(x) then g(a) = 0 — so ($x - a$) is a **factor** of g(x). Since you're given **four roots**, you have **four factors**, and that's all you need to fully factorise a quartic. Hence:

$$g(x) = x^4 - 8x^3 - 87x^2 + 342x + 1512$$
$$= (x - 12)(x - 6)(x + 3)(x + 7)$$

You could check that this factorisation is correct by expanding the brackets back out.

EXAMPLE: Show that $(2x + 1)$ is a factor of the cubic polynomial $f(x) = 2x^3 - 3x^2 + 4x + 3$.

Notice that $2x + 1 = 0$ when $x = -\frac{1}{2}$. If you show that $\mathbf{f\left(-\frac{1}{2}\right) = 0}$, then the **Factor Theorem** says that $(x + \frac{1}{2})$ is a **factor** of f(x) — which means $(2x + 1) = 2(x + \frac{1}{2})$ is **also** a factor of f(x).

Since $f\left(-\frac{1}{2}\right) = 2\left(-\frac{1}{8}\right) - 3\left(\frac{1}{4}\right) + 4\left(-\frac{1}{2}\right) + 3 = \mathbf{0}$, by the Factor Theorem, **$(2x + 1)$** is a **factor** of f(x).

When using the Factor Theorem, always remember to say 'since f(a) = 0' or 'as the remainder is 0' in your working.

Factorising Polynomials

Method 1 — use Synthetic Division when you're given a Linear Factor

Synthetic division is easiest to learn by example — let's **divide** $f(x) = -7x + x^3$ by $x - 3$.

EXAMPLE: Divide $f(x) = -7x + x^3$ by $x - 3$ using synthetic division.

Begin by setting up the **synthetic division** table:

1) Arrange $f(x)$ in **descending order** by the **degree** of its terms — if any terms are missing, include them with zero coefficients.
2) Write the **coefficients** of $f(x)$ in a table.
3) Set the **divisor** equal to zero and solve — write the **solution** in a box.

① $f(x) = -7x + x^3$
$= x^3 + 0x^2 - 7x + 0$

②

3	1	0	−7	0

③ $x - 3 = 0$
$\Rightarrow x = 3$

Now **complete the table** by following these steps:

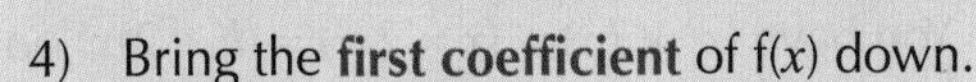

4) Bring the **first coefficient** of $f(x)$ down.

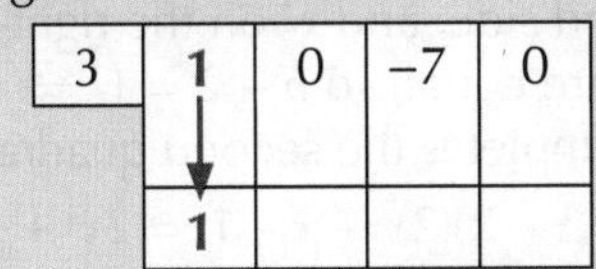

5) **Multiply** this number by the number in the box — write the answer **under** the next coefficient.

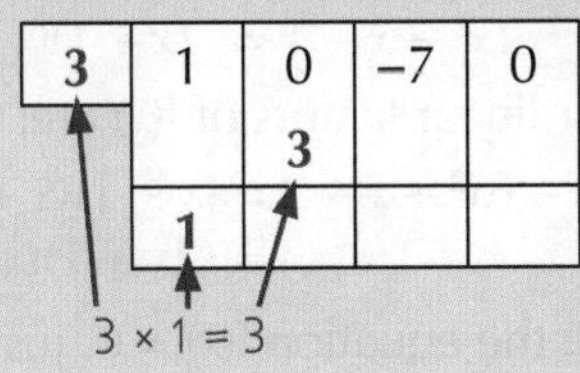

6) **Add** the two numbers in this column together — write the answer underneath.

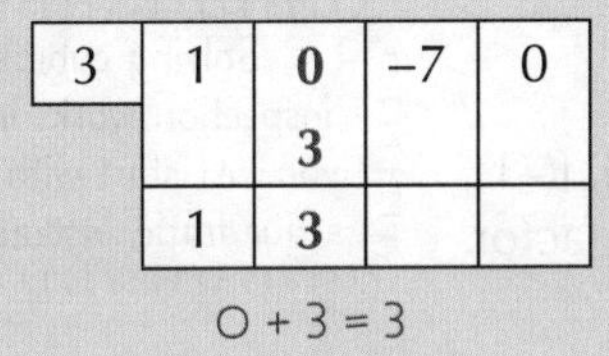

7) **Repeat** steps 5) and 6) until the table is full.

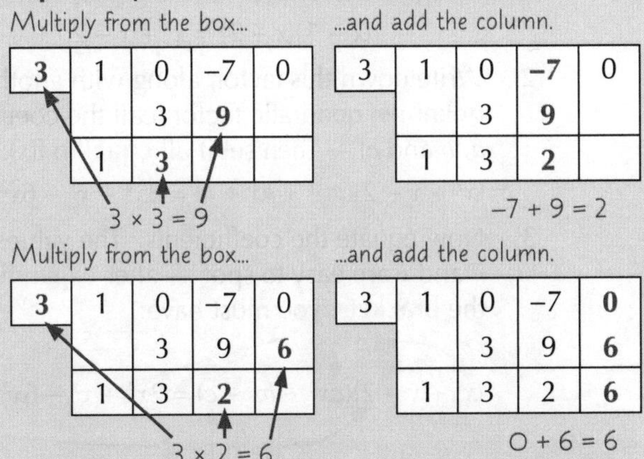

8) The **bottom row** now contains the **coefficients** of the **quotient**, starting with a power of x **one less** than the **degree** of the polynomial $f(x)$.

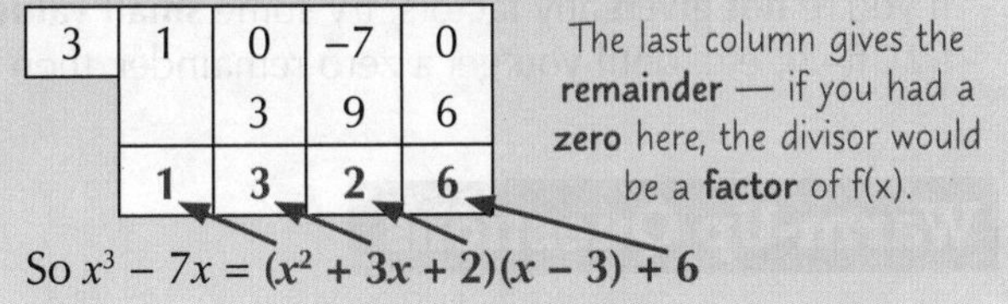

The last column gives the **remainder** — if you had a **zero** here, the divisor would be a **factor** of f(x).

So $x^3 - 7x = (x^2 + 3x + 2)(x - 3) + 6$

You can divide by any **linear term** $ax + b$, but for synthetic division to work, you **must** use $x + \frac{b}{a}$ as the **divisor**. You'll then need to adjust your quotient at the end — you can **divide the quotient** by a and **multiply the divisor** by a to get rid of the fraction. For example, $3x^3 - x^2 - 6x + 2 = (3x^2 - 6)(x - \frac{1}{3}) = 3(x^2 - 2)(x - \frac{1}{3}) = (x^2 - 2)(3x - 1)$.

Method 2 — use Algebraic Long Division instead of Synthetic Division

To divide two **algebraic** expressions, you can use **long division** (using the same method you'd use for numbers).

EXAMPLE: Factorise $2x^3 - 7x^2 - 17x + 10$, given that $x - 5$ is a factor.

Use algebraic long division to **divide**:

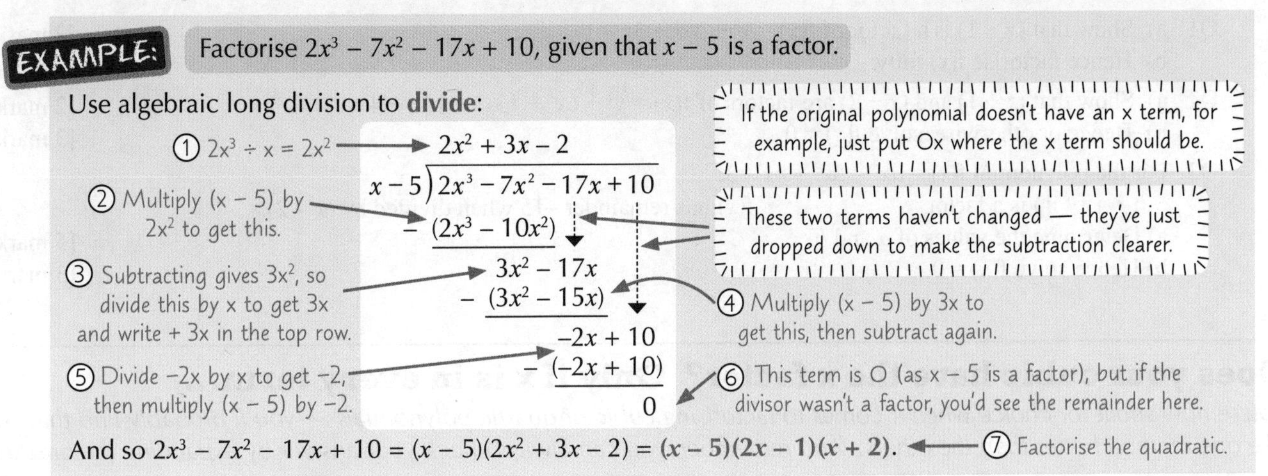

And so $2x^3 - 7x^2 - 17x + 10 = (x - 5)(2x^2 + 3x - 2) = (x - 5)(2x - 1)(x + 2)$. ⑦ Factorise the quadratic.

Factorising Polynomials

Method 3 — factorise By Inspection when you have one Factor

A **quartic** function has degree 4 — so when you factorise a quartic, you put it into (up to) **four brackets**. A **cubic** has degree 3, so when factorised it'll have (up to) **three brackets**. If the examiners are feeling nice, they'll give you **two** of the factors of a quartic, which makes it a bit **easier** to factorise.

EXAMPLE: Given that $x = 1$ and $x = -2$ are both roots of $f(x) = 2x^4 + x^3 - 6x^2 + x + 2$, express $f(x)$ as a product of four linear factors. Hence solve $f(x) = 0$.

1) The first step is to express $f(x)$ as a **product** of two **quadratic factors**. You know that $x = 1$ and $x = -2$ are **roots** so, by the **Factor Theorem**, $(x - 1)$ and $(x + 2)$ are **factors** of $f(x)$. Multiply these factors together — this will give you a **quadratic factor** of $f(x)$:

$$(x - 1)(x + 2) = x^2 + x - 2$$

2) Write down this factor, along with another **unknown** quadratic factor (call the coefficients a, b and c) — then set it all **equal** to $f(x)$:

$$(x^2 + x - 2)(ax^2 + bx + c) = 2x^4 + x^3 - 6x^2 + x + 2$$

3) Now equate the coefficients. The values of a and c are easy to spot — after **expanding** the **brackets**, you must have:

$1 \times a = 2$

$$(x^2 + x - 2)(ax^2 + bx + c) = 2x^4 + x^3 - 6x^2 + x + 2$$

$-2 \times c = 2$

So $a = 2$ and $c = -1$ — plug in these values:

$$(x^2 + x - 2)(2x^2 + bx - 1) = 2x^4 + x^3 - 6x^2 + x + 2$$

4) To find the value of b, compare x^3 coefficients.

$x^2 \times bx$

$$(x^2 + x - 2)(2x^2 + bx - 1) = 2x^4 + x^3 - 6x^2 + x + 2$$

$x \times 2x^2$

You have $(x^2 \times bx) + (x \times 2x^2) = (b + 2)x^3$ on the left-hand side, and x^3 on the right-hand side. These are equal, so $b + 2 = 1 \Rightarrow b = -1$. This completes the second quadratic factor:

$$(x^2 + x - 2)(2x^2 - x - 1) = 2x^4 + x^3 - 6x^2 + x + 2$$

5) All you have to do now is **factorise** the second quadratic (see page 2).

$$2x^2 - x - 1 = (2x + 1)(x - 1)$$

The four linear factors of $f(x)$ are:

$$2x^4 + x^3 - 6x^2 + x + 2 = (x - 1)(x + 2)(2x + 1)(x - 1) = (2x + 1)(x - 1)^2(x + 2)$$

6) To **solve** the equation $f(x) = 0$, just **write down** the roots of $f(x)$: $x = 1$, $x = -2$ and $x = -\frac{1}{2}$.

Solving cubic polynomials by inspection works in the same way — you just start with a linear factor and a quadratic, instead of two quadratics.

If you're **not given** any factors, try some **small values** of x — i.e. find $f(1)$, $f(-1)$, $f(2)$, $f(-2)$, etc. until you get a zero remainder, then use that to give your factor.

Warm-Up Questions

PRACTICE QUESTIONS

Q1 The polynomial $f(x) = x^3 - 3x^2 - 3x + a$ has remainder 5 when divided by $(x - 4)$. Use the Remainder Theorem to determine the value of a.

Q2 a) Show that $(x + 1)$ is a factor of $f(x) = x^3 - 7x - 6$.
b) Hence factorise $f(x)$ fully.

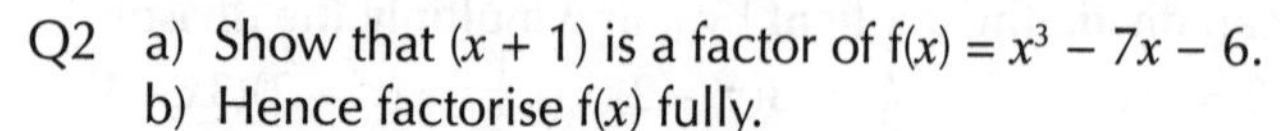

Q3 Divide $f(x) = 2x^3 + x^2 - 2x - 1$ by $(2x + 1)$ using synthetic division.

Exam Questions

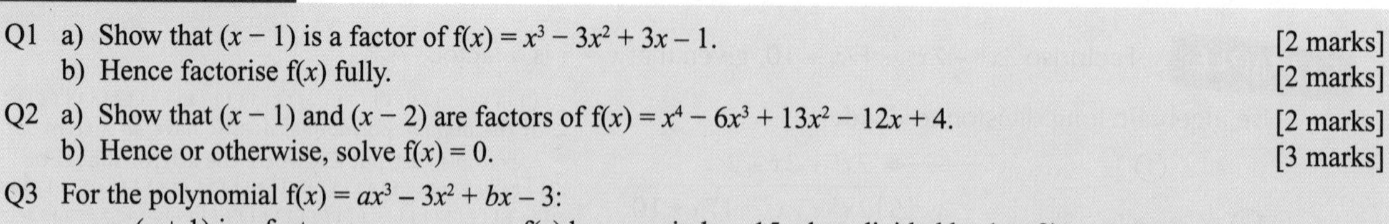

Q1 a) Show that $(x - 1)$ is a factor of $f(x) = x^3 - 3x^2 + 3x - 1$. [2 marks]
b) Hence factorise $f(x)$ fully. [2 marks]

Q2 a) Show that $(x - 1)$ and $(x - 2)$ are factors of $f(x) = x^4 - 6x^3 + 13x^2 - 12x + 4$. [2 marks]
b) Hence or otherwise, solve $f(x) = 0$. [3 marks]

Q3 For the polynomial $f(x) = ax^3 - 3x^2 + bx - 3$:
- $(x + 1)$ is a factor,
- $f(x)$ has remainder -15 when divided by $(x - 2)$.

a) Determine the values of a and b. [5 marks]
b) Hence solve $f(x) = 0$. [3 marks]

Does your cubic have the x factor? Only if x is in every term...

You're now spoilt for choice when it comes to factorising cubic or quartic polynomials — you'll probably find that you like one method better than the others. And remember, you can always check your answer by expanding the brackets.

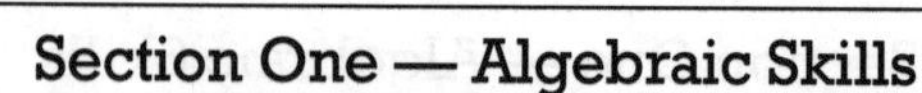

Cubic and Quartic Graphs

Now you've had fun factorising cubic and quartic polynomials, it's time to sketch their graphs. There's a lot more excitement to come sketching graphs using stationary points on p.58, but first, you need to know their general shapes...

If you know the **Factors**, the graph is easy to **Sketch**

To **sketch** a polynomial f(x), you need to know its **roots** — the **graph** of y = f(x) touches or crosses the x-axis where f(x) = 0 (i.e. at the roots). What happens at a root depends on the **power** of the factor.

The **power** of a factor $(x - a)^n$ affects what happens at $x = a$:

even power ⇒ the curve **touches** the x-axis but doesn't cross it (e.g. a '**double root**').

odd power ⇒ the curve **crosses** the x-axis (e.g. a **single** or '**triple root**').

This is true for polynomials of **any** degree.

Remember the Factor Theorem — if you know the factors, then you know the roots (see p.8).

Sketching **Cubic** polynomials with **Known Roots**

A **cubic** polynomial f(x) has up to **3 distinct roots** — its graph can **cross or touch** the x-axis up to **3 times**.

All cubics have a similar shape: '**bottom-left to top-right**' if the coefficient of x^3 is **positive**, or '**top-left to bottom-right**' if the coefficient of x^3 is **negative**.

Sketch the graphs the cubic polynomials: $f(x) = x(x - 1)(2x + 1)$, $g(x) = (1 - x)(x^2 - 2x + 2)$, $m(x) = (x - 3)^2(x + 1)$, $n(x) = (2 - x)^3$.

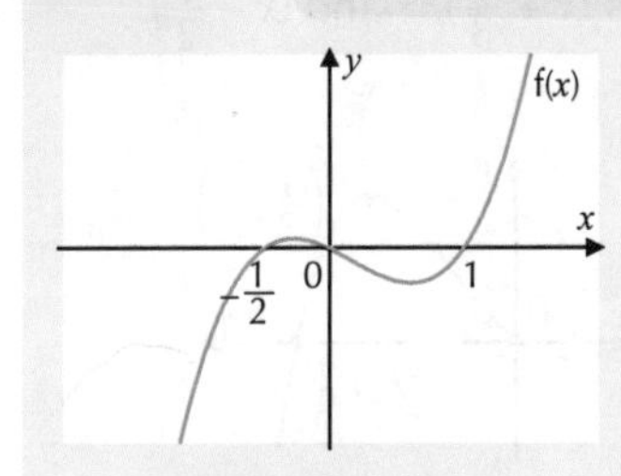

f(x) has three roots: $x = 0, 1$ and $-\frac{1}{2}$.

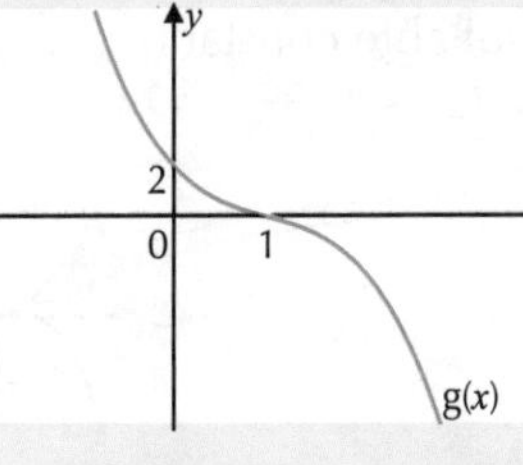

g(x) has just one root at $x = 1$ (as the quadratic factor has no real roots).

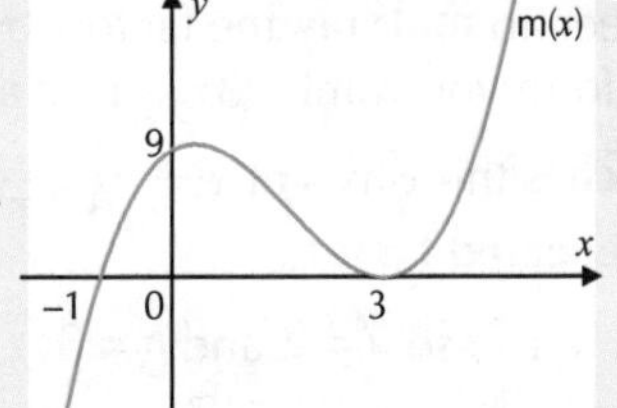

m(x) has a 'double root' at $x = 3$, so the graph just touches the x-axis there but doesn't cross it.

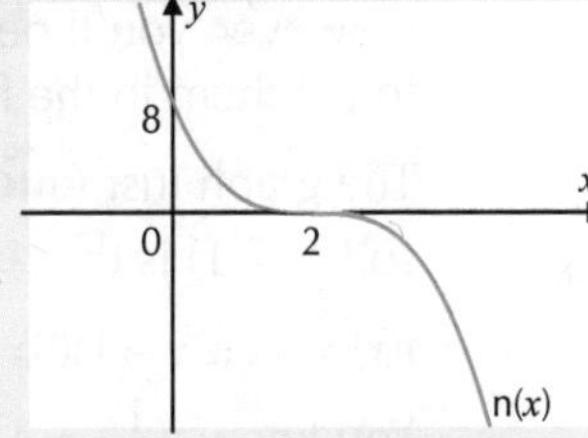

n(x) has a 'triple root' at $x = 2$, so the graph crosses the x-axis there.

Sketching **Quartic** polynomials with **Known Roots**

A **quartic** polynomial f(x) has up to **4 distinct roots** — its graph can **cross or touch** the x-axis up to **4 times**.

All quartics are: **positive** for **large** values of x (both positive and negative) if the coefficient of x^4 is **positive**, or **negative** for **large** values of x (both positive and negative) if the coefficient of x^4 is **negative**.

EXAMPLE: Sketch the graph of $f(x) = x^4 - 3x^3 + 4x = x(x + 1)(x - 2)^2$.

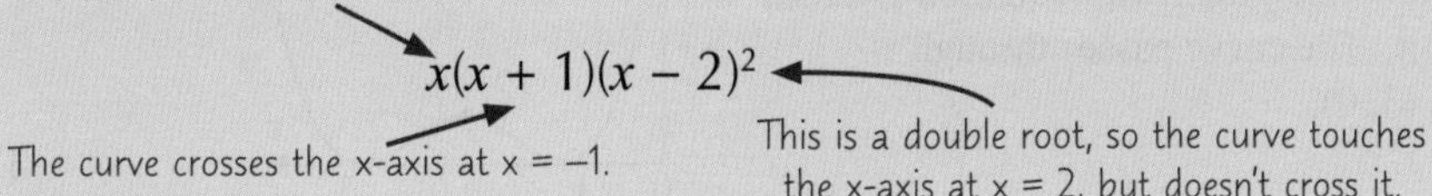

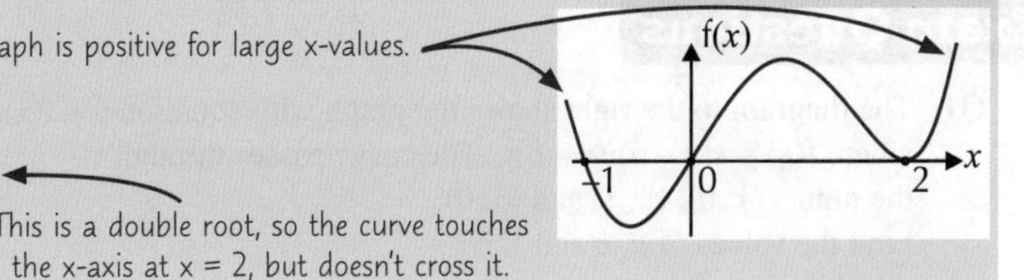

EXAMPLE: Sketch the graph of $f(x) = -x^4 - x^3 + 3x^2 + 5x + 2 = (2 - x)(x + 1)^3$.

The curve crosses the x-axis at x = 2.

$(2 - x)(x + 1)^3$

This is a triple root, so the curve crosses the x-axis at x = –1 — it flattens out too.

The coefficient of x^4 is negative, so the graph is negative for large x-values.

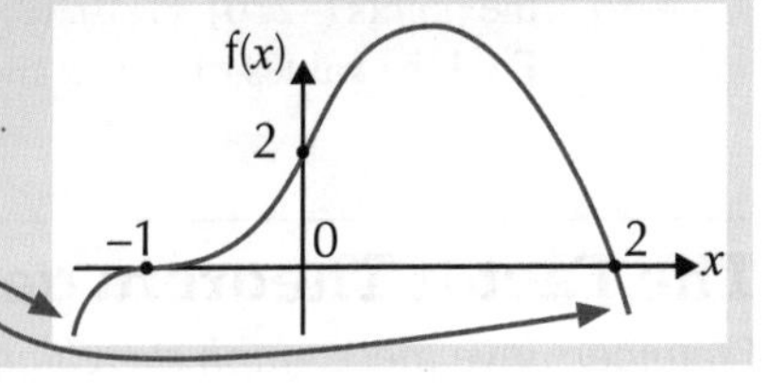

Cubic and Quartic Graphs

You can find a **Polynomial** function from a **Labelled Graph**

You can use the **coordinates** of labelled **points** to find the equation of a graph.

EXAMPLE: The diagram below is a sketch of the graph $y = f(x)$, where $f(x)$ is a cubic polynomial of the form $k(x - a)(x - b)(x - c)$. Find the values of a, b, c and k.

From the Factor Theorem, you can use the **roots** of a polynomial to find its **factors**. The roots occur when the graph crosses the x-axis, so $f(x)$ has roots at $x = -4$, $x = 1$ and $x = 3$. This gives factors $(x + 4)$, $(x - 1)$ and $(x - 3)$, so $a = -4$, $b = 1$, and $c = 3$.

To find k, use the **coordinates** of the other given point. You know $f(-2) = 10$ as $(-2, 10)$ lies on the curve, so

$$f(-2) = k(-2 + 4)(-2 - 1)(-2 - 3) = 30k \Rightarrow 30k = 10$$
$$\Rightarrow \quad k = \frac{1}{3}$$

So $f(x) = \frac{1}{3}(x + 4)(x - 1)(x - 3)$.

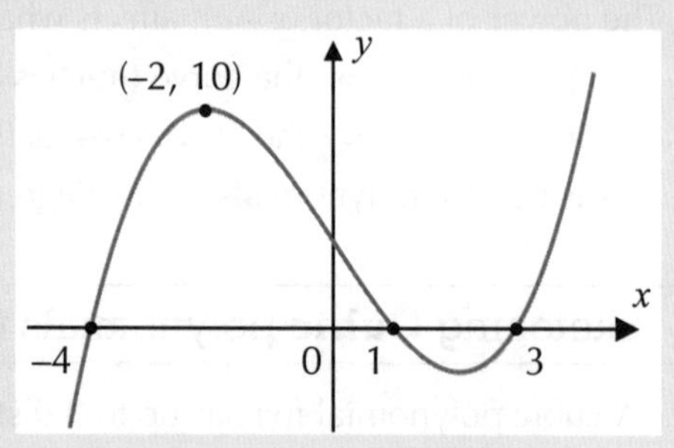

EXAMPLE: The diagram below is a sketch of the graph $y = f(x)$, where $f(x)$ is a quartic polynomial of the form $kx(ax - 1)(bx + 1)^2$. Find the values of a, b and k.

The graph **crosses** the x-axis at $x = -\frac{1}{3}$, $x = 0$ and $x = \frac{1}{2}$, so $f(x)$ has factors $(x + \frac{1}{3})$, x and $(x - \frac{1}{2})$. However, you'll need to **multiply** the factors by suitable constants to get them in the form you want: $(3x + 1)$, x and $(2x - 1)$.

The graph just **touches** the x-axis at $x = -\frac{1}{3}$, so $(3x + 1)$ is the **repeated factor**.

$f(x) = kx(2x - 1)(3x + 1)^2$, so $a = 2$ and $b = 3$.

You know $f(\frac{1}{3}) = 4$ as $(\frac{1}{3}, 4)$ **lies on** the curve, so

$$f(\tfrac{1}{3}) = \tfrac{k}{3}(2 \times \tfrac{1}{3} - 1)(3 \times \tfrac{1}{3} + 1)^2 \Rightarrow -\tfrac{4}{9}k = 4 \Rightarrow k = -9$$

The quartic is $f(x) = -9x(2x - 1)(3x + 1)^2$.

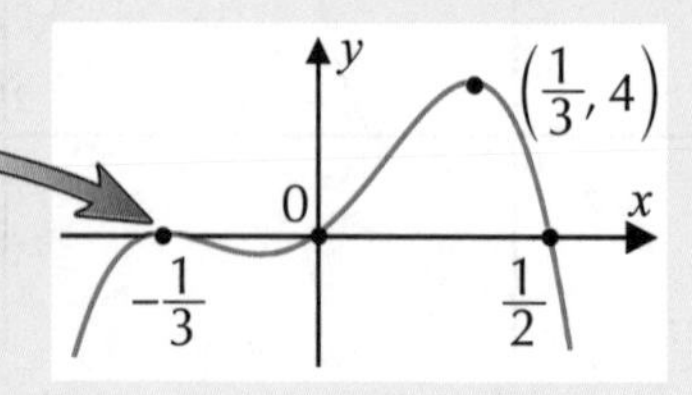

Warm-Up Questions

Q1 Sketch the graphs of the following cubic polynomials:
a) $f(x) = (x - 1)(x - 2)(x - 3)$ b) $g(x) = (x - 2)(x + 4)^2$ c) $h(x) = (x - 1)^3$

Q2 Sketch the graphs of the following quartic polynomials:
a) $f(x) = (x + 2)(x + 1)(x - 1)(x - 3)$ b) $g(x) = (2x + 1)^2(x - 1)(2 - x)$ c) $h(x) = (x + 4)^2(2 - x)^2$

Exam Questions

Q1 The diagram to the right shows the graph with equation $y = f(x)$, where $f(x) = k(x - a)^2(x - b)^2$. The curve passes through the points $(1, 0)$, $(2, 1)$ and $(3, 0)$.
Find the values of a, b and k. [2 marks]

Q2 The diagram to the right shows the graph with equation $y = f(x)$, where $f(x) = k(x - a)^2(x - b)(x - c)$. The curve passes through the points $(-2, 0)$, $(1, 0)$, $(2, 4)$ and $(3, 0)$.
Find the values of a, b, c and k. [3 marks]

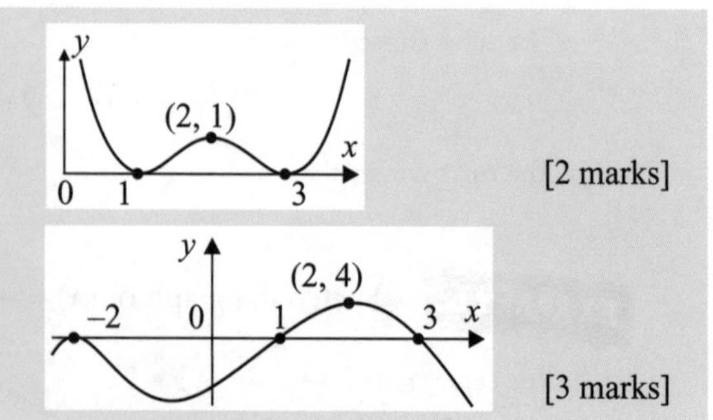

The Factor Theorem gets to the roots of the problem...

Examiners love these graph sketching questions, so don't be surprised if you find one in your exam. Best get learning...

Graph Transformations

A picture speaks a thousand words... and graphs are as close as you're going to get in maths.

There are **Four** main **Graph Transformations**

You'll have come across these graph transformations at National 5 — **translations** (adding things to **shift** the graph vertically or horizontally), **reflections** (in the x- or y-axis) and **stretches** (either vertical or horizontal). Each transformation has the same effect on any function — here they're applied to $f(x) = \sin x$:

$y = f(x + c)$

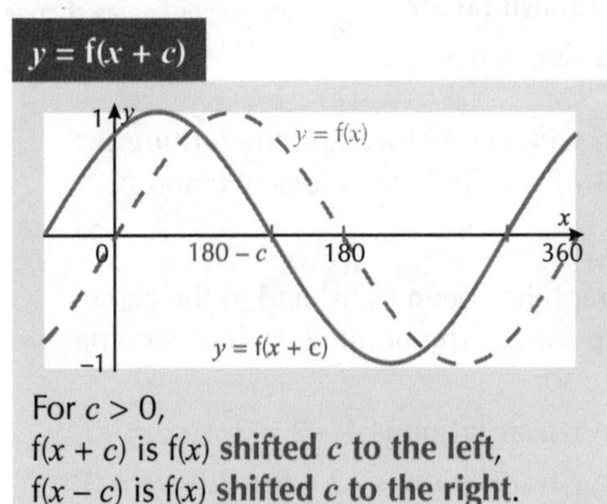

For $c > 0$,
$f(x + c)$ is $f(x)$ **shifted c to the left**,
$f(x - c)$ is $f(x)$ **shifted c to the right**.

$y = f(x) + c$

For $c > 0$, $f(x) + c$ is $f(x)$ **shifted c upwards**, and $f(x) - c$ is $f(x)$ **shifted c downwards**.

Reflections in the x-axis flip f(x) vertically and reflections in the y-axis flip f(x) horizontally.

$y = f(ax)$

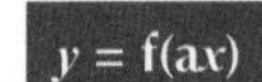

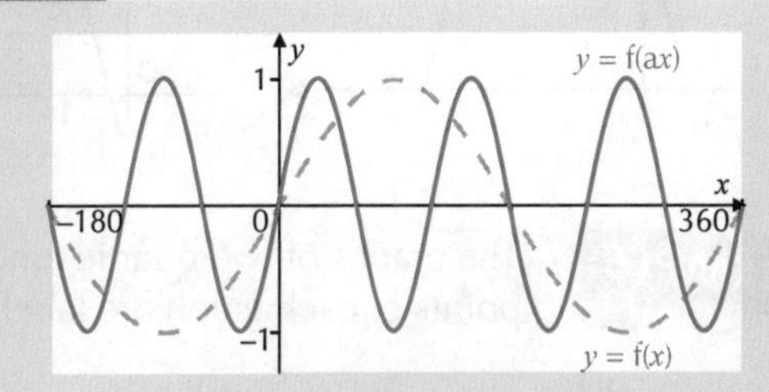

If $|a| > 1$, the graph of $f(ax)$ is $f(x)$ **squashed horizontally** by a factor of a.
If $0 < |a| < 1$, the graph is **stretched horizontally**.
And if $a < 0$, the graph is also **reflected** in the **y-axis**.

$y = af(x)$

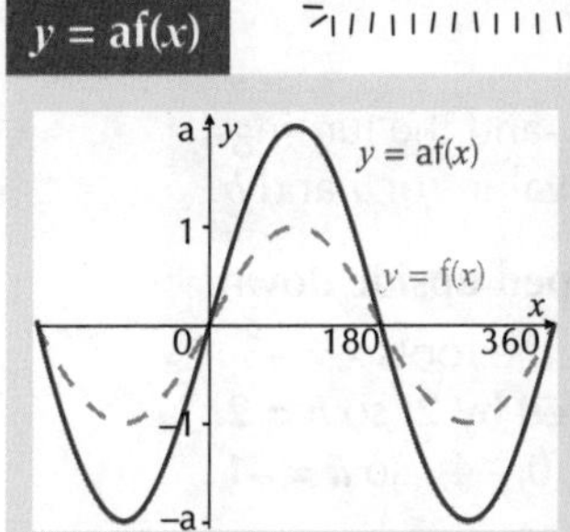

If $|a| > 1$, the graph of $af(x)$ is $f(x)$ **stretched vertically** by a factor of a.
If $0 < |a| < 1$, the graph is **squashed vertically**.
And if $a < 0$, the graph is also **reflected** in the **x-axis**.

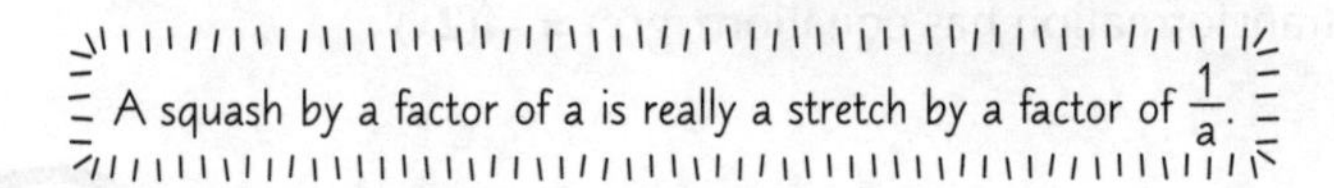

Do **Combinations** of transformations **One at a Time**

Combinations of transformations can look a bit tricky, but if you take them **one step** at a time they're not too bad. Don't do **all** the transformations at once — break it up into **separate bits** (as above) and draw a **graph** for **each stage**.

EXAMPLE: The graph below shows the function $y = f(x)$. Draw the graph of $y = 3f(x + 2)$, showing the coordinates of the turning points.

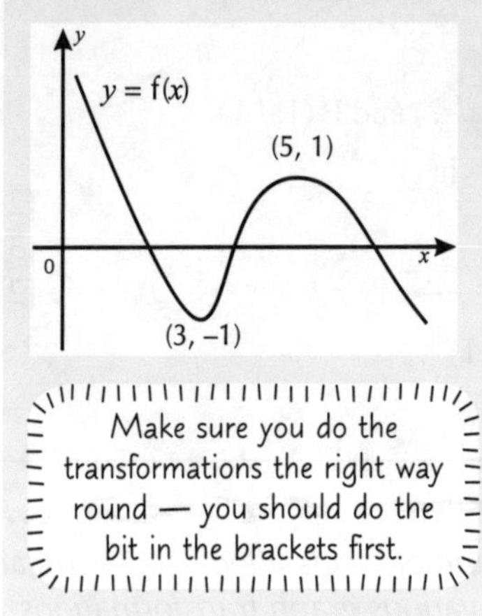

Don't try to do everything at once. First draw the graph of $y = f(x + 2)$ and work out the coordinates of the turning points.

The graph is shifted left by 2 units, so subtract 2 from the x-coordinates.

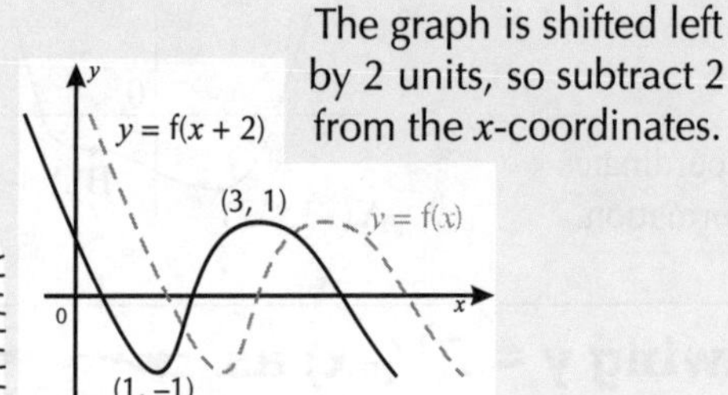

Now use your graph of $y = f(x + 2)$ to draw the graph of $y = 3f(x + 2)$.

This is a stretch in the direction of the y-axis with scale factor 3, so multiply the y-coordinates by 3.

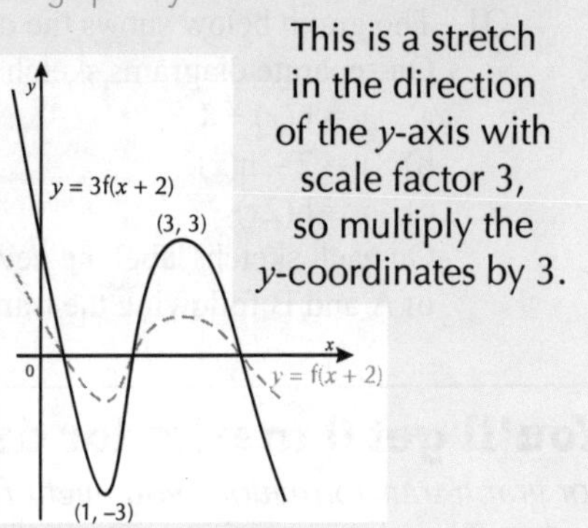

Graph Transformations

Use given **Coordinates** to find a **Graph Transformation**

You can find how one graph has been **transformed** into another, provided you have **enough information**.

- If the graph **hasn't** changed shape, you're looking at a **translation**. Look at how the x- and y- coordinates have changed in order to work out the **shift**.
- If the graph has **changed shape**, then a **stretch** is involved. See what the coordinates have been multiplied or divided by to find the **'stretch/squash factor'**.
- If the graph is flipped, then a **reflection** has taken place, so a **minus sign** is needed.

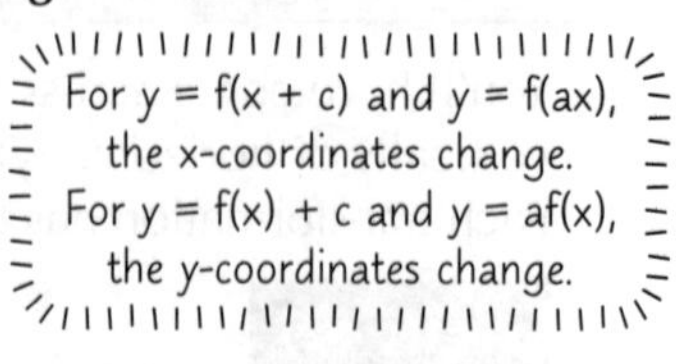

EXAMPLE: The graphs of two quadratic functions f(x) and g(x) are sketched below, and the turning point of each graph is labelled. Given that $g(x) = f(x + a) + b$, find the values of a and b.

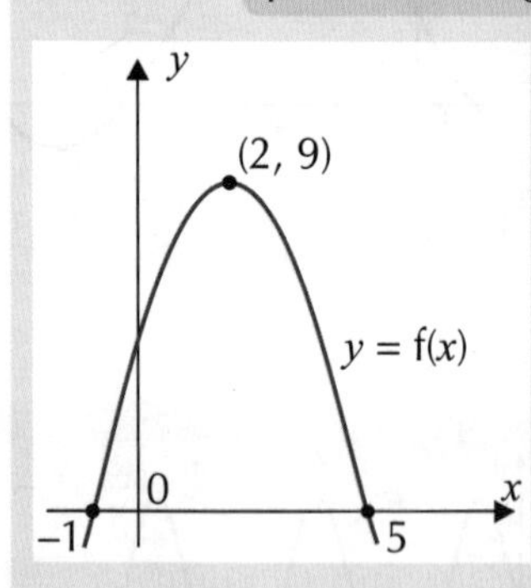

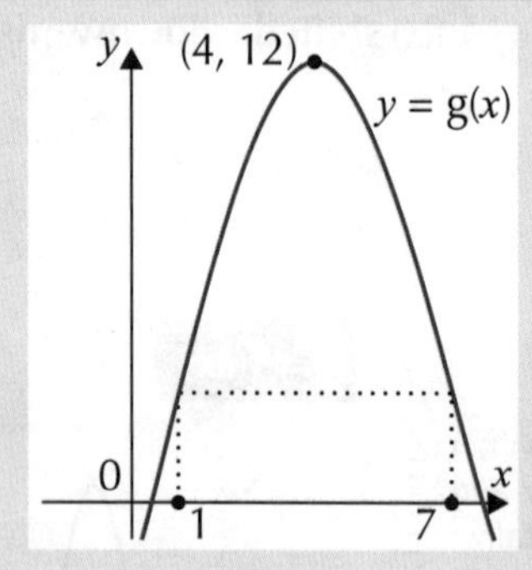

The graph has been translated to the **right** and **upwards**. The point (2, 9) has become (4, 12), so:

- the **x-translation** is $4 - 2 = 2$, so $a = -2$,
- the **y-translation** is $12 - 9 = 3$, so $b = 3$.

So the transformation has equation:
$\mathbf{g(x) = f(x - 2) + 3}$

EXAMPLE: The graphs of two quartic functions f(x) and g(x) are sketched below and the turning points of each graph are labelled. Given that $g(x) = af(bx)$, find the values of a and b.

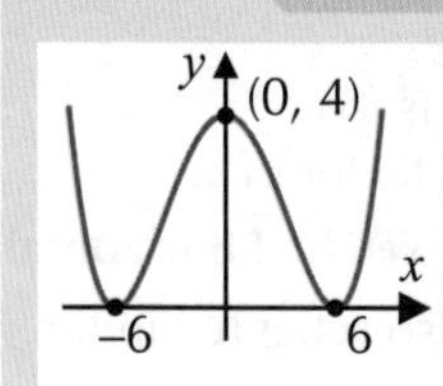

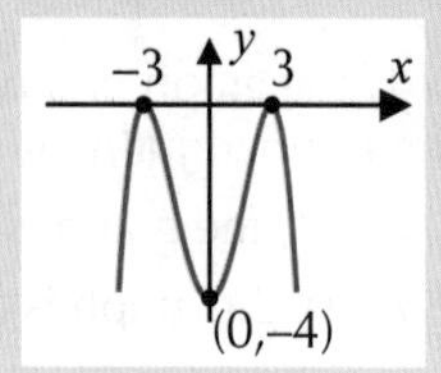

The graph has been **squashed** and **flipped upside down**.
The **roots** of f(x) ($x = \pm 6$) have become the roots $x = -3$ and $x = 3$ of g(x) — they've been **divided by 2**, so $b = 2$.
The **turning point** (0, 4) has moved to (0, –4), so $a = -1$ (this is a **reflection** in the **x-axis**).
So the transformation has equation: $\mathbf{g(x) = -f(2x)}$

Warm-Up Questions

PRACTICE QUESTIONS

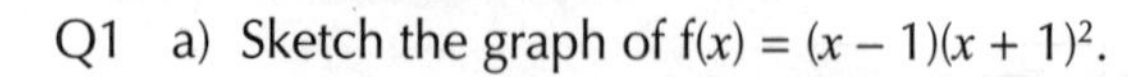

Q1 a) Sketch the graph of $f(x) = (x - 1)(x + 1)^2$.
b) Sketch the graphs of the following transformations:
(i) $y = f(x - 1)$ (ii) $y = 2f(x) - 1$ (iii) $y = f(\frac{1}{2}x) + 2$

Q2 The function $y = f(x)$ is shown on the graph to the right.
Sketch the graphs of the following:
a) $y = \frac{1}{4}f(x)$ b) $y = 2f(x) + 1$ c) $y = -f(x + 90°)$

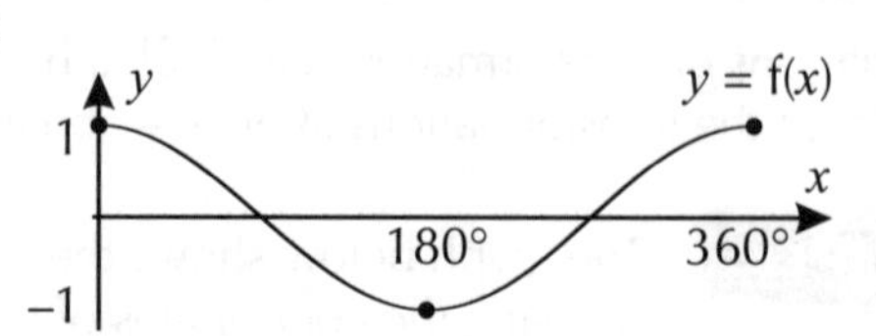

Exam Question

Q1 The graph below shows the curve $y = h(x)$. It goes through the points A (–1, –2) and B (1, –1).
On separate diagrams sketch of the following:
a) $y = h(x) + 1$ [2 marks]
b) $y = 2 - h(x)$ [3 marks]
c) $y = h(2x)$ [2 marks]
On each sketch, label the new coordinates of A and B following the transformation.

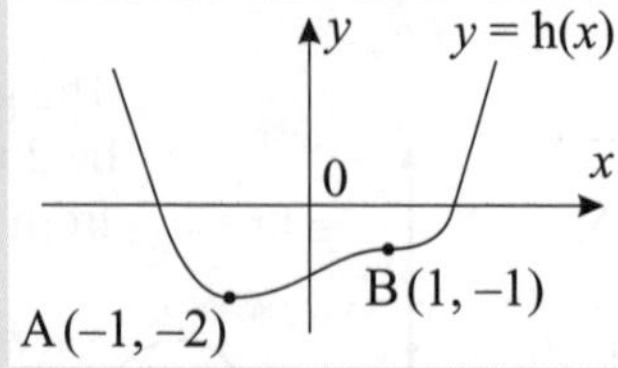

You'll get 0 marks for drawing y = f(1⁄10x) as y = f(x) ...

For graph transformations you might find it useful to remember that stuff outside the brackets affects f(x) vertically and stuff inside affects f(x) horizontally. Now get out there and get exploring the various graph transformations.

Exponentials and Logs

Logs have a bad reputation, but they're all soft and fluffy once you get to know them.

An **Exponential Graph y = a^x** never reaches **Zero**

An **exponential function** is a function of the form $f(x) = a^x$, for some constant $a > 0$.

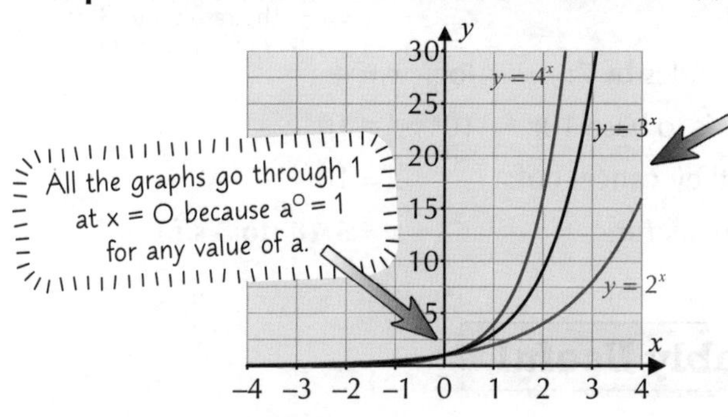

All the graphs of $y = a^x$ (**exponential graphs**) where $a > 1$ have the **same basic shape**. The graphs for $a = 2$, $a = 3$ and $a = 4$ are shown on the left.

- a is greater than 1 — so **y increases as x increases**.
- The **bigger** a is, the **quicker** the graphs increase.
- As x **decreases**, y **decreases** at a **smaller and smaller rate** — y will approach zero, but never actually get there.

The graphs on the right are for $y = a^x$ where $0 < a < 1$ (they're for $a = \frac{1}{2}, \frac{1}{3}$ and $\frac{1}{4}$).

- a is less than 1 — so **y decreases as x increases**.
- As x **increases**, y **decreases** at a **smaller and smaller rate** — y will approach zero, but never actually get there.

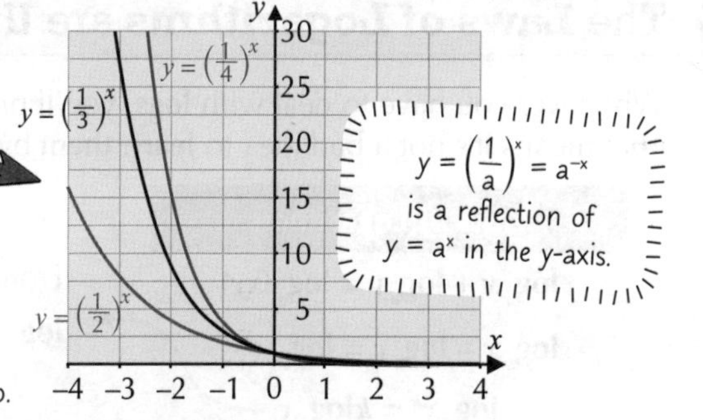

All the transformations from p.13 can be applied to the graphs on this page too.

You need to be able to **Switch** between **Different Notations**

Exponential and **logarithms** (or '**logs**') can describe the same thing — they're **inverses** of each other (see below).

$\log_a b = c$ means the same as $a^c = b$

So $\log_a a = 1$ and $\log_a 1 = 0$

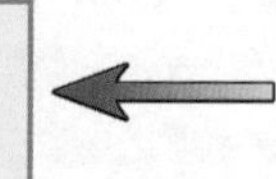

The little number 'a' after 'log' is called the base. Logs can be to any base but the log button on your calculator is actually base 10 (i.e. $\log_{10}$) — and that's what we mean in this book if we just say log.

You'll need to learn both notations — here are some examples to get you started.

EXAMPLE: Write down the values of: a) $\log_2 8$ b) $\log_5 5$

a) 8 is 2 raised to the power of 3, so $2^3 = 8$ and $\log_2 8 = 3$.

b) Anything raised to the power of 1 is itself, so $\log_5 5 = 1$.

EXAMPLE: Write the following in log notation: a) $5^3 = 125$ b) $3^0 = 1$

a) 3 is the power (or logarithm) that 5 (the base) is raised to to get 125, so $\log_5 125 = 3$.

b) This is one of the rules in the orange box above: $\log_a 1 = 0$ for any a, so $\log_3 1 = 0$.

Logs and **Exponentials** are **Inverses**

The **log function** $\log_a x$ is the **inverse** of the exponential function a^x (see p.21-22 for more on inverses).

The diagram on the left is a sketch of $y = a^x$ and $y = \log_a x$ (for $a > 1$).

1) $y = \log_a x$ is the **reflection** of $y = a^x$ in the line $y = x$.
2) It **crosses the x-axis** at **(1, 0)** (as $\log_a 1 = 0$) — a^x crosses the y-axis at (0, 1) and the point has been **reflected** in $y = x$.
3) As $x \to \infty$, $\log_a x \to \infty$ (but slowly), and as $x \to 0$, $\log_a x \to -\infty$.
4) $\log_a x$ **does not exist** for $x \le 0$ (i.e. **x can't be zero or negative**).

→ means 'tends to'

$y = \log_a x$ has an asymptote at $x = 0$ (see p.27 for more on asymptotes).

Because $\log_a x$ is the **inverse** of a^x, we get these juicy **formulas**:

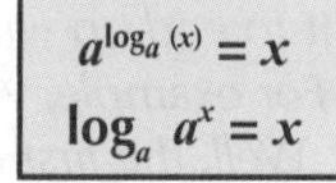
$a^{\log_a(x)} = x$

$\log_a a^x = x$

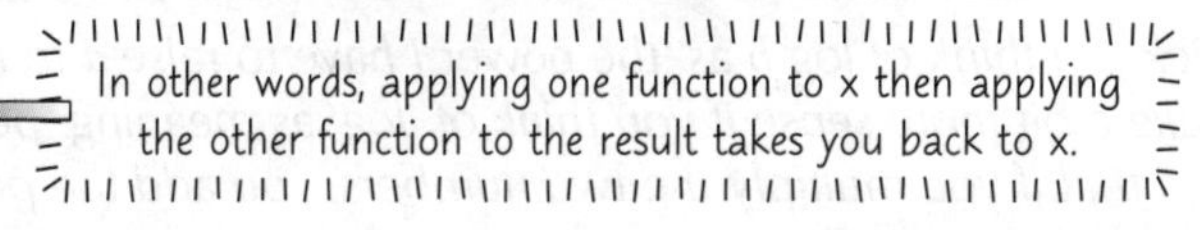

Exponentials and Logs

You can use **Logs** and **Exponentials** to **Solve Equations**

You can use exponentials to get rid of logs from equations — and vice versa.

> To solve an equation like $3^x = 5$, take $\log_3$ of both sides and use the result $\log_3 3^x = x$.

EXAMPLE: Solve $7 \log_{10} x = 5$ to 3 significant figures.

1) You want x on its own, so begin by **dividing** both sides **by 7**: $\log_{10} x = \frac{5}{7}$
2) Do '10 to the power of' both sides (since the log is to base 10): $10^{\log_{10} x} = 10^{\frac{5}{7}}$
3) Logs and exponentials are **inverse** functions, so they **cancel out**: $x = 10^{\frac{5}{7}}$
4) But $10^{\frac{5}{7}}$ is just a number you can **find** using a **calculator**: $x = 5.18$ **(to 3 s.f.)**

The **Laws of Logarithms** are **Unbelievably Useful**

Whenever you have to deal with **logs**, you'll probably end up using the **laws** below.
That means it's not a bad idea to **learn them** by heart right now.

Laws of Logarithms

$$\log_a x + \log_a y = \log_a (xy)$$

$$\log_a x - \log_a y = \log_a \left(\frac{x}{y}\right)$$

$$\log_a x^k = k \log_a x$$

From this **law** you'll find that: $\log_a \frac{1}{x} = \log_a x^{-1} = -\log_a x$

Alasdair's new shoes didn't improve his logarithm.

EXAMPLE: Write $\log_a 5 + \log_a 4$ in the form $\log_a n$, where n is a number.

Use $\log_a x + \log_a y = \log_a (xy)$: $\log_a 5 + \log_a 4 = \log_a (5 \times 4) = \mathbf{\log_a 20}$

> Remember, fractional powers are the same as roots — $x^{\frac{1}{2}}$ is the same as $\sqrt{x}$.

EXAMPLE: Evaluate $\log_2 72 - \frac{1}{2}\log_2 81$.

Apply $k\log_a x = \log_a x^k$ to **simplify** $\frac{1}{2}\log_2 81$: $\frac{1}{2}\log_2 81 = \log_2 81^{\frac{1}{2}} = \log_2 9$

Now use $\log_a x - \log_a y = \log_a \left(\frac{x}{y}\right)$:

$$\log_2 72 - \frac{1}{2}\log_2 81 = \log_2 72 - \log_2 9 = \log_2 \frac{72}{9} = \log_2 8 = \mathbf{3} \quad (\text{as } 2^3 = 8)$$

Warm-Up Questions

PRACTICE QUESTIONS

Q1 Evaluate the following: a) $\log_3 27$ b) $\log_3 \left(\frac{1}{27}\right)$ c) $\log_3 18 - \log_3 2$

Q2 Simplify the following: a) $\log 3 + 2 \log 5$ b) $\frac{1}{2}\log 36 - \log 3$ c) $\log 2 - \frac{1}{4}\log 16$

Q3 For the following functions, sketch the function and its inverse on the same set of axes.
a) 5^x b) $\log_3 x$

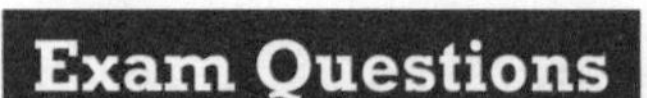

Exam Questions

Q1 Solve the equation $\log_7 (y + 3) + \log_7 (2y + 1) = 1$, where $y > 0$. [4 marks]

Q2 Find the value of n that makes the following equation correct: $\log_n 45 - 2 \log_n 3 = \frac{1}{3}$. [4 marks]

It's sometimes hard to see the wood for the trees — especially with logs...

Tricky... I think of $\log_a b$ as 'the power I have to raise a to if I want to end up with b' — that's all it is. And the log laws make a bit more sense if you think of 'log' as meaning 'power'. For example, you know that $2^a \times 2^b = 2^{a+b}$ — this just says that if you multiply the two numbers, you add the powers. Well, the first law of logs is saying the same thing.

Using Exponentials and Logs

Now that you're familiar with the log laws, it's time to reveal their true power. Okay, maybe that's a slight exaggeration, but they are pretty useful in a variety of situations. Read on to find out more.

Use the **Calculator Log Button** whenever you can

Your calculator will have a 'log' button (meaning $\log_{10}$) — you'll need it in this next example. If you have a 'log■□' button, you can enter any base.

You can choose any base, but pick one that uses $\log_a a = 1$ — and make sure you use the same base on each side.

EXAMPLE: Use logarithms to solve $10^{3x} = 4000$ for x, giving your answer to 4 s.f.

As x is in the **power**, take **logs** of both sides: $\log_{10} 10^{3x} = \log_{10} 4000$

Use $\log_{10}$ here, as you've got a power of 10 on one side.

Use the log law $\log_a x^k = k\log_a x$: $3x \log_{10} 10 = \log_{10} 4000$

Solve the equation to **find** x. $\log_{10}10 = 1$ so: $3x = \log_{10} 4000$, and $x = \mathbf{1.201}$ **(4 s.f.)**

You might have to **Combine** the **Laws of Logs** to **Solve** equations

If the examiners are feeling particularly mean, they might make you use **more than one** law to solve an equation.

EXAMPLE: Solve the equation $\log_3 (2 - 3x) - 2\log_3 x = \log_4 16$.

You have two different bases here, so you must evaluate the right-hand side.

1) **Evaluate** the **log** on the right-hand side: $\log_4 16 = \log_4 4^2 = 2\log_4 4 = 2$
2) **Combine** the log terms on the left-hand side into one term, using the **laws of logs**: $\log_3 (2 - 3x) - 2\log_3 x = \log_3 (2 - 3x) - \log_3 x^2 = \log_3 \frac{2-3x}{x^2}$

It's helpful to simplify both sides of an equation before trying to solve it.

3) Take **exponentials** to get rid of the log (use **base 3** here): $\log_3 \frac{2-3x}{x^2} = 2 \Rightarrow 3^{\log_3 \frac{2-3x}{x^2}} = 3^2 \Rightarrow \frac{2-3x}{x^2} = 9$
4) **Rearrange** into a standard quadratic: $2 - 3x = 9x^2 \Rightarrow 9x^2 + 3x - 2 = 0$
5) Finally, **solve** for x: $(3x - 1)(3x + 2) = 0 \Rightarrow x = \frac{1}{3}$

Ignore the negative solution because you can't take logs of a negative number.

Exponential Growth and **Decay** applies to **Real-Life** problems

Logs can even be used to model **real-life** situations — see pages 19-20 for more on this.

EXAMPLE: The radioactivity of a substance decays by 20 percent over a year. The initial level of radioactivity is 400. Find the time taken for the radioactivity to fall to 200 (the half-life).

$R = 400 \times 0.8^T$ where R is the **level of radioactivity** at time T years.

You need $R = 200$, so solve $200 = 400 \times 0.8^T$

The 0.8 comes from 100% – 20% decay.

$0.8^T = \frac{200}{400} = 0.5 \Rightarrow T\log 0.8 = \log 0.5 \Rightarrow T = \frac{\log 0.5}{\log 0.8} = \mathbf{3.106}$ **years** (4 s.f.)

Exponential **models** often have a **time restriction** — after a long time, the numbers might get too big or small.

Exponential equations can be **Reduced to Linear Form**

Equations like $y = ax^b$ and $y = ab^x$ can be a bit awkward to use. Fortunately, using the **laws of logs**, they can be rewritten to look like a form you've seen before — good old $y = mx + c$. Just take **logs** of both sides and rearrange:

You can use any base here, but base 10 is usually the easiest — that way you can just use the log button on your calculator.

$$y = ax^b \Rightarrow \log y = b \log x + \log a$$

$$y = ab^x \Rightarrow \log y = x \log b + \log a$$

By taking the log of each side, you get $\log y = \log (ax^b)$. Then you can use the log laws to show $\log (ax^b) = \log a + b \log (x)$. The other equation can be found similarly.

Once the equations are in this form you can draw their **straight-line graphs** — you just need to **label** the axes **log x** (top) or x (bottom) against **log y**. Now your graph is **easier** to work with than the original graph.

Using Exponentials and Logs

The number of employees, p, working for a company t years after it was founded can be modelled by the equation $p = at^b$. The table below shows data collected over 25 years:

Age of company (t years)	2	5	8	13	25
Number of employees (p)	3	7	10	16	29

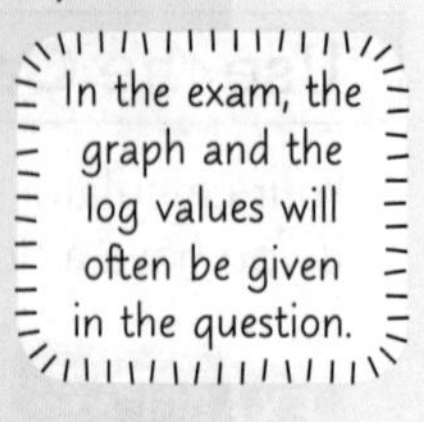

a) Show that $p = at^b$ can be written in the form $\log p = b \log t + \log a$.

b) Plot a graph of $\log t$ against $\log p$ and draw a line of best fit for your graph.

c) Use your graph to estimate the values of a and b in the equation $p = at^b$.

a) Starting with $p = at^b$ and take **logs** of both sides: $\log p = \log at^b$

Use the **laws of logs** to rearrange into the required form: $= \log a + \log t^b = b\log t + \log a$

b) Make a **table** of the **values** of $\log t$ and $\log p$, using the values of p and t given in the question:

$\log t$	0.301	0.699	0.903	1.114	1.398
$\log p$	0.477	0.845	1.000	1.204	1.462

Now **plot** a graph of $\log t$ against $\log p$ and draw a line of best fit.

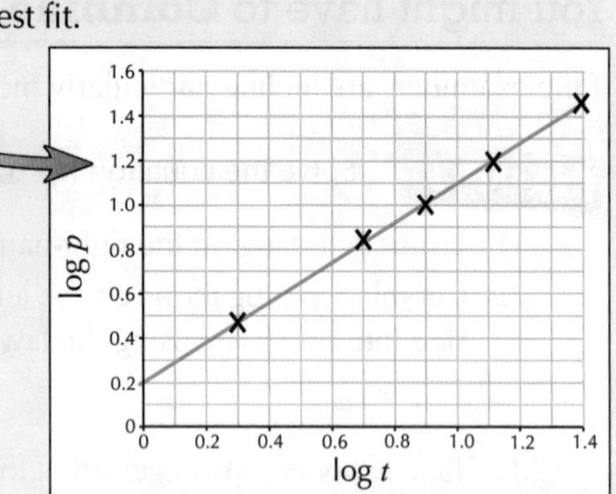

c) From part a), the graph has equation:

$\log p = b \log t + \log a$.

Compare this to $y = mx + c$:

b is the **gradient** of the line and

$\log a$ is the **vertical intercept** of the line.

Use the coordinates of **two points** on the line to find the gradient:

E.g. use coordinates (1.0, 1.1) and (0, 0.2):

$$b = \frac{y_2 - y_1}{x_2 - x_1} = \frac{1.1 - 0.2}{1.0 - 0} = \mathbf{0.9}$$

You can also read the vertical intercept **off the graph**: 0.2.

BUT this value is equal to $\log a$, so **take exponentials** of both sides:

$a = 10^{0.2} = \mathbf{1.585 \text{ to 3 d.p.}}$

So the original equation $p = at^b$ is $\mathbf{p = 1.585t^{0.9}}$.

Be careful when using models like this to predict values outside the range of the given data — this is extrapolation, and can be unreliable.

Warm-Up Questions

PRACTICE QUESTIONS

Q1 If $6^{(3x+2)} = 9$, find x to 3 significant figures.

Q2 Solve $2\log_4 (x - 1) - \log_4 x = \log_2 \frac{1}{\sqrt{2}}$, where $x > 1$.

Q3 The value of a painting is modelled as increasing by 5% each year. If the initial price of the painting is £1000, find the time taken in years for the price to reach £2000. Give your answer to 1 d.p.

Exam Question

Q1 The yearly income from book sales of a particular author has tended to increase with time. The table below shows his income from book sales over the first five years after his book was published.

Number of years after book published (t)	1	2	3	4	5
Income (£p thousand)	10	13	17	24	35

The relationship is modelled by the equation $p = ab^t$, where a and b are constants to be found.

a) Plot a graph of t against $\log_{10}p$. Draw, by eye, a line of best fit for your graph. [2 marks]

b) State, in terms of a and b, the gradient and vertical-axis intercept of your graph. Hence use your graph to estimate the values of a and b. [4 marks]

c) Predict the author's income 10 years after his book was published. [1 mark]

Reducing to linear form is hard work — you'll sleep like a log tonight...

If you're given a straight line graph with labelled points, you should use those points to find the gradient and y-intercept like in part c) of the example above. Remember to 'de-log' the y-intercept and gradient by taking exponentials.

Modelling Using Exponentials and Logs

*Of all the exponential functions in the world (and there are infinitely many exponential functions), only one can be called **the** exponential function. The most powerful, most incredible — e^x. Wait, what do you mean, "anticlimactic"?*

The **Number e** and the **Natural Log ln** have special properties

e and ln x

- There's a value 'a' for which the **gradient** of $y = a^x$ is **exactly the same** as a^x. That value is known as **e** — it's an **irrational number** around 2.7183 (it's stored in your calculator, just like π). e^x is known as **the** exponential function, and it's used in a lot of **real-life situations** (see below).
- **ln x** (also know as **$\log_e x$**, or **'natural log'**) is the **inverse function** of e^x. This means $e^{\ln x} = x$ and $\ln e^x = x$. $\ln x$ is read as 'lin x'.
- The **log laws** from p.16 also apply to $\ln x$.

The graphs of e^x and $\ln x$ have all the properties of the exponential and log graphs you saw on p.15.

EXAMPLE: If $e^{2x} = 9$, find the exact value of x.

Take **ln** of both sides: $\ln e^{2x} = \ln 9$

Using $\ln x^k = k \ln x$: $2x \ln e = \ln 9 \Rightarrow 2x = \ln 9$

$\Rightarrow x = \frac{1}{2}\ln 9 = \ln 9^{\frac{1}{2}} = \mathbf{\ln 3}$

The 'exact value of x' means 'leave x in terms of e or ln.'

EXAMPLE: If $\ln(x - 5) = 3$, find the exact value of x.

Take **exponentials** of both sides: $e^{\ln(x-5)} = e^3$

Using $e^{\ln x} = x$: $\Rightarrow x - 5 = e^3$

$\Rightarrow \mathbf{x = 5 + e^3}$

All logs and no play makes Jill a dull girl.

Use **Exponential Functions** to **Model** real-life **Growth**...

In the **exam**, you might be given a background story to an exponential equation. You may then be asked to **find** some **values** or work out a **missing part** of the equation. There's nothing here you haven't seen before — you just need to know how to deal with all the **wordy** bits.

The exponential growth of a colony of bacteria can be modelled by the equation $B = 60e^{kt}$, where B is the number of bacteria, k is a constant, and t is the time in hours from the point at which the colony is first monitored ($t \geq 0$). It takes 24 hours for the colony to double in size.

a) Show that $k = 0.03$ to 1 s.f.

The colony size at $t = 0$ is $60e^{0k} = 60$, so double this size is $60 \times 2 = 120$. Hence:

$60e^{24k} = 120 \Rightarrow e^{24k} = 2$

$\Rightarrow 24k = \ln 2$

$\Rightarrow k = \frac{\ln 2}{24} = 0.02888...$

$= \mathbf{0.03\ (1\ s.f.)}$

b) Predict the number of bacteria after 8 hours.

You need to find B when $t = 8$, so plug in the numbers — use the **exact** value of k here:

$B = 60 \times e^{(0.02888... \times 8)}$

$= 60 \times 1.2599...$

$= 75.5952...$

So B = **75 bacteria**

You shouldn't round up here — there are only 75 whole bacteria, not 76.

c) Find the time taken for the colony to grow to 1000.

- You need to find t when $B = 1000$, so put the numbers into the equation:

  $1000 = 60e^{0.02888...t}$

  $\Rightarrow e^{0.02888...t} = 1000 \div 60 = 16.6666...$

- Now take 'ln' of both sides:

  $\ln e^{0.02888...t} = \ln(16.6666...)$

  $\Rightarrow 0.02888...t = 2.8134...$

  $\Rightarrow t = 2.8134... \div 0.02888...$

  $= 97.4134...$

  $=$ **97.4 hours (3 s.f.)**

Modelling Using Exponentials and Logs

...and Decay

EXAMPLE:

The concentration (C) of a drug in the bloodstream, t hours after taking an initial dose, decreases exponentially according to $C = Ae^{-kt}$, where k is a constant.
The initial concentration is 0.72, and this halves after 5 hours.
a) Find the values of A and k.
b) After 7 hours, what is the percentage decrease in concentration, to 1 d.p.?

a) The **initial concentration** is **0.72** when **$t = 0$**.
Put this information into the equation to **find A**:
$0.72 = A \times e^0 \Rightarrow 0.72 = A \times 1 \Rightarrow A = 0.72$

The question says that when $t = 5$, C is **half** of 0.72:
$C = 0.72e^{-kt}$ so $0.72 \div 2 = 0.72 \times e^{(-k \times 5)}$

$\Rightarrow 0.36 = 0.72 \times e^{-5k} \Rightarrow 0.36 = \frac{0.72}{e^{5k}}$

$\Rightarrow e^{5k} = \frac{0.72}{0.36} = 2$

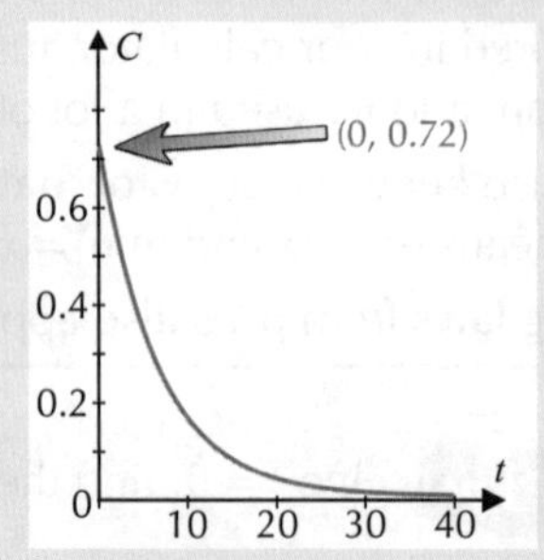

The graph of $C = 0.72e^{-0.139t}$

Now take 'ln' of **both sides** to solve:
$\ln e^{5k} = \ln 2 \Rightarrow 5k = \ln 2 \Rightarrow k = \frac{\ln 2}{5} = 0.139$ **(3 s.f.)**.

Use the exact value of k where possible.

b) Find the **concentration**, C, at $t = 7$ hours **in terms of** the initial concentration A:
$C = Ae^{-7 \times \frac{\ln 2}{5}} = A \times 0.3789...$

You don't actually need the value of A here — the answer can be found without it.

Work out the **decrease** in concentration:
$A - C = A - (A \times 0.3789...) = A(1 - 0.3789...) = A \times 0.6210...$

So as a **percentage**, the decrease is **62.1% to 1.d.p.**

Warm-Up Questions

Q1 Solve the following equations, giving your answers as exact values of x.
a) $\ln(x + 3) = 1$ b) $e^{2x} = 6$ c) $2 \ln x - \ln 3 = \ln 12$ d) $3e^{-4x+1} = 5$

Q2 Solve the equation $\ln x + \frac{24}{\ln x} = 10$, giving your answers as exact values of x.

Q3 The value of a motorbike (£V) varies with age (in t years from new) according to $V = 7500e^{-0.2t}$.
a) How much did it originally cost?
b) What will its value be after 10 years (to the nearest £)?
c) After how many years will the motorbike's value have fallen to £500? Give your answer to 1 d.p.

Exam Question

Q1 A breed of mink is introduced to a new habitat.
The number of mink, M, after t years in the habitat, is modelled by: $M = 74e^{0.6t}$ ($t \geq 0$)
a) State the number of mink that were introduced to the new habitat originally. [1 mark]
b) Predict the number of mink after 3 years in the habitat. [2 marks]
c) Predict the number of complete years it would take for the population of mink to exceed 10 000. [2 marks]

Q2 A radioactive substance decays exponentially so that its activity, A, can be modelled by $A = Be^{-kt}$, where t is the time in days, and $t \geq 0$.
Some experimental data is shown in the table.

t	0	5	10
A	50	42	

a) State the value of B. [1 mark]
b) Find the value of k, to 3 significant figures. [2 marks]
c) Estimate the missing value from the table, to the nearest whole number. [2 marks]
d) The half-life of a substance is the time it takes for the activity to halve.
Find the half-life of this substance, in days. Give your answer to the nearest day. [3 marks]

Learn this and watch your knowledge grow exponentially...

For these wordy problems, the key is just to extract the relevant information and solve like you did on the previous pages. The more you practise, the more familiar they'll become — soon you'll be able to do them with your eyes shut.

Composite and Inverse Functions

A function takes one number and transforms it into another — e.g. 'multiply by 5' and 'divide by 7' are both functions.

A Function is a type of Mapping

1) A **function** is an operation that takes numbers and **maps** each one to only one number — e.g. x^2 is written $f(x) = x^2$.
2) The set of starting numbers is the **domain** and the numbers they become is the **range**.
3) A **one-to-one** function maps **one** element in the **domain** to **one** element in the **range**.
4) A **many-to-one** function maps **more than one** element in the **domain** to **one** element in the **range**.

Some **common sets** you might come across for the domain and range include:

- $\mathbb{N}$ — natural numbers, i.e. { 1, 2, 3... }
- $\mathbb{W}$ — whole numbers, i.e. { 0, 1, 2, 3... }
- $\mathbb{Z}$ — all integers
- $\mathbb{Q}$ — all rational numbers
- $\mathbb{R}$ — all real numbers

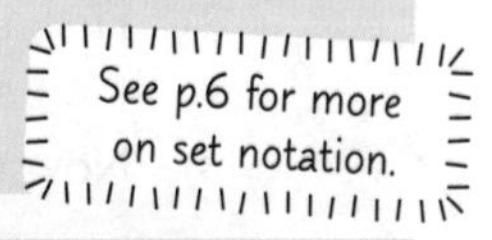

- f(x) is a function — it maps **every** value of x to **only one** value of $2x$.
- f(x) has **domain** $x \in \mathbb{R}$ and **range** $f(x) \in \mathbb{R}$.
- f(x) is a **one-to-one function.**

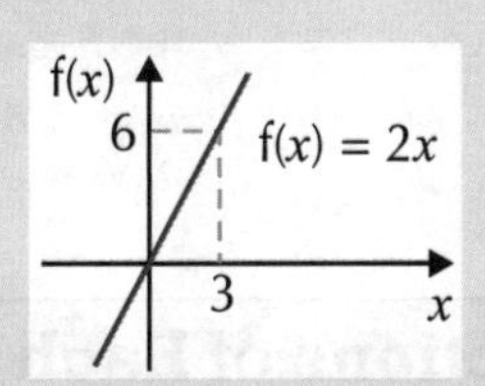

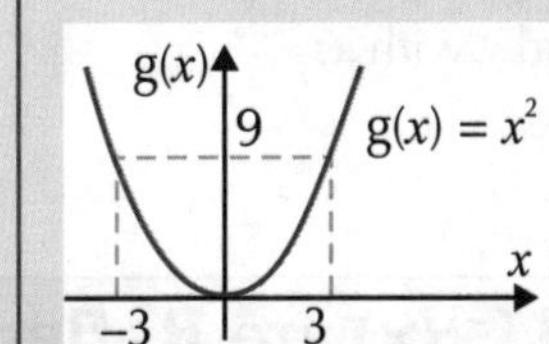

- g(x) is a function — it maps **each** value of x to **only one** value of x^2.
- g(x) has **domain** $x \in \mathbb{R}$ and **range** $g(x) \geq 0$.
- g(x) is a **many-to-one function.**

Functions can be Combined to make a Composite Function

1) If you have two functions f and g, you can **combine** them (do one followed by the other) to make a new function. This is called a **composite function.**
2) Composite functions are written fg(x) — this means do g first, then f. **Brackets** can be handy here, so $fg(x) = f(g(x))$. The **order** is really important — usually $fg(x) \neq gf(x)$.
3) Composite functions made up of **more than two** functions work in the same way.

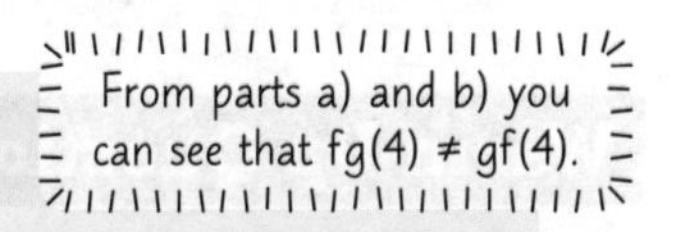

For the functions $f(x) = 2x^3$, $x \in \mathbb{R}$ and $g(x) = x - 3$, $x \in \mathbb{R}$, find:
a) fg(4) b) gf(4) c) fg(x) d) ff(x).

a) $fg(4) = f(g(4)) = f(4 - 3) = f(1) = 2 \times 1^3 = \mathbf{2}$

b) $gf(4) = g(f(4)) = g(2 \times 4^3) = g(128) = 128 - 3 = \mathbf{125}$

c) $fg(x) = f(g(x)) = f(x - 3) = \mathbf{2(x - 3)^3}$

d) $ff(x) = f(f(x)) = f(2x^3) = 2(2x^3)^3 = \mathbf{16x^9}$

4) If you're asked to **solve** an equation involving a composite function, start by finding fg(x).

EXAMPLE:

For the functions $f(x) = x + 1$, $x \in \mathbb{R}$ and $g(x) = \sin x$, $0 \leq x \leq 2\pi$, solve the equation $fg(x) = 1$.

First, **find** the function fg(x): $fg(x) = f(\sin x) = \sin x + 1$

Now **solve** the equation: $fg(x) = 1 \Rightarrow \sin x + 1 = 1$
$\Rightarrow \sin x = 0$
$\Rightarrow \mathbf{x = 0, \pi, \text{or } 2\pi}$

The domain of g is $0 \leq x \leq 2\pi$ so these are the only solutions.

5) Be careful — composite functions may **not exist**. This might happen if the domain or range of one function **excludes** values that are needed for the other function to work.

Only One-to-One Functions have Inverses

1) An **inverse function** does the **opposite** to the function. For a function f(x), the inverse is written $\mathbf{f^{-1}(x)}$.
2) An inverse function **maps** an element in the original function's **range** to an element in the **domain**. This means that only **one-to-one functions** have inverses, otherwise it wouldn't be a function by definition.
3) For **any** inverse $f^{-1}(x)$, doing the function and then the inverse is the same as doing the inverse then doing the function — both just give you x. ⟹ $f^{-1}f(x) = x = ff^{-1}(x)$
4) If you know that $\mathbf{f(g(x)) = x}$, then f(x) and g(x) **must** be inverses of each other.
5) The **domain** of $f^{-1}(x)$ is the **range** of f(x), and the **range** of $f^{-1}(x)$ is the **domain** of f(x).

Composite and Inverse Functions

Work out the **Inverse Function** using **Algebra**

For **simple** functions it's easy to work out what the inverse is just by **looking** at it — e.g. $f(x) = x + 1$ has the inverse $f^{-1}(x) = x - 1$. But for more **complex** functions, you need to **rearrange** the original function to **change** the **subject**.

EXAMPLE: Find the inverse of the function $f(x) = \ln(3x^2 + 1)$ with domain $x \in \mathbb{R}$.

1) **Replace** $f(x)$ with y — it's easier to work with:
$y = \ln(3x^2 + 1)$

2) First, use the **exponential** e to remove the 'ln': ← See p.19 for more on this.
$y = \ln(3x^2 + 1) \Rightarrow e^y = 3x^2 + 1$

3) Now **rearrange** the equation to make x the **subject**:
$e^y = 3x^2 + 1 \Rightarrow e^y - 1 = 3x^2 \Rightarrow \sqrt{\frac{e^y - 1}{3}} = x$

4) Replace x with $f^{-1}(x)$ and y with x:
$f^{-1}(x) = \sqrt{\frac{e^x - 1}{3}}$

You're told in the question that f has domain $x \in \mathbb{R}$. $3x^2 + 1$ is always ≥ 1, so $\ln(3x^2 + 1)$ is always ≥ 0. This means the range of $f(x)$ is $f(x) \geq 0$.

By swapping domain and range, the inverse $f^{-1}(x)$ has domain $x \geq 0$ and range $f^{-1}(x) \in \mathbb{R}$.

The **Graphs** of **f(x)** and **f⁻¹(x)** are **Reflections** of **Each Other**

The graph of the **inverse** of a function is a **reflection** of the original graph in the line $y = x$.

The inverse function is $f^{-1}(x) = \sqrt{x + 8}$.

EXAMPLE: Sketch the graph of the inverse of the function $f(x) = x^2 - 8$ with domain $x \geq 0$.

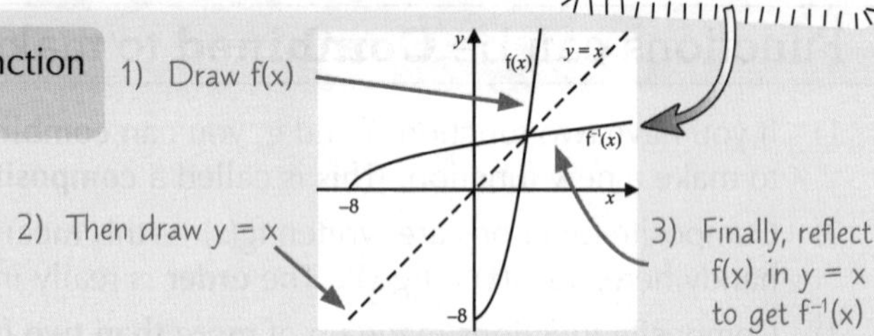

It's easy to see what the **domains** and **ranges** are from the graph — $f(x)$ has domain $x \geq 0$ and range $f(x) \geq -8$, so $f^{-1}(x)$ has domain $x \geq -8$ and range $f^{-1}(x) \geq 0$.

Warm-Up Questions

PRACTICE QUESTIONS

Q1 For each pair of functions f and g, find: (i) fg(2) (ii) gf(1) (iii) fg(x)

a) $f(x) = \frac{3}{x}$, $x > 0$ and $g(x) = 2x + 3$, $x \in \mathbb{R}$

b) $f(x) = 3x^2$, $x \geq 0$ and $g(x) = x + 4$, $x \in \mathbb{R}$

Q2 State the domains and ranges of the following functions:

a) $\sin x$ b) $\cos x$ c) $\tan x$ d) e^x e) $\ln x$

Q3 Using algebra, find the inverse of the function $f(x) = \sqrt{2x - 4}$, $x \geq 2$.

Exam Questions

Q1 The functions f and g, defined on suitable domains, are given by $f(x) = \frac{1}{x^2 - 9}$ and $g(x) = x - 2$.

a) Find an expression for $h(x)$, where $h(x) = f(g(x))$. Give your answer as a single fraction. [2 marks]

b) State a suitable domain for h. [1 mark]

Q2 Using the functions $f(x) = \cos x$ and $g(x) = 2\pi x$, find expressions for:

a) $f(g(x))$ [2 mark]

b) $g(f(x))$ [1 mark]

Q3 A function is defined by $f(x) = e^{x+1}$ for $x \in \mathbb{R}$.

a) Find an expression for $f^{-1}(x)$. [3 marks]

b) What values of x cannot be in the domain of $f^{-1}(x)$? [1 mark]

Inverses — putting the 'nuf' in functions since 1877...

If you think of a function as like a pipe (stuff goes in one end, and comes out the other), then a composite function is like two pipes joined end to end. But unlike pipes, it makes a big difference which function comes first — here's a trick to help you remember: in 'fg(x)', the function g is closest to the x, so you do g first and then f second.

Recurrence Relations

If you attempted to list an infinite sequence of numbers, you'd probably miss your dinner. That's why recurrence relations were invented — even mathematicians need to eat.

A **Recurrence Relation** describes a **Sequence**

1) A **sequence** is just a list of numbers that follow a certain **pattern** or **rule**.
2) The notation u_n is used to represent a **term** in a sequence. The first term is usually written as u_0, and u_{n+1} is the term after u_n.
3) A **recurrence relation** tells you how to work out a term in a sequence from the **previous term** — it gives you a rule to work out u_{n+1} if you know u_n.
4) To **define** a sequence, you need a **recurrence relation** and a **value** for at least **one term** (usually the first term).

The rule here is: tread carefully.

EXAMPLE: Describe fully the sequence that begins 3, 7, 11, 15, ... using a recurrence relation.

First, find the **relationship** between each term and the next.
The terms are **increasing by 4** at each step, so the rule is:
'add 4 to the previous term', or $u_{n+1} = u_n + 4$ ← This isn't enough to describe the sequence fully — e.g. the sequence 4, 8, 12, 16, ... fits the same pattern.
To describe the sequence fully, you need to give **one term**.
It's usually easiest to give the **first term** — here it's 3.
So the full answer is: $u_{n+1} = u_n + 4$, $u_0 = 3$.

Complete a **Recurrence Relation** from **Partial Information**

You may have to **set up** and **solve equations** in order to **complete** a recurrence relation.

A sequence is defined by the recurrence relation $u_{n+1} = 2u_n + b$ with $u_0 = 2$.
a) Find u_2 in terms of b. b) Given that $u_3 = 23$, find b.

a) You're given the **first term**, u_0, so use the **recurrence relation** to find u_1 and u_2:

$u_{n+1} = 2u_n + b$, so $u_1 = 2u_0 + b = 2 \times 2 + b = 4 + b$
$u_2 = 2u_1 + b = 2(4 + b) + b$ ← Put in the expression for u_1 you just found.
$= 8 + 3b$

b) Form an **expression** for u_3 using the **recurrence relation**:

$u_{n+1} = 2u_n + b$, so $u_3 = 2u_2 + b = 2(8 + 3b) + b$ ← Put in the expression for u_2 found in a).
$= 16 + 7b$

The question tells you $u_3 = 23$, so form an **equation** and **solve** it to find b:

$23 = 16 + 7b \Rightarrow 7b = 7 \Rightarrow b = 1$

Some sequences **Converge** to a **Limit**

A **linear** recurrence relation has the form $u_{n+1} = au_n + b$. The **behaviour** of the generated sequence **depends** on the **value of** a — there are three different cases:

1) If $a \geq 1$ **or** $a < -1$, then the sequence **diverges** and the terms just keep getting **bigger**.
2) If $a = -1$, then the sequence **bounces** between **two values**.
3) If $-1 < a < 1$, then the sequence **converges** and the terms approach a **limit** as $n \to \infty$.

There's one exception — when a = 1 and b = 0, the sequence is constant and just repeats u_0.

The Limit Formula

The **limit** of the recurrence relation $u_{n+1} = au_n + b$ (when $-1 < a < 1$), is the value L that satisfies: $L = aL + b$.
Rearrange to get the **limit formula**:

$$L = aL + b \Rightarrow L - aL = b$$
$$\Rightarrow (1 - a)L = b$$
$$\Rightarrow L = \frac{b}{1-a}$$

This doesn't depend on u_0 or any of the terms in the sequence.

EXAMPLE: Calculate the limit of the sequence generated by $u_{n+1} = 0.5u_n + 1$, $u_0 = 1$.

The recurrence relation has the form $u_{n+1} = au_n + b$ where $a = 0.5$ and $b = 1$.
As $a = 0.5$ lies in the range $-1 < a < 1$, the sequence has a **limit**, L. ← Always state this in your answers.
The **limit formula** gives:

$$L = \frac{b}{1-a} = \frac{1}{1-0.5} = 2$$

So $u_n \to 2$ as $n \to \infty$.

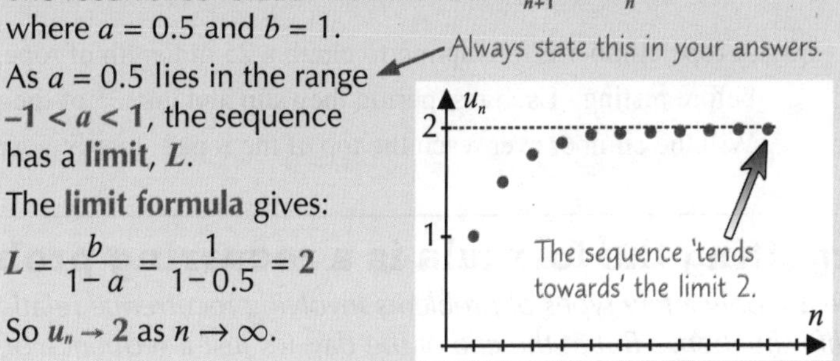

Recurrence Relations

Model Real-Life Situations using Recurrence Relations

Recurrence relations can provide simple **models** for many **real-life situations**.

A patient must take medicine every morning. The medicine contains a drug that increases in concentration in the body over a number of days. The concentration level c_n (mg/ml), after the dose on the nth day, is given by the recurrence relation:

$c_{n+1} = pc_n + q$ for some constants p and q.

The concentration levels after the first three doses are 0.1 mg/ml, 0.3 mg/ml and 0.38 mg/ml.

a) Use the information above to find the values of p and q.

b) The drug is dangerous if the concentration exceeds 0.5 mg/ml. Will this ever happen?

a) Write down the **information** you're given:

$c_0 = 0.1,\ c_1 = 0.3,\ c_2 = 0.38$

Use the **recurrence relation** to form two equations:

$c_1 = pc_0 + q \Rightarrow 0.3 = 0.1p + q \quad (1)$

$c_2 = pc_1 + q \Rightarrow 0.38 = 0.3p + q \quad (2)$

Now **solve simultaneously** for p and q:

$(2) - (1): \quad 0.38 - 0.3 = 0.3p - 0.1p$

$\Rightarrow 0.08 = 0.2p \Rightarrow \mathbf{p = 0.4}$

Substitute p into equation (1):

$0.3 = 0.1p + q \Rightarrow q = 0.3 - (0.1 \times 0.4)$

$\Rightarrow \mathbf{q = 0.26}$

b) From a), the recurrence relation is:

$c_{n+1} = 0.4c_n + 0.26$

Since $\mathbf{-1 < 0.4 < 1}$, the recurrence relation has a **limit**. Use the **formula** to calculate the limit:

$$L = \frac{q}{1-p} = \frac{0.26}{1-0.4} = \mathbf{0.433...}$$

The **concentration level** approaches, but never exceeds, 0.433... This is < 0.5, so the concentration level **never exceeds** 0.5 mg/ml.

p = 0.4, which means that 40% of the drug is left in the body by the next morning.

Warm-Up Questions

Q1 Describe fully each of these sequences using a recurrence relation:

a) 2, 4, 6, 8, ... b) 5, 9, 13, 17, ... c) 5, 4, 3, 2, ... d) $9, 3, 1, \frac{1}{3}, ...$

Q2 Find the 4th term of the sequence described by the following recurrence relations:

a) $a_{n+1} = 0.5a_n + 2$ with $a_0 = 12$ b) $b_{n+1} = 2b_n + 10$ with $b_0 = -5$

Q3 Calculate the limit of each the following recurrence relations:

a) $u_{n+1} = 0.3u_n - 1$ b) $u_{n+1} = -0.1u_n + 5$

Q4 A sequence is defined by the recurrence relation $u_{n+1} = \frac{1}{2}u_n + 2$ with $u_0 = 2$.

a) Calculate the first four terms of the sequence.

b) Explain why this sequence approaches a limit as $n \to \infty$.

c) Calculate this limit.

Exam Questions

Q1 A sequence satisfies the recurrence relation $u_{n+1} = au_n - 5$ with $u_1 = 2a + 1$.

a) State the value of u_2 in terms of a. [1 mark]

b) Given that the sequence has a limit and that $u_2 + 4 = 0$, find the value of a. [3 marks]

Q2 a) A sequence is given by $a_{n+1} = -a_n$ with $a_2 = -1$. Determine the values of a_0 and a_1. [1 mark]

b) A different sequence is given by $27, 6, 13, 10\frac{2}{3}, ...$ It is generated by the recurrence relation $b_{n+1} = pb_n + q$ with $b_0 = 27$. Determine the values of p and q. [3 marks]

c) (i) Explain why the sequence in part a) does not have a limit. [1 mark]

(ii) Calculate the limit of the sequence in part b). [2 marks]

Q3 A rope climber is attempting to climb a 25 m length of rope. They climb in stretches of 10 m before resting. Each rest period they slip and lose $\frac{1}{3}$ of their total progress.
Will the climber ever reach the top of the rope? Justify your answer. [3 marks]

Forgetting the formula is a recurring problem of mine...

There are only a few types of problems involving recurrence relations — so examiners like to dress them up using real-life situations. But at the end of the day, it's just a sequence of numbers — and totally within your limits.

Revision Summary for Section One

From quadratics to quartics and logs to limits — that's the algebra section finished.

- Try these questions and tick off each one when you get it right.
- When you've done all the questions for a topic and are completely happy with it, tick off the topic.

Quadratic Equations and Inequalities (p.2-7)

1) a) Express $f(x) = -2x^2 + 16x - 27$ in the form $p(x + q)^2 + r$.
   b) State the coordinates of the turning point on the graph of $y = f(x)$.

2) Given that $f(x) = mx^2 + 6x + m$ has no real roots, find the range of values of m.

3) Determine the exact values of k for which the quadratic $f(x) = x^2 + (k - 2)x + k$ has one repeated root.

4) Solve the inequalities: a) $x^2 > 49$ b) $3x^2 - 23 \leq 1$ c) $3x^2 + 5x - 2 > 0$

Cubic and Quartic Polynomials (p.8-12)

5) The cubic polynomial $f(x) = ax^3 - 5x^2 - 8x + b$ can be expressed as $f(x) = g(x)(x - 1) - 4$ and $f(x) = h(x)(x + 1)$ for quadratics $g(x)$ and $h(x)$.
   a) Determine the values of a and b.
   b) Factorise $f(x)$ fully.

6) The diagram to the right is the graph of the quartic polynomial $f(x) = -2x^4 - 3x^3 + 20x^2 + 27x - 18$. Two points where the curve intercepts the x-axis have been labelled. Find all solutions to $f(x) = 0$.

Graph Transformations (p.13-14)

7) a) Sketch the graph of $f(x) = 2x(x - 4)^2(x + 3)$.
   b) Sketch the graph of each of the following transformations:
   (i) $y = f(x - 1)$ (ii) $y = f(-2x)$ (iii) $y = -f(x)$

Exponentials and Logs (p.15-20)

8) a) Write $2\log_6 3 + \log_6 4$ in the form $\log_2 p$ where $p \in \mathbb{Z}$.
   b) Hence solve $\log_2 \sqrt{x} = 2\log_6 3 + \log_6 4$, where $x > 0$.

9) The mass of a radioactive substance after t years is denoted by N. The decay of the substance is measured by the equation $N = Ae^{-pt}$, where A is the initial mass, p is a constant and t measures time in years.
   a) The substance takes 45 years to decay to half its original mass. Determine the value of p to 2 s.f.
   b) After 90 years, the substance has a mass of 12 units. Determine the value of A.

Composite and Inverse Functions (p.21-22)

10) Functions f and g are defined by $f(x) = 2x - 3$ and $g(x) = x^3$.
   a) Find an expression for $h(x)$, where $h(x) = f(g(x))$.
   b) Find an expression for $h^{-1}(x)$.

Recurrence Relations (p.23-24)

11) The third term generated by the recurrence relation $u_{n+1} = pu_n - 2$ is $u_2 = 4p - 1$.
   a) Given that $u_1 = 2$, find the value of p.
   b) Calculate the limit of the sequence.

12) A sequence is generated by the recurrence relation $u_{n+1} = ru_n + t$ with $u_0 = 5r + t$.
   a) Determine the value of u_1 in terms of r and t.
   b) Given that $u_1 = 2$ and that the sequence has a limit of 1, find all possible values of r.
   c) For each value of r calculated in part b), give the value of u_2.

Angles and Identities

You should be familiar with angles measured in degrees. For Highers, you also need to measure them in radians.

Radians are another way of **Measuring Angles**

You need to know how radians relate to **degrees**.
In short, **180 degrees = π radians**. The table below shows you how to convert between the two units:

Converting angles	
Radians to degrees: Divide by π, multiply by 180.	Degrees to radians: Divide by 180, multiply by π.

If there isn't a degree symbol, you should assume the question is in radians — so sin x would be radians but sin x° is degrees.

"...and bake in an oven preheated to π radians for around 40 minutes."

Here's a table of some of the **common angles** that often come up — in degrees and radians:

Degrees	0	30	45	60	90	120	180	270	360
Radians	0	$\frac{\pi}{6}$	$\frac{\pi}{4}$	$\frac{\pi}{3}$	$\frac{\pi}{2}$	$\frac{2\pi}{3}$	π	$\frac{3\pi}{2}$	2π

Some angles have **Exact Trig Values**

At National 5 you came across the three **trig formulas** and saw how to use them on right-angled triangles.

Remember: SOH CAH TOA...

$\sin = \frac{\text{opp}}{\text{hyp}}$ $\quad \cos = \frac{\text{adj}}{\text{hyp}}$ $\quad \tan = \frac{\text{opp}}{\text{adj}}$

You can use these on two **special triangles** to find some **exact trig values**:

Half an equilateral triangle with sides of length 2:
Get the height $\sqrt{3}$ by **Pythagoras' Theorem:**
$1^2 + (\sqrt{3})^2 = 2^2$
Then you can use the triangle to work out **sin, cos** and **tan** of **30°** and **60°**.

So $\sin 30° = \frac{1}{2}$, $\cos 30° = \frac{\sqrt{3}}{2}$,
$\tan 30° = \frac{1}{\sqrt{3}}$, $\sin 60° = \frac{\sqrt{3}}{2}$,
$\cos 60° = \frac{1}{2}$ and $\tan 60° = \sqrt{3}$

Right-angled triangle with two sides of length 1:
The $\sqrt{2}$ just comes from **Pythagoras:**
$1^2 + 1^2 = \sqrt{2}^2$
This triangle gives you **sin, cos** and **tan** of **45°**.

So $\sin 45° = \frac{1}{\sqrt{2}}$,
$\cos 45° = \frac{1}{\sqrt{2}}$
and $\tan 45° = 1$

You don't need to memorise these values, but you need to be able to find them.

You can use this method on different triangles to find other exact values.

EXAMPLE: Given that $\sin x = \frac{7}{12}$, find the exact value of $\cos x$ and $\tan x$.

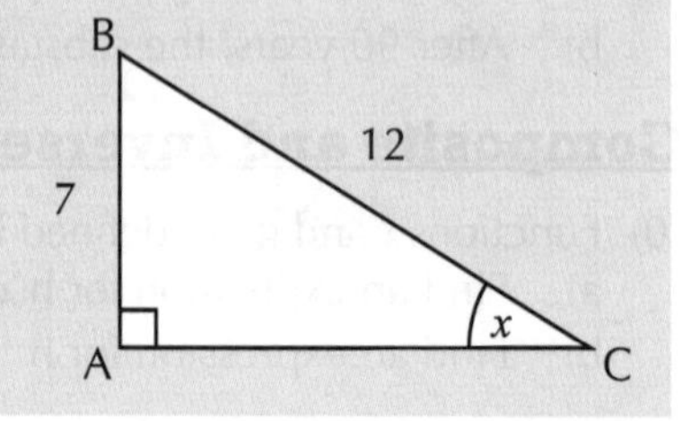

1) You can find the length of the missing side by using Pythagoras:
$AC^2 = 12^2 - 7^2 = 95$ so $AC = \sqrt{95}$

2) So $\cos x = \frac{\sqrt{95}}{12}$ and $\tan x = \frac{7}{\sqrt{95}}$

There are two **Important Trig Identities**

You'll have seen these identities at National 5, but make sure you **learn them** as they often come up in trig questions.

$$\tan x \equiv \frac{\sin x}{\cos x} \qquad \sin^2 x + \cos^2 x \equiv 1 \quad \Rightarrow \quad \begin{array}{l}\sin^2 x \equiv 1 - \cos^2 x \\ \cos^2 x \equiv 1 - \sin^2 x\end{array}$$

When I graduated from university, I got a radian instead of a degree...

There should be two modes on your calculator, one for degrees and one for radians. Make sure you know how to swap between them — and always check which mode you're in before doing your calculations in the exam.

Trig Graphs and Transformations

Most of what's on this page you should have come across at National 5, but here's a recap (I'm kind like that). You'll also need to know all the graphs in radians as well degrees, so let's get stuck in...

You have to know the angles in **Radians** as well as degrees

The values of sin x, cos x and tan x are exactly the **same** whether x is in **radians** or **degrees** — you just need to remember the **key values** in both units.

$x°$	–360	–270	–180	–90	0	90	180	270	360
x radians	-2π	$-\frac{3\pi}{2}$	$-\pi$	$-\frac{\pi}{2}$	0	$\frac{\pi}{2}$	π	$\frac{3\pi}{2}$	2π
sin x	0	1	0	–1	0	1	0	–1	0
cos x	1	0	–1	0	1	0	–1	0	1
tan x	0	—	0	—	0	—	0	—	0

The '—' here means tan x is undefined, so draw an asymptote (see below).

sin x and cos x are always in the range –1 to 1

Both **sin x** and **cos x** just bounce up and down between –1 and 1 — these functions **never** take a value outside this range.

You saw amplitude at N5 — it's half the distance from the maximum value of a function to the minimum value. sin x and cos x have an amplitude of 1.

sin x and cos x are both **periodic** (repeat themselves) with **period 2π**:

$\cos(x + 2\pi) = \cos x$

$\sin(x + 2\pi) = \sin x$

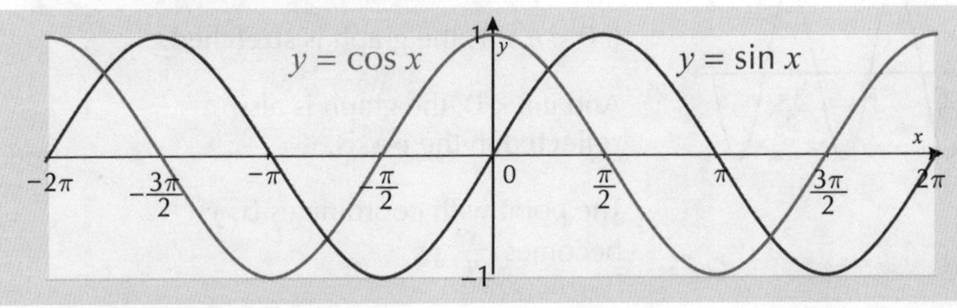

sin x goes through the **origin** — that means **sin 0 = 0.**

cos x crosses the y-axis at $y = 1$ — that means **cos 0 = 1.**

Symmetry in the **vertical** axis:

$\sin(-x) = -\sin x$

$\cos(-x) = \cos x$

...but not beyond?

tan x can be **Any Value** at all

tan x is **different** from sin x or cos x.
It doesn't go gently up and down between –1 and 1 — it goes **between $-\infty$ and $+\infty$.**

tan x is also periodic — but with **period π**

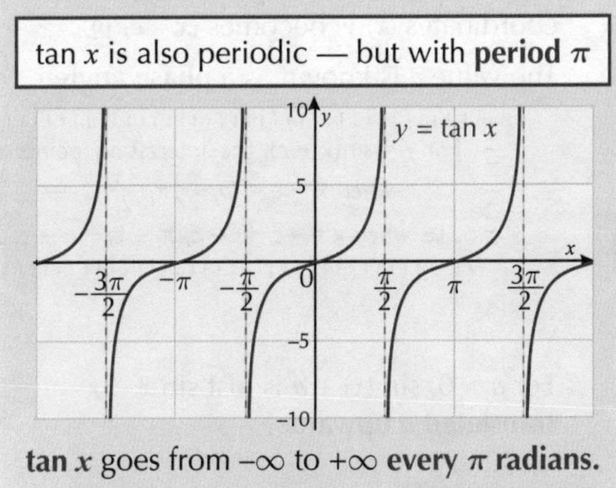

tan x goes from $-\infty$ to $+\infty$ **every π radians.**
So it has period π, and takes **every possible value** in each interval of π radians.

$\tan(x + \pi) = \tan x$

tan x is **undefined** at $\pm\frac{\pi}{2}, \pm\frac{3\pi}{2}, \pm\frac{5\pi}{2}, \ldots$

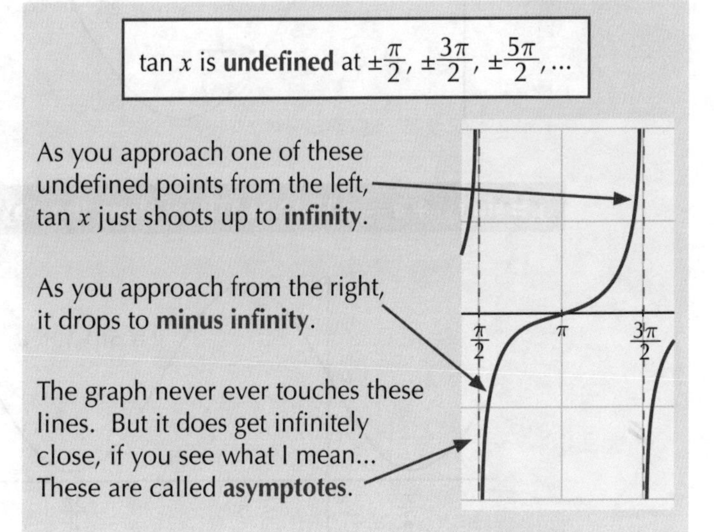

As you approach one of these undefined points from the left, tan x just shoots up to **infinity**.

As you approach from the right, it drops to **minus infinity**.

The graph never ever touches these lines. But it does get infinitely close, if you see what I mean... These are called **asymptotes**.

The easiest way to sketch any of these graphs is to plot the **important points** which happen **every $\frac{\pi}{2}$** (i.e. $-\pi$, $-\frac{\pi}{2}$, **0**, $\frac{\pi}{2}$, π, $\frac{3\pi}{2}$, 2π) and then just join up the dots.

Trig Graphs and Transformations

There are 4 basic types of **Transformed Trig Graph**

Transformed trigonometric graphs look much the same as the bog-standard ones, just a little **different**. There are four main types of transformation.

$y = n \sin x$ — a VERTICAL STRETCH or SQUASH

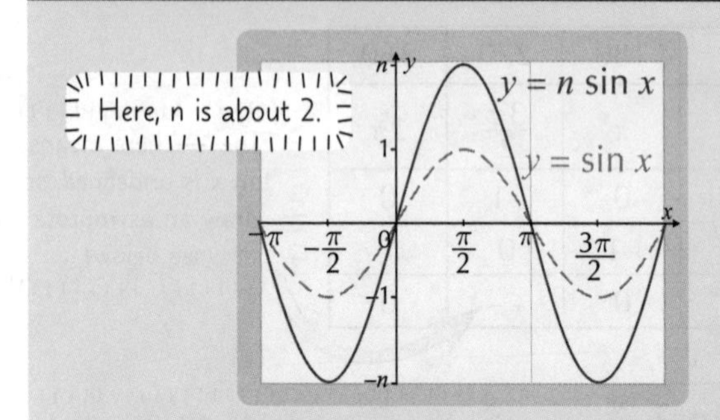

If $n > 1$, the graph of $y = \sin x$ is **stretched vertically** by a factor of n.

If $0 < n < 1$, the graph is **squashed**.

And if $n < 0$, the graph is also **reflected** in the ***x*-axis**.

The point with coordinates (x, y) becomes $(\boldsymbol{x}, \boldsymbol{ny})$.

$y = \sin nx$ — a HORIZONTAL SQUASH or STRETCH

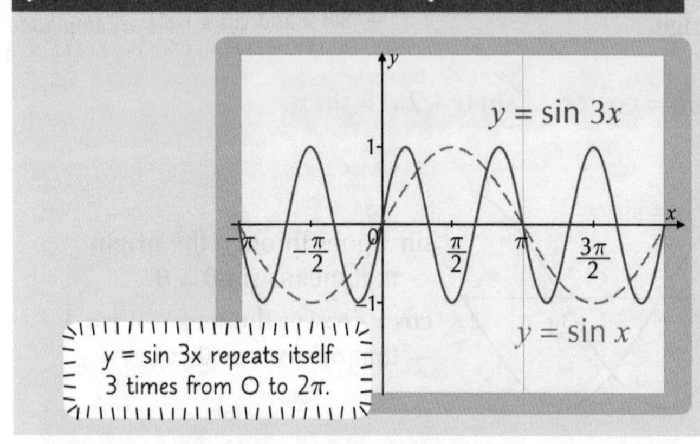

If $n > 1$, the graph of $y = \sin x$ is **squashed horizontally** by a factor of n. (The squash is actually a **stretch** of $\frac{1}{n}$.)

If $0 < n < 1$, the graph is **stretched**.

And if $n < 0$, the graph is also **reflected** in the ***y*-axis**.

The point with coordinates (x, y) becomes $(\frac{\boldsymbol{x}}{\boldsymbol{n}}, y)$.

$y = \sin (x + c)$ — a TRANSLATION along the x-axis

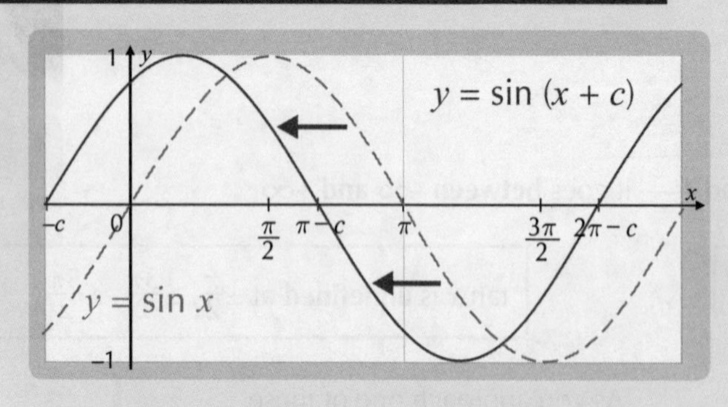

For $c > 0$, $\sin (x + c)$ is just $\sin x$ **translated *c* to the left.**

Similarly, $\sin (x - c)$ is just $\sin x$ **translated *c* to the right.**

For $y = \sin (x + c)$, the point with coordinates (x, y) becomes $(\boldsymbol{x - c}, \boldsymbol{y})$.

The value c is known as a **phase angle.**

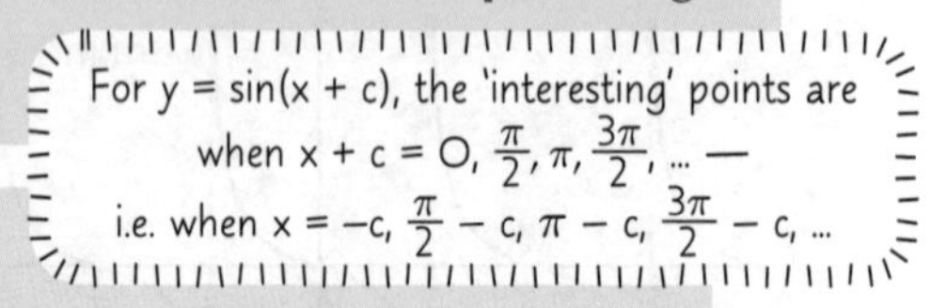

$y = \sin (x) + a$ — a TRANSLATION along the y-axis

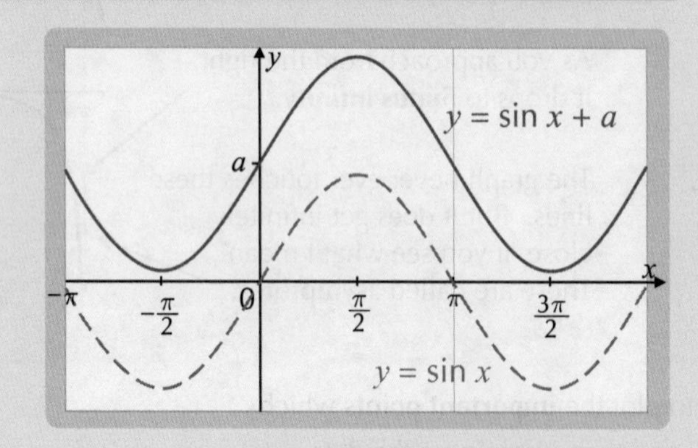

For $a > 0$, $\sin (x) + a$ is just $\sin x$ **translated *a* upwards.**

Similarly, $\sin (x) - a$ is just $\sin x$ **translated *a* downwards.**

The point with coordinates (x, y) becomes $(\boldsymbol{x}, \boldsymbol{y + a})$.

Trig Graphs and Transformations

Consider **Multiple Transformations** one at a time

If you need to sketch a graph with **multiple transformations** (like $y = 3 \sin x + 2$), draw one transformation at a time.

So first sketch $\boldsymbol{y = 3 \sin x}$ (the **vertical stretch**) and then apply the **vertical shift** to get the full graph $\boldsymbol{y = 3 \sin x + 2}$.

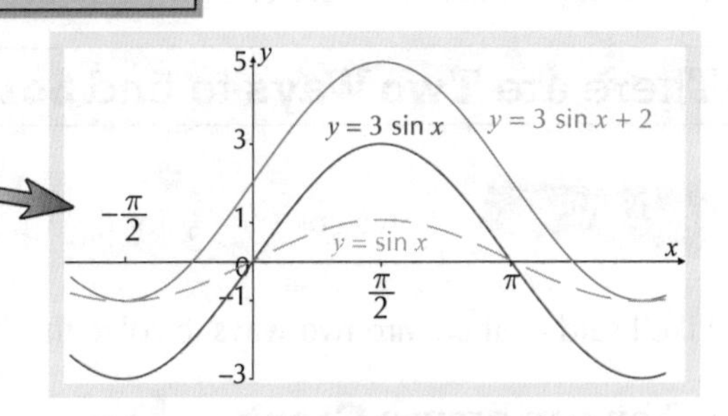

If you need a reminder on graph transformations, have a look back at page 13 in Section One.

You can use a **Transformed Graph** to work out the **Transformation...**

EXAMPLE: The graph on the right is of the form $y = p \sin qx + r$. Find the values of p, q and r.

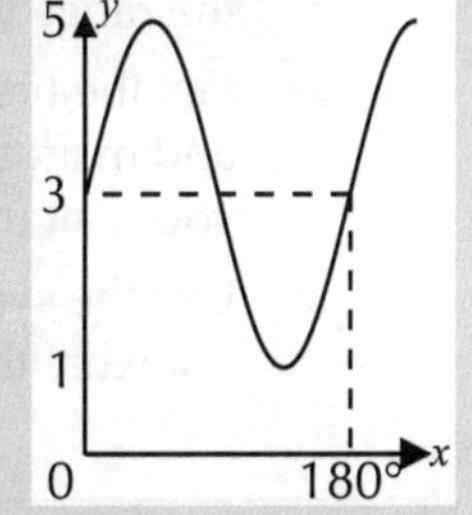

1) The graph of $y = \sin x$ takes values between –1 and 1, so has an amplitude of 1. This transformed graph takes values between 1 and 5, so has an amplitude of 2. The graph has been **stretched** in the ***y*-direction** by a factor of 2, so $\boldsymbol{p = 2}$.
2) The transformed graph has one complete 'loop' between 0° and 180°, so between 0° and 360°, there will be two complete 'loops', so $\boldsymbol{q = 2}$.
3) Lastly, $y = \sin x$ normally **intersects** the ***y*-axis** at 0, whereas the transformed graph intersects at 3. The graph has been shifted up by 3, so $\boldsymbol{r = 3}$. (So the equation of the graph is $y = 2 \sin 2x + 3$.)

...or to find out **Information** about **Specific Points**

EXAMPLE: The frequency of a sound wave can be described by the function $F(x) = 50 \cos 16x - 40$. Determine the period of $F(x)$ and its maximum value.

1) The function has been **stretched** in the ***x*-direction** by a factor of $\frac{1}{16}$. To find its period, you need to multiply 2π (the period of cos) by $\frac{1}{16}$. So the period of $F(x)$ is $\frac{1}{16} \times 2\pi = \boldsymbol{\frac{\pi}{8}}$.
2) For the **maximum value**, you know that the **largest** value cos can take is 1. So the maximum value of $\cos 16x$ is 1 and the maximum value of $F(x) = 50 \times 1 - 40 = \mathbf{10}$.

Warm Up Questions

Q1 Sketch the graph $y = 2 \cos x - 1$ for $0 \le x \le 2\pi$

Q2 Sketch:
a) $y = \frac{1}{2} \cos x°$ (for $0 \le x \le 360$)
b) $y = \sin\left(x + \frac{\pi}{6}\right)$ (for $0 \le x \le 2\pi$)
c) $y = \tan 3x°$ (for $0 \le x \le 180$).

Q3 The graph on the right is of the form $y = p \cos qx + r$. Find the values of p, q and r.

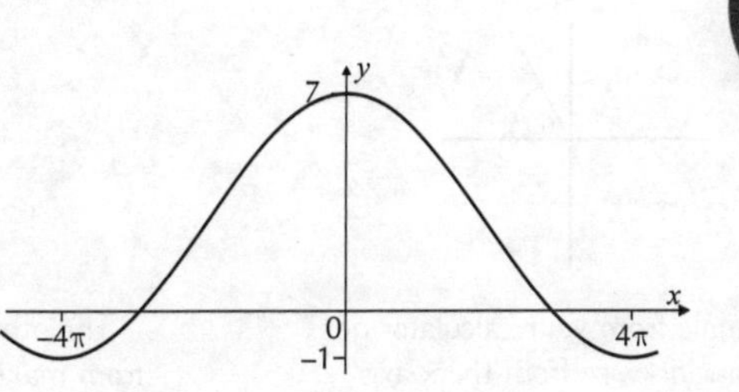

Exam Questions

Q1 a) Sketch, for $0 \le x \le 360$, the graph of $y = \cos(x° + 60°)$. [2 marks]
b) Write down all the values of x, for $0 \le x \le 360$, where $\cos(x° + 60°) = 0$. [2 marks]

Q2 Sketch, for $0 \le x \le \pi$, the graph of $y = \sin 4x$. [2 marks]

Curling up on the sofa with 2 cos x — that's my idea of cosiness...

It's really really really really really important that you can draw and transform the trig graphs on these pages. Trust me.

Solving Trig Equations

I used to really hate trig stuff like this. But once I'd got the hang of it, I just couldn't get enough. I stopped going out, lost interest in romance — the CAST method became my life. Learn it, but be careful. It's addictive.

There are **Two Ways** to find **Solutions** in an **Interval**

Solve $\cos x° = \frac{1}{2}$ for $0 \le x \le 720$.

Like I said — there are **two ways** to solve this kind of question. Just use the one you prefer...

You can draw a **Graph...**

1) Draw the **graph** of $y = \cos x°$ for the range you're interested in...
2) Get the first solution from your **calculator** and mark this on the graph. Make sure your calculator is set to **degrees**.
3) Use the **symmetry of the graph** to work out what the other solutions are:

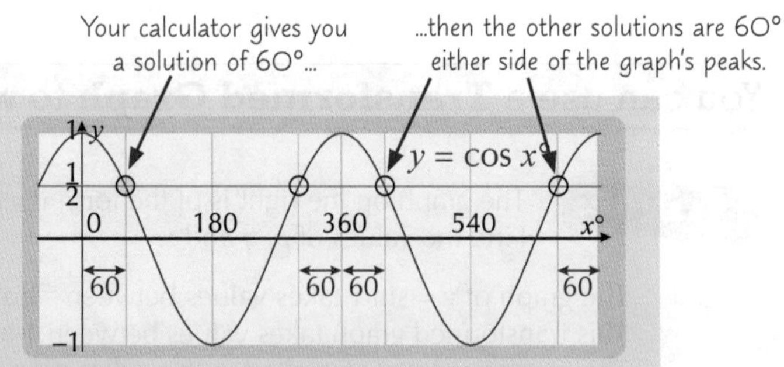

The solutions are: **60**, **300**, **420** and **660**.

...or you can use the **CAST Diagram**

CAST stands for **COS**, **ALL**, **SIN**, **TAN** — the CAST diagram shows you where these functions produce **positive** values:

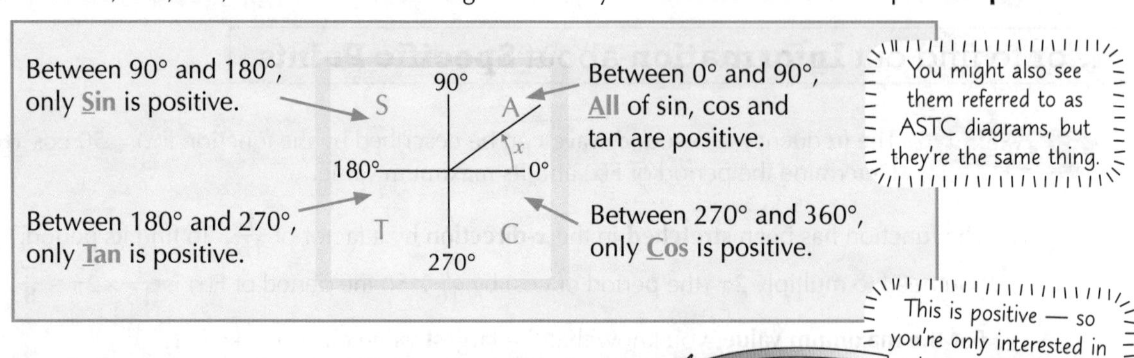

This is positive — so you're only interested in where cos is positive.

First, to find all the values of x between 0 and 360 where $\cos x = \frac{1}{2}$, you do this:

Put the **first solution** onto the **CAST diagram**.

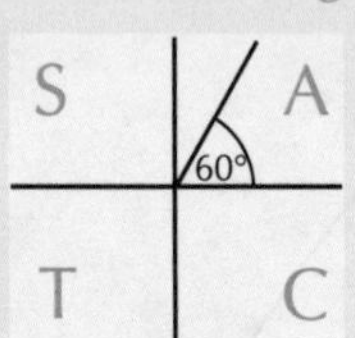

The angle from your calculator goes anticlockwise from the x-axis (unless it's negative — then it would go clockwise into the 4th quadrant).

Find the **other angles** between 0 and 360 that might be solutions.

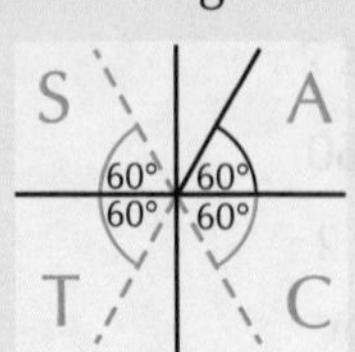

The other possible solutions come from making the same angle from the horizontal axis in the other 3 quadrants.

Ditch the ones that are the **wrong sign**.

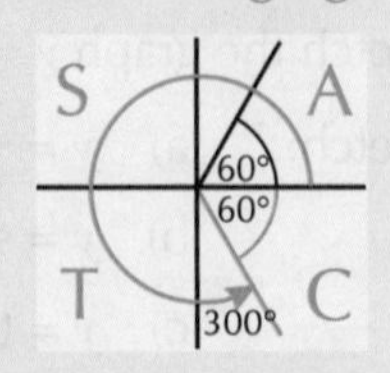

cos x° = ½, which is positive. The CAST diagram tells you cos is positive in the 4th quadrant, but not the 2nd or 3rd, so ditch those two angles.

So you've got solutions 60 and 300 in the range 0 to 360. But you need **all the solutions** in the range 0 to 720. Get these by repeatedly **adding** (or subtracting) **360** onto each until you go out of range:

$x = 60 \Rightarrow$ (adding 360) $x = 420$, 780 (too big)
and (subtracting 360) $x = -300$ (too small)

$x = 300 \Rightarrow$ (adding 360) $x = 660$, 1020 (too big)
and (subtracting 360) $x = -60$ (too small)

sin and cos have a period of 360°, so adding 360° to a solution gives another solution.

So the solutions are: $x =$ **60**, **300**, **420** and **660**.

Solving Trig Equations

Sometimes you end up with **sin kx = number...**

For these, it's definitely easier to draw the **graph** rather than use the CAST method — that's one reason why being able to sketch trig graphs properly is so important.

EXAMPLE: Solve $\sin 3x = -\frac{1}{\sqrt{2}}$ for $0 \le x \le 2\pi$.

1) You've got $3x$ instead of x, which means the interval you need to find solutions in is $\mathbf{0 \le 3x \le 6\pi}$. So draw the graph of $y = \sin x$ between 0 and 6π.
2) On p.26, you saw that $\frac{1}{\sqrt{2}} = \sin\frac{\pi}{4}$,
   and so $-\frac{1}{\sqrt{2}} = \sin\left(-\frac{\pi}{4}\right)$, which gives $\mathbf{3x = -\frac{\pi}{4}}$
   — but this is **outside the interval** for $3x$, so use the pattern of the graph to find a solution in the interval.
   As the sin curve repeats every 2π, there'll be a solution at $2\pi - \frac{\pi}{4} = \mathbf{\frac{7\pi}{4}}$.

These are the solutions — but remember that this is for 3x. You'll need to divide by 3 to get your final answers.

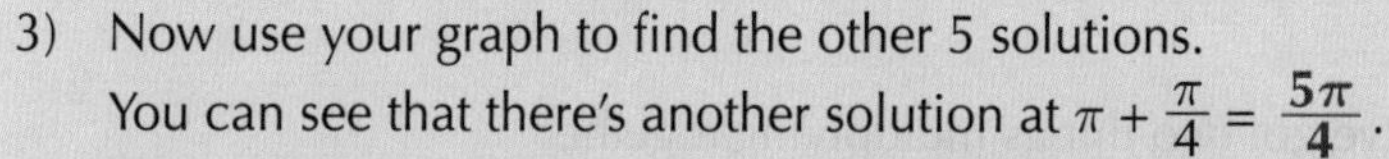

3) Now use your graph to find the other 5 solutions.
   You can see that there's another solution at $\pi + \frac{\pi}{4} = \mathbf{\frac{5\pi}{4}}$.
4) Then add on 2π and 4π to both $\frac{5\pi}{4}$ and $\frac{7\pi}{4}$ to get: $3x = \frac{5\pi}{4}, \frac{7\pi}{4}, \frac{13\pi}{4}, \frac{15\pi}{4}, \frac{21\pi}{4}$ and $\frac{23\pi}{4}$
5) **Divide by 3** to get the solutions for x: $x = \mathbf{\frac{5\pi}{12}, \frac{7\pi}{12}, \frac{13\pi}{12}, \frac{15\pi}{12}, \frac{21\pi}{12}}$ and $\mathbf{\frac{23\pi}{12}}$
6) **Check** your answers by putting these values into your calculator.

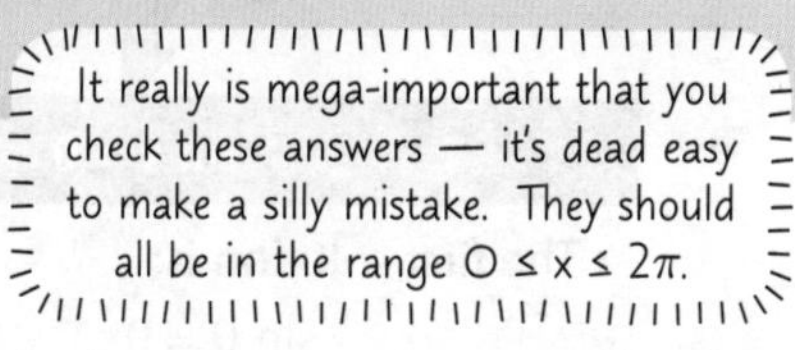

...or **Something More Complicated**

All the steps in this example are basically the same as in the one above, although at first sight it looks rather tricky. Just take it step by step and enjoy the modellinginess* of it all...

EXAMPLE: A simplified model of the phases of the moon is given by $P = 50\sin\left(\left(\frac{90t}{7}\right)^\circ + 90^\circ\right) + 50$, where P is the percentage of the moon visible at night, and t is the number of days after a full (100%) moon was recorded. On which days, over 12 weeks, will there be a half moon?

1) Start by figuring out the interval for the solutions. 12 weeks = 84 days, so $0 \le t \le 84$.
   But you've got $\left(\left(\frac{90t}{7}\right)^\circ + 90^\circ\right)$, so the interval is:
   $$\left(\frac{90\times 0}{7}\right)^\circ + 90^\circ \le \left(\left(\frac{90t}{7}\right)^\circ + 90^\circ\right) \le \left(\frac{90\times 84}{7}\right)^\circ + 90^\circ \Rightarrow \mathbf{90^\circ \le \left(\left(\frac{90t}{7}\right)^\circ + 90^\circ\right) \le 1170^\circ}$$
2) The question is asking you to find the values of t when $P = 50$, so put this into the model:
   $$50 = 50\sin\left(\left(\frac{90t}{7}\right)^\circ + 90^\circ\right) + 50$$
   $$\Rightarrow 0 = \sin\left(\left(\frac{90t}{7}\right)^\circ + 90^\circ\right)$$
   $$\Rightarrow \left(\frac{90t}{7}\right)^\circ + 90^\circ = \sin^{-1} 0 = \mathbf{0^\circ}$$
   This is **outside the interval** for solutions, so consult the graph of $y = \sin x$ again.
3) You should know the x-intercepts of this graph off by heart by now — they're every 180° from zero.
   So $\left(\frac{90t}{7}\right)^\circ + 90^\circ = 180^\circ, 360^\circ, 540^\circ, 720^\circ, 900^\circ, 1080^\circ, 1260^\circ...$

This is above 1170° so it's not in the interval.

4) To solve for t, subtract 90° from each answer and divide by $\frac{90}{7}$: $t = \mathbf{7, 21, 35, 49, 63}$ and $\mathbf{77}$.
   So there will be a half moon **7, 21, 35, 49, 63** and **77** days after the first recorded full moon.

*Almost certainly a proper word somewhere.

Solving Trig Equations

For equations with **tan x** in, it often helps to use this...

$$\tan x \equiv \frac{\sin x}{\cos x}$$

This is a handy thing to know. Basically, if you've got a trig equation with a tan in it, together with a sin or a cos, chances are you'll be better off if you rewrite the tan using this formula.

EXAMPLE: Solve $3 \sin x - \tan x = 0$ for $0 \le x \le 2\pi$.

If you're struggling with radians, solve it in degrees and convert to radians at the end.

1) It's got **sin** and **tan** in it — so writing $\tan x$ as $\frac{\sin x}{\cos x}$ is probably a good move:

$$3 \sin x - \tan x = 0$$

$$\Rightarrow 3 \sin x - \frac{\sin x}{\cos x} = 0$$

2) Get rid of the **cos x** on the bottom by multiplying the whole equation by $\cos x$.

$$\Rightarrow 3 \sin x \cos x - \sin x = 0$$

3) Now — there's a **common factor** of $\sin x$. Take that outside a bracket.

$$\Rightarrow \sin x (3 \cos x - 1) = 0$$

4) And now you're almost there. You've got two things multiplying together to make zero. That means either **one or both** of them is **equal to zero**.

$$\Rightarrow \sin x = 0 \text{ or } 3 \cos x - 1 = 0$$

CAST gives any solutions in the interval $0 \le x \le 2\pi$.

$\sin x = 0$

The first solution is:

$$\sin 0 = 0$$

Now find the other points where $\sin x$ is zero in the interval $0 \le x \le 2\pi$.

Remember the sin graph is zero every π radians.

$\Rightarrow x = 0, \pi, 2\pi$ radians

Having memorised the roots of sin x, smug young Sherlock had ample time to entertain his classmates as they caught up.

$3 \cos x - 1 = 0$

Rearrange:

$$\cos x = \frac{1}{3}$$

So the first solution is:

$$\cos^{-1}\left(\frac{1}{3}\right) = 1.23095...$$

$$= 1.231 \text{ (3 d.p.)}$$

S A T C — 1.231, 5.052

CAST (or the graph of $\cos x$) gives another positive solution in the 4th quadrant, where $x = 2\pi - 1.23095... = 5.052$ (3 d.p.)

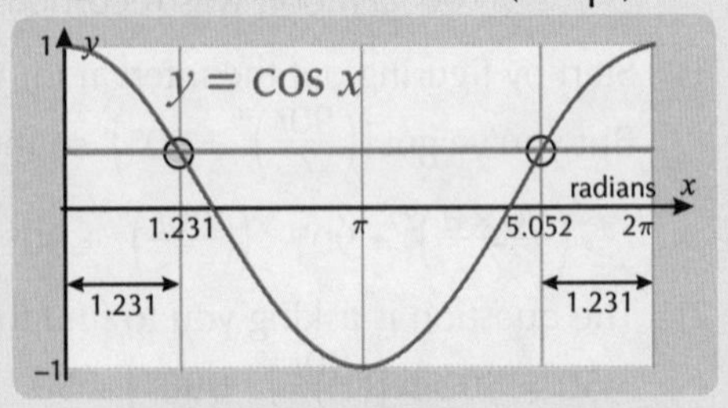

And the two solutions from this part are:

$$\Rightarrow x = 1.231, 5.052 \text{ radians}$$

If you're solving in radians, make sure your calculator is in radian mode.

So altogether you've got **five** possible solutions:

$$x = 0, 1.231, \pi, 5.052, 2\pi \text{ radians}$$

Be warned — you might be tempted to simplify an equation by **dividing** by a trig function. For example, at step 2, you might have tried rearranging like this:

$$3 \sin x \cos x = \sin x$$

$$3 \cos x = 1$$

You would have still found the solutions $x = 1.231$ and 5.052, but lost the solutions that come from $\sin x = 0$. So you can **only** divide by a trig function if the trig function you're dividing by is **never zero** in the range the equation is valid for. Dividing by zero is not big or clever, or even possible.

Solving Trig Equations

And if you have $\sin^2 x$ or $\cos^2 x$, think of this straight away...

$$\sin^2 x + \cos^2 x \equiv 1 \quad \Rightarrow \quad \begin{array}{l} \sin^2 x \equiv 1 - \cos^2 x \\ \cos^2 x \equiv 1 - \sin^2 x \end{array}$$

Use this identity to get rid of a $\sin^2$ or a $\cos^2$ that's making things awkward...

EXAMPLE: Solve $2\sin^2 x° + 5\cos x° = 4$ for $0 \le x \le 360$.

1) You can't do much while the equation's got both sin's and cos's in it.
   So replace the $\sin^2 x$ bit with $1 - \cos^2 x$:

   $2(1 - \cos^2 x°) + 5\cos x° = 4$ ← Now the only trig function is cos.

2) Multiply out the bracket and rearrange it so that you've got zero on one side — and you get a **quadratic** in $\cos x$:

   $\Rightarrow 2 - 2\cos^2 x° + 5\cos x° = 4$
   $\Rightarrow 2\cos^2 x° - 5\cos x° + 2 = 0$

3) It's easier to factorise this if you make the substitution $y = \cos x$.

   $2y^2 - 5y + 2 = 0$
   $\Rightarrow (2y - 1)(y - 2) = 0$
   $\Rightarrow (2\cos x° - 1)(\cos x° - 2) = 0$

   You need to substitute $y = \cos x°$ back into the brackets to get the marks.

4) Now, one of the brackets must be **0**. So you get 2 equations as usual:

   $2\cos x° - 1 = 0$ or $\cos x° - 2 = 0$

   $\cos x° = \frac{1}{2} \Rightarrow x = 60$ and $x = 300$ and $\cos x° = 2$

   See p.26 for some common angles.

   This is a bit weird. $\cos x$ is always between -1 and 1, so you don't get any solutions from this bracket.

So at the end of all that, the only solutions you get are $x = 60$ and $x = 300$. How boring.

Warm Up Questions

PRACTICE QUESTIONS

Q1 a) Solve each of these equations for $0 \le x \le 2\pi$:

(i) $\sin x = \frac{\sqrt{3}}{2}$ (ii) $\tan x = 1$ (iii) $\cos x = -\frac{1}{\sqrt{2}}$

b) Solve each of these equations for $0 \le x \le 360$ (giving your answer to 1 d.p.):

(i) $\cos 4x° = -\frac{2}{3}$ (ii) $\sin(x° + 35°) = 0.3$ (iii) $\tan\left(\frac{1}{2}x°\right) = 500$

Q2 Find all the solutions to $6\sin^2 x = \cos x + 5$ in the range $0 \le x \le 2\pi$ (answers to 3 s.f. where appropriate).

Q3 Solve $3\tan x° + 2\cos x° = 0$ for $-90 \le x \le 90$.

Q4 Simplify: $(\sin y + \cos y)^2 + (\cos y - \sin y)^2$.

Exam Questions

Q1 a) Solve $2\cos\left(x - \frac{\pi}{4}\right) = \sqrt{3}$, for $0 \le x \le 2\pi$. [3 marks]

b) Solve $\sin 2x° = -\frac{1}{2}$, for $0 \le x \le 360$. [3 marks]

Q2 a) Show that the equation $2(1 - \cos x) = 3\sin^2 x$ can be written as $3\cos^2 x - 2\cos x - 1 = 0$. [2 marks]

b) Use this to solve the equation $2(1 - \cos x°) = 3\sin^2 x°$ for $0 \le x \le 360$, giving your answers to 1 d.p. [5 marks]

Q3 Find the points where the graphs of $y = 3\cos^2 x$ and $y = \sin^2 x$ intersect for $0 \le x \le 2\pi$. [6 marks]

Trig equations are sinful (and cosful and tanful)...

Take a bit of time to really get your head around the skills you're learning here — they're going to be very useful later on in this section. Remember to use the CAST diagram or the graph to find all the possible solutions in the given interval, not just the one on your calculator display. Okay then, let's move on to some more formulas...

Addition and Double Angle Formulas

You might have noticed that there are quite a lot of formulas lurking in this here trigonometry jungle. There are some more coming up on these pages too I'm afraid, so brace yourself.

You can use the **Addition Formulas** for **Sums of Angles**

You can use the **addition formulas** to find the sin, cos or tan of the **sum** or **difference** of two angles. When you have an expression like $\sin(x + 60°)$ or $\cos\left(n - \frac{\pi}{2}\right)$, you can use these formulas to **expand the brackets**.

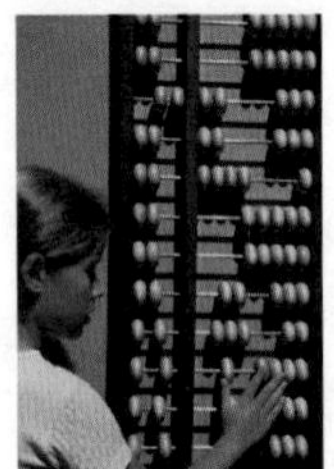

Ailsa activated the 'hard trig' setting on her new-fangled adding machine.

$$\sin(A \pm B) \equiv \sin A \cos B \pm \cos A \sin B$$

$$\cos(A \pm B) \equiv \cos A \cos B \mp \sin A \sin B$$

The sin and cos formulas are given on the formula sheet.

Watch out for the ± and ∓ signs in the cos formulas. If you use the sign on the top on the RHS, you have to use the sign on the top on the left-hand side too — so cos(A + B) = cos A cos B – sin A sin B.

You can derive the addition formulas for tan from the sin and cos formulas and the identity $\frac{\sin x}{\cos x} \equiv \tan x$.

This gives: $\tan(A + B) = \dfrac{\tan A + \tan B}{1 - \tan A \tan B}$

and: $\tan(A - B) = \dfrac{\tan A - \tan B}{1 + \tan A \tan B}$

Use the **Formulas** to find the **Exact Value** of trig expressions

On p.26 you saw that there are some **special angles** that give you exact trig values. Here's a table to remind you but you can always find them by sketching the triangles from p.26.

	0° / 0	30° / $\frac{\pi}{6}$	45° / $\frac{\pi}{4}$	60° / $\frac{\pi}{3}$	90° / $\frac{\pi}{2}$
sin	0	$\frac{1}{2}$	$\frac{1}{\sqrt{2}}$	$\frac{\sqrt{3}}{2}$	1
cos	1	$\frac{\sqrt{3}}{2}$	$\frac{1}{\sqrt{2}}$	$\frac{1}{2}$	0
tan	0	$\frac{1}{\sqrt{3}}$	1	$\sqrt{3}$	—

You can use these angles and the addition formulas to find **exact values** of the trig functions of other angles too.

Find a **pair of angles** from the table which **add or subtract** to give the angle you're after. Then plug them into the **addition formula**, and work it through.

EXAMPLE: Using the addition formula for cos, show that $\cos 75° = \frac{\sqrt{6} - \sqrt{2}}{4}$.

1) Pick two angles that **add or subtract to give 75°**, and put them into the cos addition formula. You need to use **30°** and **45°** here.

   Using cos (A + B) = cos A × cos B – sin A × sin B

   $\cos 75° = \cos(30° + 45°) = \cos 30° \times \cos 45° - \sin 30° \times \sin 45°$

2) **Substitute** the values for cos 30°, cos 45°, sin 30° and sin 45° into the equation:

   $= \frac{\sqrt{3}}{2} \times \frac{1}{\sqrt{2}} - \frac{1}{2} \times \frac{1}{\sqrt{2}} = \frac{\sqrt{3} - 1}{2\sqrt{2}}$

3) Now **rationalise** the denominator of the fraction to get rid of the $\sqrt{2}$:

   $= \frac{\sqrt{3} - 1}{2\sqrt{2}} \times \frac{\sqrt{2}}{\sqrt{2}} = \mathbf{\frac{\sqrt{6} - \sqrt{2}}{4}}$

You should have covered rationalising denominators at N5. Have a look back at your notes if you need a reminder.

EXAMPLE: Using the addition formula for sin, find $\sin(A + B)$, where $\sin A = \frac{4}{5}$ and $\sin B = \frac{7}{25}$.

1) Look at the **addition formula** for sin: $\sin(A + B) \equiv \sin A \cos B + \cos A \sin B$

2) You're given sin A and sin B, but you need cos A and cos B too. The numbers in the fractions should make you think of **right-angled triangles**:

   The triangles which have $\sin A = \frac{4}{5}$ and $\sin B = \frac{7}{25}$ have $\cos A = \frac{3}{5}$ and $\cos B = \frac{24}{25}$.

   As $\sin = \frac{\text{opp}}{\text{hyp}}$ and $\cos = \frac{\text{adj}}{\text{hyp}}$.

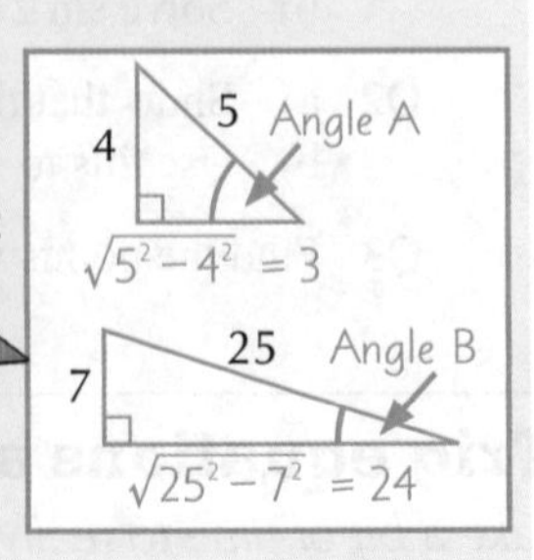

3) Putting these values into the formula gives:

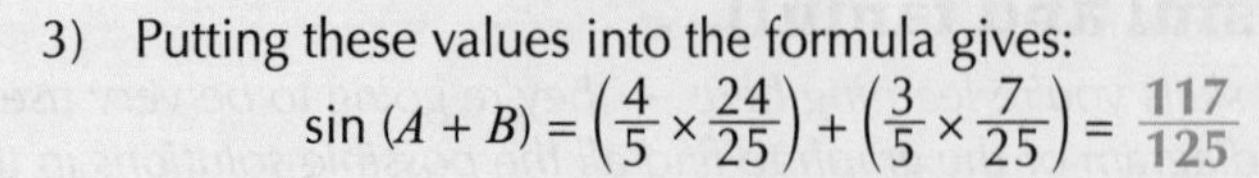

   $\sin(A + B) = \left(\frac{4}{5} \times \frac{24}{25}\right) + \left(\frac{3}{5} \times \frac{7}{25}\right) = \mathbf{\frac{117}{125}}$

Addition and Double Angle Formulas

There's a **Double Angle Formula** for **Each Trig Function**

Whenever you see a trig expression with an **even multiple of x** in it, like sin $2x$, you can use one of the **double angle formulas** to prune it back to an expression just in terms of a **single x**. You need to know about the double angle formulas for **sin** and **cos**:

$$\sin 2A \equiv 2 \sin A \cos A$$

You get these formulas by writing 2A as A + A and using the addition formulas from the previous page.

$$\cos 2A \equiv \cos^2 A - \sin^2 A$$
or $\equiv 2\cos^2 A - 1$
or $\equiv 1 - 2\sin^2 A$

You can use the identity $\cos^2 A + \sin^2 A \equiv 1$ to get the other versions of the cos 2A formula.

You can use the sin and cos formulas to derive the double angle formula for tan: $\tan 2A = \dfrac{2\tan A}{1-\tan^2 A}$.

Use the **Double Angle Formulas** to **Simplify** and **Solve Equations**

If an equation has a **mixture** of **sin x** and **sin $2x$** (or cos x and cos $2x$) terms in it, there's not much that you can do with it. So that you can **simplify** it, and then **solve** it, you have to use one of the **double angle formulas**.

EXAMPLE: Solve the equation $\cos 2x - 5\cos x = 2$ in the interval $0 \le x \le 2\pi$.

1) First use the **double angle formula** $\cos 2A \equiv 2\cos^2 A - 1$ to get rid of $\cos 2x$:
   $2\cos^2 x - 1 - 5\cos x = 2$

   Use this version so that you don't end up with a mix of sin and cos terms.

2) **Simplify** so you have zero on one side, then **factorise** and **solve** the quadratic that you've made:
   $2\cos^2 x - 5\cos x - 3 = 0$
   $(2\cos x + 1)(\cos x - 3) = 0$
   $(2\cos x + 1) = 0$ or $(\cos x - 3) = 0$
3) The **second bracket** gives you $\cos x = 3$, which has **no solutions** since $-1 \le \cos x \le 1$.
4) So all that's left is to solve the **first bracket** to find x:

   $2\cos x + 1 = 0$
   $\cos x = -\frac{1}{2}$
   $\Rightarrow x = \frac{2}{3}\pi$ or $x = \frac{4}{3}\pi$

Sketch the graph of cos x to find all values of x in the given interval: $\cos x = -\frac{1}{2}$ twice, once at $\frac{2}{3}\pi$ and once at $2\pi - \frac{2}{3}\pi = \frac{4}{3}\pi$.

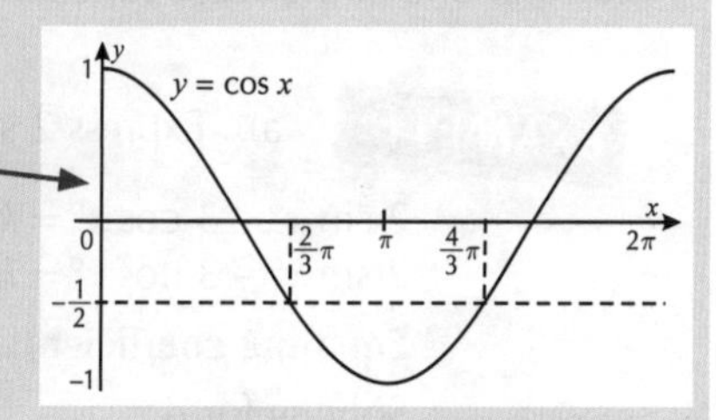

(Or you can use the CAST method if you prefer — see p.30.)

Warm Up Questions

PRACTICE QUESTIONS

Q1 Use an addition formula and the values of $\cos\frac{\pi}{3}$ and $\cos\frac{\pi}{4}$ to find the exact value of $\cos\frac{\pi}{12}$.

Q2 Use the double angle formula to solve the equation: $\sin 2x° = -\sqrt{3}\sin x°$, $0 \le x \le 360$.

Q3 Use the double angle formulas to write: a) $\sin\frac{x}{2}\cos\frac{x}{2}$ in terms of $\sin x$, b) $6 - 12\sin^2 2a$ in terms of $\cos 4a$.

Exam Questions

Q1 Using the double angle and addition formulas, show that $\sin 3x = 3\sin x - 4\sin^3 x$. [4 marks]

Q2 Solve $\cos 2x + \sin^2 x + 4\cos x + 3 = 0$ for $0 < x < 2\pi$. [3 marks]

Q3 Find the values of p and q such that $\sin 3x = \sin x\,(p\cos^2 x + q)$. [3 marks]

Double the angles, double the fun...

The double angle and addition formulas for sin and cos will be on the formula sheet, but make sure you're comfortable using them. And watch out for sneaky questions that need a double angle formula but don't contain a "2x" bit.

The Wave Function

Now for a different kind of formula — one that lets you go from an expanded expression to one with brackets...

Use the **Wave Function** when you've got a **Mix** of **Sin** and **Cos**

If you're solving an equation that contains **both** $\sin x$ and $\cos x$ terms, e.g. $3 \sin x + 4 \cos x = 1$, you need to **rewrite** it so that it only contains **one** trig function. The formulas that you use to do that are known as the **Wave Functions**:

One set for **sin**: $a \sin x \pm b \cos x \equiv k \sin (x \pm \alpha)$

And one set for **cos**: $a \cos x \pm b \sin x \equiv k \cos (x \mp \alpha)$

...where a, b and k are **positive**. Again, you need to be careful with the + and – signs here — see p.34.

Using the Wave Function

1) You'll start with an **identity** like $2 \sin x + 5 \cos x \equiv k \sin (x + \alpha)$, where k and α need to be found.
2) First, **expand the RHS** using the **addition formula** for sin (see p.34): $2 \sin x + 5 \cos x \equiv k \sin x \cos \alpha + k \cos x \sin \alpha$.
3) **Equate the coefficients** of $\sin x$ and $\cos x$. You'll get two equations: ① $k \cos \alpha = 2$ and ② $k \sin \alpha = 5$.
4) To find α, **divide** equation ② by equation ①, then take $\tan^{-1}$ of the result.
5) To find k, **square** equations ① and ② and **add** them together, then take the **square root** of the answer.

This is because $\frac{k \sin \alpha}{k \cos \alpha} = \tan \alpha$.

$(k \sin \alpha)^2 + (k \cos \alpha)^2 \equiv k^2(\sin^2 \alpha + \cos^2 \alpha) \equiv k^2$ (using the identity $\sin^2 \alpha + \cos^2 \alpha \equiv 1$).

This method looks a bit scary, but follow the example below through and it should make more sense.

Solve the equation in **Stages**

You'll almost always be asked to solve equations like this in **different stages** — first **writing out** the equation in the form of one of the wave functions, then **solving** it. You might also have to find the **maximum** or **minimum** value.

EXAMPLE: a) Express $2 \sin x° - 3 \cos x°$ in the form $k \sin (x° - \alpha°)$, given that $k > 0$ and $0 \le \alpha \le 90$.

$2 \sin x° - 3 \cos x° = k \sin (x° - \alpha°)$, so expand the RHS to get
$2 \sin x° - 3 \cos x° = k(\sin x° \cos \alpha° - \cos x° \sin \alpha°)$.

Equating coefficients of $\sin x$ and $\cos x$ gives the equations $2 = k \cos \alpha°$ and $3 = k \sin \alpha°$.

Look at the coefficients of sin x° on each side of the equation — on the LHS it's 2 and on the RHS it's k cos α°, so 2 = k cos α°. You do the same with the coefficients of cos x°.

Solving for α:

$$\frac{k \sin \alpha°}{k \cos \alpha°} = \frac{3}{2} = \tan \alpha°$$

$$\alpha = \tan^{-1} \frac{3}{2} = 56.30... = 56.3 \text{ (1 d.p.)}$$

This value fits into the correct range so you can leave it as it is.

Solving for k: $(k \cos \alpha°)^2 + (k \sin \alpha°)^2 = 2^2 + 3^2 = k^2$

$\Rightarrow k = \sqrt{2^2 + 3^2} = \sqrt{13}$ So $2 \sin x° - 3 \cos x° = \sqrt{13} \sin (x° - 56.3°)$

b) Hence solve $2 \sin x° - 3 \cos x° = 1$ in the interval $0 \le x \le 360$, giving your answers to 1 d.p.

If $2 \sin x° - 3 \cos x° = 1$, that means $\sqrt{13} \sin (x° - 56.30...°) = 1$, so $\sin (x° - 56.30...°) = \frac{1}{\sqrt{13}}$.
$0 \le x \le 360$, so $-56.30... \le x - 56.30... \le 303.69...$

Help with solving trig equations is on p.30-31.

Solve the equation using $\sin^{-1}$: $x - 56.30... = \sin^{-1}\left(\frac{1}{\sqrt{13}}\right) = 16.10...$ or $180 - 16.1 = 163.89...$

So $x = 16.10... + 56.30... = 72.4$ (1 d.p.) or $x = 163.89... + 56.30... = 220.2$ (1 d.p.)

Careful — you're looking for solutions between –56.3° and 303.7° here.

c) What are the maximum and minimum values of $2 \sin x° - 3 \cos x°$?

The maximum and minimum values of sin (and cos) are ± 1.
So the maximum and minimum values of $k \sin (x° - \alpha°)$ are $\pm k$.
From part a), $k = \sqrt{13}$, so the maximum and minimum values are $\pm\sqrt{13}$.

The Wave Function

Wave Function Questions could involve Real Life Contexts or Graphs

EXAMPLE: The amplitude of a sound wave, A, can be modelled by $A = 5 \sin 2.5t - 12 \cos 2.5t$, where t is time in seconds. Express the amplitude in the form $k \sin (2.5t - \alpha)$ and hence find the two values of t for $0 \le t \le \frac{\pi}{2}$ at which the amplitude is 10.

1) First **expand** $k \sin (2.5t - \alpha)$ using the addition formula:
   $k \sin (2.5t - \alpha) = k \sin 2.5t \cos \alpha - k \cos 2.5t \sin \alpha$
2) **Comparing coefficients** with the formula for A gives: $k \cos \alpha = 5$ and $k \sin \alpha = 12$
3) To find α, **divide** the second equation by the first to get $\tan \alpha = \frac{12}{5}$. So $\alpha = \tan^{-1}\left(\frac{12}{5}\right) = 1.176...$
4) To find k, **square** both equations and add them: $(k \cos \alpha)^2 + (k \sin \alpha)^2 = 5^2 + 12^2 = 169$.
   $k^2 (\cos^2 \alpha + \sin^2 \alpha) = 169$ and $\cos^2 \alpha + \sin^2 \alpha \equiv 1$, so $k^2 = 169$, which means $k = 13$.
5) You now know that $A = 13 \sin (2.5t - 1.176...)$.
   Now you need to set this equation equal to 10 and solve for t.
   $13 \sin (2.5t - 1.176...) = 10 \Rightarrow \sin (2.5t - 1.176...) = \frac{10}{13}$
   Solve the equation using $\sin^{-1}$:
   $2.5t - 1.176... = \sin^{-1}\left(\frac{10}{13}\right) = 0.877...$ and $2.5t - 1.176... = \pi - 0.877... = 2.263...$
   $\Rightarrow$ $t = 0.821$ **seconds** (3 d.p.) and $t = 1.376$ **seconds** (3 d.p.)

Use the symmetry of the sin graph to find the second solution. Don't forget to adjust the range to match 2.5t – 1.176...

EXAMPLE: Sketch the graph of $y = 3 \cos x + 4 \sin x$.

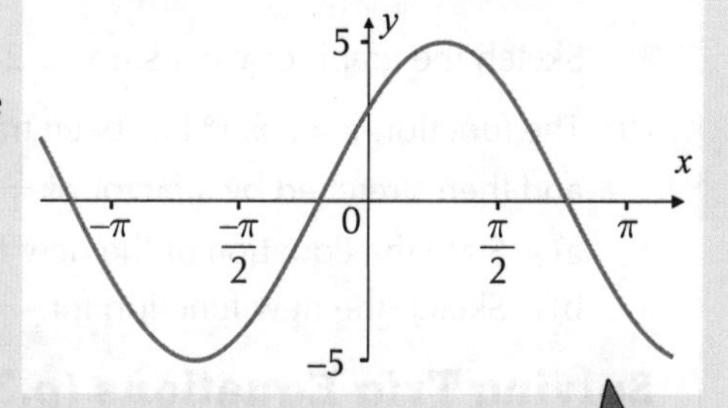

1) At the moment, you **can't sketch** this graph — but you can use the **wave function** to turn it into a form that you **can** sketch.
2) You can use the wave function in the form $y = k \cos (x - \alpha)$.
   Expanding this using the **cos addition formula** gives:
   $y = k \cos x \cos \alpha + k \sin x \sin \alpha$
3) **Equating coefficients** gives the equations:
   $k \cos \alpha = 3$ and $k \sin \alpha = 4$
4) Dividing the second equation by the first gives: $\tan \alpha = \frac{4}{3}$ and so $\alpha = \tan^{-1}\left(\frac{4}{3}\right) = 0.927...$
5) **Squaring** both equations and adding them gives:
   $(k \cos \alpha)^2 + (k \sin \alpha)^2 = 3^2 + 4^2 = 25 \Rightarrow k^2 (\cos^2 \alpha + \sin^2 \alpha) = 25 \Rightarrow k^2 = 25 \Rightarrow k = 5$
6) So the graph is also given by $y = 5 \cos (x - 0.927...)$ and you can now **sketch** it.
7) It's a **cos x** graph with a **vertical stretch of 5** (so goes between –5 and 5) and **shifted 0.927...** to the **right**.

Warm Up Questions

Q1 Which two forms of the wave function could you use to write $a \cos x + b \sin x$ $(a, b > 0)$ in terms of just sin or just cos?

Q2 Write $5 \sin x° - 6 \cos x°$ in the form $k \sin (x° - \alpha°)$, where $k > 0$ and $0 \le \alpha \le 90$.

Exam Questions

Q1 a) Write $9 \sin x + 12 \cos x$ in the form $k \sin (x + \alpha)$, where $k > 0$ and $0 \le \alpha \le \frac{\pi}{2}$. [3 marks]
b) Using the result from part a), solve $9 \sin x + 12 \cos x = 3$, giving all solutions for x in the range $0 \le x \le 2\pi$. [5 marks]
c) $f(x) = 10 - 9 \sin x - 12 \cos x$. Find the maximum and minimum values of $f(x)$. [3 marks]

Q2 a) Write $5 \cos x° + 12 \sin x°$ in the form $k \cos (x° - \alpha°)$, where $k > 0$ and $0 \le \alpha \le 90$. [3 marks]
b) Hence solve $5 \cos x° + 12 \sin x° = 2$ for $0 \le x \le 360$, giving your answers to 2 decimal places. [5 marks]
c) Use your results from part a) above to find the minimum value of $(5 \cos x° + 12 \sin x°)^3$. [2 marks]

A great function for saying hello to people...

Keep doing examples until you're happy with the method, and be careful when adjusting the interval for solutions.

Revision Summary for Section Two

That's all the trigonometry you need to know — phew. Before you go, get stuck in to these questions...

- Try these questions and tick off each one when you get it right.
- When you've done all the questions for a topic and are completely happy with it, tick off the topic.

Angles and Identities (p.26)

1) How do you convert degrees to radians?
2) Change the following values in degrees into exact values in radians:
   a) 60° b) 270° c) 87°
3) Change the following radian values into degrees:
   a) $\frac{\pi}{4}$ b) $\frac{2\pi}{5}$ c) $\frac{16\pi}{9}$
4) State the identity that relates $\sin^2 x$ and $\cos^2 x$.
5) Express $\tan x$ in terms of $\sin x$ and $\cos x$.
6) Simplify $\sin x \tan x \cos x + \cos^2 x$.

Trig Graphs and Transformations (p.27-29)

7) Write down the period of: a) $\sin x$ b) $\cos x°$ c) $\tan x$
8) Which transformation can be used to turn the graph of $y = \cos x$ into $y = \cos (x + 2)$?
9) Sketch the graph of $y = 4 \sin x° + 2$ for $0 \leq x \leq 360$.
10) The function $y = \cos x°$ has been translated 20° to the right and then stretched by a factor of $\frac{1}{2}$ in the y-direction.
    a) State the equation of the new function.
    b) Sketch the new function for $-360 \leq x \leq 360$.

Solving Trig Equations (p.30-33)

11) Sketch the CAST diagram.
12) Solve $\sin 4x° = \frac{1}{2}$ for $0 \leq x \leq 180$.
13) Solve: a) $\cos (x - \frac{\pi}{6}) = \frac{1}{\sqrt{2}}$ for $0 \leq x \leq 2\pi$
    b) $3 \sin^2 x° - 4 \cos x° = -1$ for $0 \leq x \leq 360$ (to 1 d.p.).
14) a) Sketch the graph $y = 3 \sin x$ for $0 \leq x \leq 3\pi$.
    b) Use your graph to solve the equation $3 \sin x = \frac{3}{2}$ for $0 \leq x \leq 3\pi$ (Hint: $\sin^{-1} \frac{1}{2} = \frac{\pi}{6}$).

Addition and Double Angle Formulas (p.34-35)

15) If $\sin x = \frac{8}{15}$, find the exact value of: a) $\cos x$ b) $\tan x$
16) Using the addition formulas, show that: a) $\sin 105° = \frac{1 + \sqrt{3}}{2\sqrt{2}}$ b) $\cos \frac{5\pi}{6} = -\frac{\sqrt{3}}{2}$
17) Write: a) $\sin 2x$ in terms of $\sin x$ b) $\cos 2x$ in terms of $\cos x$
18) Simplify the following expression: $2 - \frac{\cos^2 x}{1 - \sin^2 x} + \frac{\sin 2x}{\cos^2 x}$.
19) Solve $\cos 2x + 4 \sin x + 5 = 0$, for $0 \leq x \leq 2\pi$.

The Wave Function (p.36-37)

20) What are the four forms of the wave function?
21) a) Express $15 \cos x - 8 \sin x$ in the form $k \cos (x + \alpha)$.
    b) Hence solve $15 \cos x - 8 \sin x = 4$ with $0 \leq x \leq 2\pi$. Give your answers to 2 d.p.
    c) What are the minimum and maximum values of this function?

Linear Coordinate Geometry

You'll have seen some of this stuff on straight lines at National 5, but don't worry, there's still plenty to learn...

Finding the **Equation of a Line**

It's easy to convert between the different forms.

There are **three different ways** of writing the equation of a straight line:

$$y - b = m(x - a) \qquad y = mx + c \qquad ax + by + c = 0$$

where a, b and c are **constants**

You should **multiply out** the brackets of an equation in the first form and **rearrange** to give one of the other forms.

EXAMPLE: Find the equation of the line that passes through the points (–3, 10) and (1, 4) in the forms $y - b = m(x - a)$, $y = mx + c$ and $ax + by + c = 0$.

Label the points: $(x_1, y_1) = (-3, 10)$ and $(x_2, y_2) = (1, 4)$ ← It doesn't matter which way round you label them.

Find m, the **gradient** of the line: $m = \frac{y_2 - y_1}{x_2 - x_1} = \frac{4 - 10}{1 - (-3)} = \frac{-6}{4} = -\frac{3}{2}$ ← Remember, the formula for the gradient is: $\frac{\text{change in } y}{\text{change in } x}$

Write down the equation of the line: $y - b = m(x - a)$

(a, b) is a point on the line — I've used (–3, 10), but you could use (1, 4).

$y - 10 = -\frac{3}{2}(x - (-3)) \Rightarrow \mathbf{y - 10 = -\frac{3}{2}(x + 3)}$

Now you can **rearrange** into the two other forms:

For the form $y = mx + c$, take **everything except the** y over to the right-hand side and expand the brackets.

$$y - 10 = -\frac{3}{2}(x + 3)$$
$$\Rightarrow y = -\frac{3}{2}x - \frac{9}{2} + 10$$
$$\Rightarrow \mathbf{y = -\frac{3}{2}x + \frac{11}{2}}$$

To get it in the form $ax + by + c = 0$, take **everything** over to one side — and then get rid of any fractions.

$$y = -\frac{3}{2}x + \frac{11}{2}$$
$$\Rightarrow \frac{3}{2}x + y - \frac{11}{2} = 0$$
$$\Rightarrow \mathbf{3x + 2y - 11 = 0}$$

If the coefficients a, b or c are fractions, it's good practice to make them **all integers**, so multiply everything here by 2.

Parallel lines have equal **Gradient**

That's what makes them parallel — the fact that the gradients are the **same**.

If lines l_1 and l_2 have gradients m_1 and m_2, and the lines are parallel, then $m_1 = m_2$.

The equation of the line l_1 can be written as $y = \frac{3}{4}x - \frac{7}{4}$ or $3x - 4y - 7 = 0$. Find the line parallel to l_1 that passes through the point (3, –1).

Method 1

Parallel lines have the **same gradient**.

The original equation is: $y = \frac{3}{4}x - \frac{7}{4}$

So the new equation will be: $y = \frac{3}{4}x + c$

You know that the line passes through (3, –1), so stick $x = 3$, $y = -1$ into the equation to find c.

At (3, –1): $-1 = \frac{3}{4} \times 3 + c \Rightarrow c = -1 - \frac{9}{4} = -\frac{13}{4}$

So the equation of the line is: $\mathbf{y = \frac{3}{4}x - \frac{13}{4}}$

Method 2

With the $\mathbf{ax + by + c = 0}$ form it's even easier:

The original line is: $3x - 4y - 7 = 0$

So the new line is: $3x - 4y + k = 0$

Then use the values of x and y at (3, –1) to find k.

$$(3 \times 3) - (4 \times (-1)) + k = 0$$
$$\Rightarrow 9 + 4 + k = 0$$
$$\Rightarrow k = -13$$

So the equation is: $\mathbf{3x - 4y - 13 = 0}$

EXAMPLE: P and Q have coordinates (17, 12) and (a, –9) respectively, and the line PQ is parallel to $2y - 7x + 3 = 0$. Find the value of a.

Find the **gradient** of $2y - 7x + 3 = 0$ — you can **rewrite** this as $y = \frac{7}{2}x - \frac{3}{2}$, so the **gradient** of the line is $\frac{7}{2}$.

Since the lines are **parallel**, they have the **same gradient**, so $m = \frac{12 - (-9)}{17 - a} = \frac{7}{2} \Rightarrow \frac{21}{17 - a} = \frac{7}{2}$

$$\Rightarrow 21 \times 2 = 7(17 - a)$$
$$\Rightarrow 42 = 119 - 7a \Rightarrow 7a = 77 \Rightarrow \mathbf{a = 11}$$

Linear Coordinate Geometry

Points are **Collinear** if they lie on the **Same Line**

You can prove that a set of points is **collinear** by showing that they lie on **parallel lines** which have a **common point** — i.e. the points A, B and C are collinear if AB and BC are parallel, since AB and BC have a common point B.

EXAMPLE: Show that points P (–2, 3), Q (1, 4) and R (4, 5) are collinear.

See p.50 for more on collinearity.

Find the **gradient** of the line PQ using the gradient formula: $m_{PQ} = \frac{4-3}{1-(-2)} = \mathbf{\frac{1}{3}}$

Now find the **gradient** of the line QR: $m_{QR} = \frac{5-4}{4-1} = \mathbf{\frac{1}{3}} = m_{PQ}$

PQ and QR are **parallel** and have a **common point Q** so P, Q and R must be **collinear**.

The gradient of a **Perpendicular** line is **–1 ÷ the Other Gradient**

Finding **perpendicular** lines isn't too bad — as long as you remember that the **product** of the two gradients is **–1**. To find the gradient of a perpendicular line, turn the gradient you already have **upside down** and change its **sign**.

EXAMPLE: The line l_1 has the equation $y = \frac{1}{3}x - 1$. Find the equation of the line l_2 which is perpendicular to l_1 and passes through the point (–2, 4).

If line l_1 with gradient m_1 is perpendicular to line l_2 with gradient m_2, then $m_1 m_2 = -1$ (or $m_1 = -\frac{1}{m_2}$).

l_1 has gradient $m_1 = \frac{1}{3}$, so the **gradient** of l_2 is $m_2 = -1 \div \frac{1}{3} = -3$

Using $y = mx + c$ with $x = -2$ and $y = 4$: $4 = (-3 \times -2) + c \Rightarrow c = 4 - 6 = -2$

You could also use $y - b = m(x - a)$.

So the equation of l_2 is $\mathbf{y = -3x - 2}$

You can find the **Angle** between a **Line** and the **x-axis**

From National 5, you know that $\tan\theta = \frac{\text{opposite}}{\text{adjacent}}$.

Looking at the **graph** on the right, $\tan\theta = \frac{\text{opposite}}{\text{adjacent}} = \frac{y_2 - y_1}{x_2 - x_1} = m$.

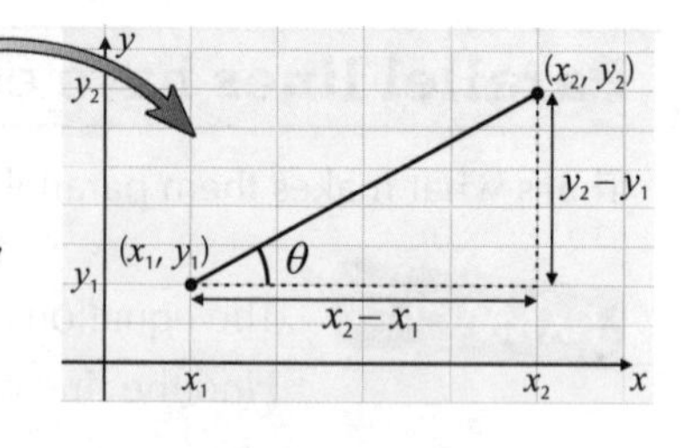

You'll recognise this from the previous page — it's the equation of the **gradient** of the line joining the **two points**. If you extend the line until it meets the ***x*-axis**, the angle θ between the line and x-axis will be the **same** (due to the properties of similar triangles). So you can use the **gradient *m*** to find the angle θ between a line and the **positive** direction of the ***x*-axis**.

You want the angle measured **anti-clockwise** from the positive x-axis, so if you get a **negative** angle (i.e. the angle measured clockwise) you need to **subtract** its **magnitude** from π to get the correct answer.

EXAMPLE: Line l_1 has equation $\sqrt{5}y - 2x - 3 = 0$.

a) Find the equation of line l_2 which is perpendicular to l_1 and passes through the point $(1, \sqrt{5})$.

b) Find the angle l_2 makes with the positive x-axis.

a) **Rearrange** l_1 to find the **gradient:** $\sqrt{5}y = 2x + 3 \Rightarrow y = \frac{2}{\sqrt{5}}x + \frac{3}{\sqrt{5}}$

The gradient of l_1 is $\frac{2}{\sqrt{5}}$, so the **gradient of** l_2 is $-\frac{\sqrt{5}}{2}$.

l_2 has equation $y - \sqrt{5} = -\frac{\sqrt{5}}{2}(x - 1) \Rightarrow \mathbf{y = -\frac{\sqrt{5}}{2}x + \frac{3\sqrt{5}}{2}}$

b) The gradient of l_2 is $-\frac{\sqrt{5}}{2}$, so $\tan\theta = -\frac{\sqrt{5}}{2} \Rightarrow \theta = \tan^{-1}\left(-\frac{\sqrt{5}}{2}\right) = -0.841$ radians

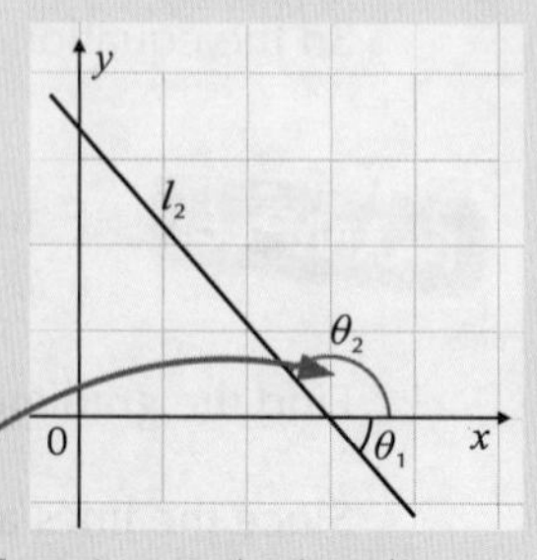

This gives you the angle θ_1 on the diagram to the right, but you want the angle measured **anti-clockwise** from the positive x-axis, shown here by the angle θ_2.

So the angle is $\pi - 0.841 = \mathbf{2.30}$ **radians (3 s.f.)**

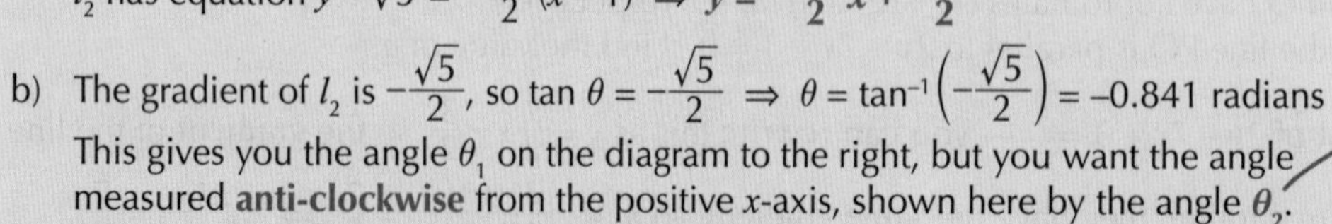

You want the **size** of the angle θ_1, so ignore the fact that it's negative (it just means it's below the x-axis). If it's easier, think of it as adding π to the negative solution.

Linear Coordinate Geometry

You need to know about **Important Lines** in **Triangles**

Triangles have some lines with **special properties** that you could be asked to find in your exam.

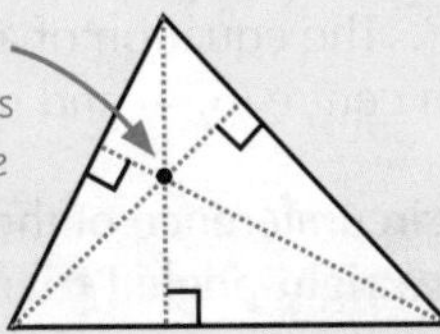

The **altitude** is the line from a vertex that is **perpendicular** to the opposite side.

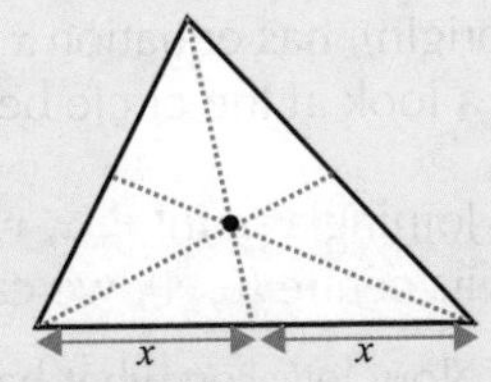

A **median** goes from a vertex to the **midpoint** of the opposite side.

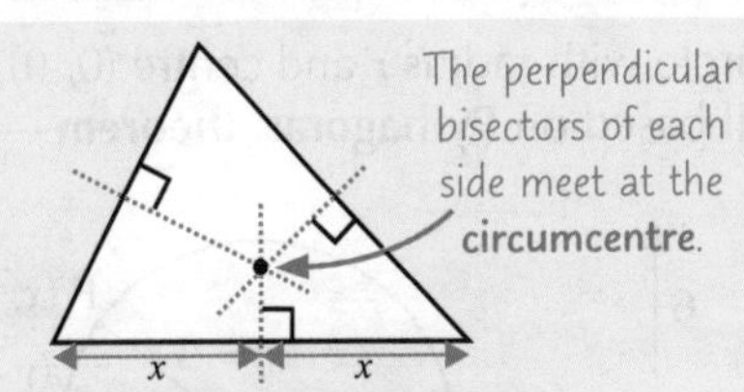

The **perpendicular bisector** of a side is **perpendicular** to the side at its midpoint.

The points A (2, 5), B (4, 3) and C (–1, –7) form a triangle. Find the equation of:
a) the altitude through C, b) the median through A, c) the perpendicular bisector of AB.

a) The **altitude through C** is **perpendicular** to the line AB, so its **gradient** is –1 ÷ gradient of AB (or m_{AB}).
First find the **gradient** of AB: $m_{AB} = \frac{5-3}{2-4} = \frac{2}{-2} = -1$, so the gradient of the **altitude** is 1.
The altitude goes through C (–1, –7). You have the **gradient** and a **point**, so you can find the equation: $y - (-7) = 1(x - (-1)) \Rightarrow \mathbf{y = x - 6}$

b) The **median** goes from A (2, 5) to the **midpoint** of the line BC. You can find the coordinates of the **midpoint** by taking the **mean** of the x-coordinates and the **mean** of the y-coordinates of B and C:
Midpoint of BC $= \left(\frac{x_B + x_C}{2}, \frac{y_B + y_C}{2}\right) = \left(\frac{-1+4}{2}, \frac{-7+3}{2}\right) = \left(\frac{3}{2}, -2\right)$
Now you can find the **gradient** of the line through A and the midpoint of BC: $m = \frac{5-(-2)}{2-\frac{3}{2}} = \frac{7}{\left(\frac{1}{2}\right)} = 14$
So the equation of the median through A is: $y - 5 = 14(x - 2) \Rightarrow \mathbf{y = 14x - 23}$

c) The **perpendicular bisector** of AB goes through the **midpoint** of AB, and has a **gradient** of $-1 \div m_{AB}$
Use the formula above to find the **midpoint** of AB: $\left(\frac{2+4}{2}, \frac{5+3}{2}\right) = (3, 4)$
In part a), you found the **gradient** of AB is –1, and the gradient of the perpendicular bisector is 1.
So the equation of the **perpendicular bisector** of AB is $y - 4 = 1(x - 3) \Rightarrow \mathbf{y = x + 1}$

Warm-Up Questions

Q1 Find the equation of the line parallel to $y = \frac{3}{2}x - \frac{2}{3}$ that passes through the point (4, 2).

Q2 The line l_2 passes through the point (6, 1) and is perpendicular to $2x - y - 7 = 0$.
a) Find the equation of l_2. b) Find the angle l_2 makes with the positive x-axis.

Exam Questions

Q1 The line PQ has equation $4x + 3y = 15$. The point R lies on PQ and has coordinates (3, 1).
a) Find the equation of line L which is perpendicular to PQ at the point R. [3 marks]
b) Calculate the angle between the x-axis and line L. [2 marks]

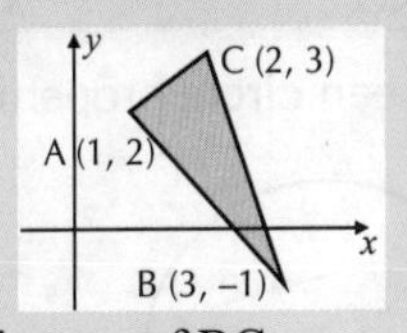

Q2 The points A (1, 2), B (3, –1) and C (2, 3) are the vertices of a triangle.
a) Find the equation of the median from A. [3 marks]
b) Find the equation of the perpendicular bisector of side BC. [3 marks]
c) Find the point of intersection of the median from A and the perpendicular bisector of BC. [3 marks]

The tragedy of parallel lines — so alike, but destined never to meet...

There's another special triangle word you might want to know — concurrency. That's when three (or more) lines all meet at the same point. The orthocentre and the circumcentre are both points of concurrency, and so's your favourite shopping centre when you go there to meet up with your friends. As long as there are at least three of you, that is...

Circle Geometry

I always say a beautiful shape deserves a beautiful formula, and here you've got one of my favourite double-acts...

Circle Equations can be written in Two Ways

A circle with radius r and centre (0, 0) (the origin), has equation $x^2 + y^2 = r^2$. The equation of a circle is all based on **Pythagoras' theorem** — take a look at the circle below, with centre (6, 4) and radius 3.

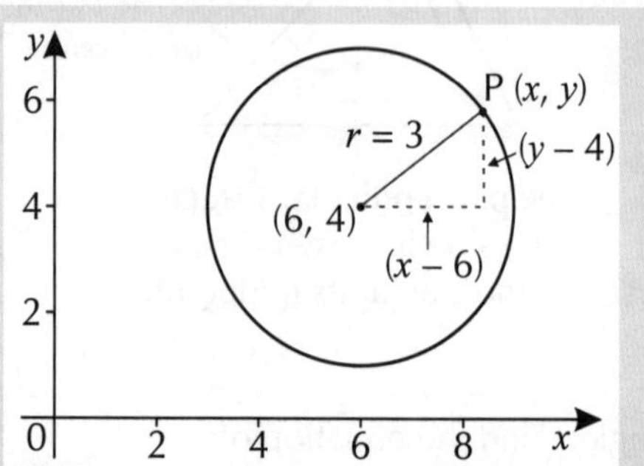

Joining a point P (x, y) on the circumference of the circle to its centre (6, 4), we can create a **right-angled triangle.**

Now let's see what happens if we use **Pythagoras' theorem:**

$(x - 6)^2 + (y - 4)^2 = 3^2$

or: $(x - 6)^2 + (y - 4)^2 = 9$ ← This is the equation for the circle. It's as easy as that.

In general, a circle with radius r and centre (a, b) has the equation:

$$(x - a)^2 + (y - b)^2 = r^2$$

Both versions of the circle equation are on the formula sheet.

You might also see the equation of a circle written in the form $x^2 + y^2 + 2gx + 2fy + c = 0$ — this equation gives a circle with the **centre** $(-g, -f)$ and **radius** $\sqrt{g^2 + f^2 - c}$.

For the circle above, you can write its equation as $x^2 + y^2 - 12x - 8y + 43 = 0$ by **multiplying out** the brackets.

Find the centre and radius of the circle with equation:
a) $(x - 2)^2 + (y + 3)^2 = 16$ b) $x^2 + y^2 + 8x - 12y + 3 = 0$

a) Compare $(x - 2)^2 + (y + 3)^2 = 16$ with the **general form** $(x - a)^2 + (y - b)^2 = r^2$
$a = 2$, $b = -3$ and $r = 4$, so the centre is **(2, –3)** and the radius is **4**.

b) Compare $x^2 + y^2 + 8x - 12y + 3 = 0$ with the **general form** $x^2 + y^2 + 2gx + 2fy + c = 0$
$g = 4$, $f = -6$, $c = 3$ and $r = \sqrt{4^2 + (-6)^2 - 3} = \sqrt{49} = 7$, so the centre is **(–4, 6)** and the radius is **7**.

You can Switch between the Forms

If you have an equation of the form $x^2 + y^2 + 2gx + 2fy + c = 0$, you can **convert** it to the $(x - a)^2 + (y - b)^2 = r^2$ form by **completing the square** (see p.2). Or, if you have an equation like $(x - a)^2 + (y - b)^2 = r^2$, you can **convert** it to $x^2 + y^2 + 2gx + 2fy + c = 0$ form by **expanding the brackets** and **collecting like terms**.

EXAMPLE: Write the equation $x^2 + y^2 - 6x + 4y + 4 = 0$ in the form $(x - a)^2 + (y - b)^2 = r^2$.

Complete the square on the x and y terms:

$x^2 + y^2 - 6x + 4y + 4 = 0$ ← Collect the x and y terms together...

$x^2 - 6x + y^2 + 4y + 4 = 0$

$(x - 3)^2 - 9 + (y + 2)^2 - 4 + 4 = 0$ ← ...then find squares that give the terms you need, and subtract constants to balance things up.

$\mathbf{(x - 3)^2 + (y + 2)^2 = 9}$

So the centre is (3, –2) and the radius is $\sqrt{9} = 3$.

Don't forget the Properties of Circles

You'll have seen circle properties at National 5, but here's a reminder of some that might come in handy.

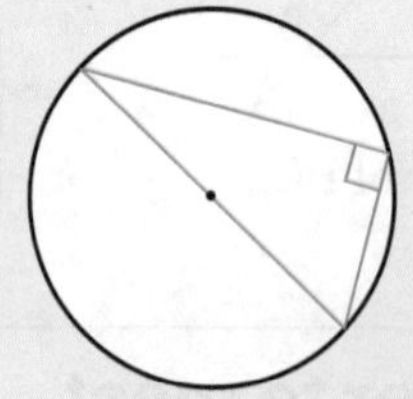

The angle in a **semicircle** is a **right angle**.

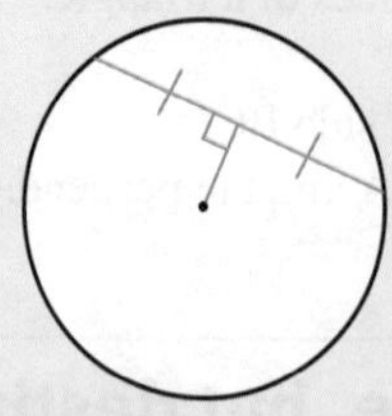

The **perpendicular** from the centre to a chord **bisects** the **chord**.

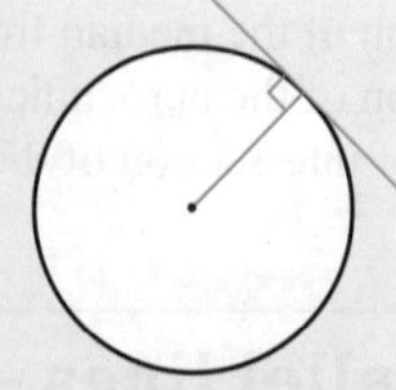

A **radius** and **tangent** to the **same point** will meet at **right angles**.

Bob thinks the Magic Circle rules. Bunnykin isn't so sure.

Circle Geometry

Use the **Gradient Rule** for **Perpendicular Lines**

Remember that the **tangent** at a given point will be **perpendicular** to the **radius** at that same point.

Point A (6, 4) lies on a circle with the equation $(x-2)^2 + (y-1)^2 = 25$.
Find the equation of the tangent to the circle at A.

The equation of the circle tells you the centre is **(2, 1)**.
The tangent you're interested in is at **right angles** to the radius at (6, 4).

The gradient of the **radius** at (6, 4) $= \frac{4-1}{6-2} = \frac{3}{4}$,

so the gradient of the **tangent** at (6, 4) $= \frac{-1}{\frac{3}{4}} = -\frac{4}{3}$.

It often helps with questions like this to use what you know at the start to sketch the graph.

So using $y - b = m(x - a)$, the tangent at (6, 4) is $y - 4 = -\frac{4}{3}(x-6) \Rightarrow \mathbf{y = -\frac{4}{3}x + 12}$

Use **Other Information** to find the **Equation of a Circle**

When you're finding the equation of a circle, there's no getting around the fact that you'll need to know its **centre** and its **radius**. If you're not given them in the question, you'll have to use everything you know about circles to **figure them out** from the information you're given — often, this will be some points on the **circumference**.

Two points P (–2, –4) and Q (6, 2) lie on the circumference of a circle, and PQ is a diameter. Find the equation of the circle.

PQ is a diameter, so the **midpoint** of PQ is the **centre** of the circle.

midpoint of PQ $= \left(\frac{-2+6}{2}, \frac{-4+2}{2}\right) = \mathbf{(2, -1)}$

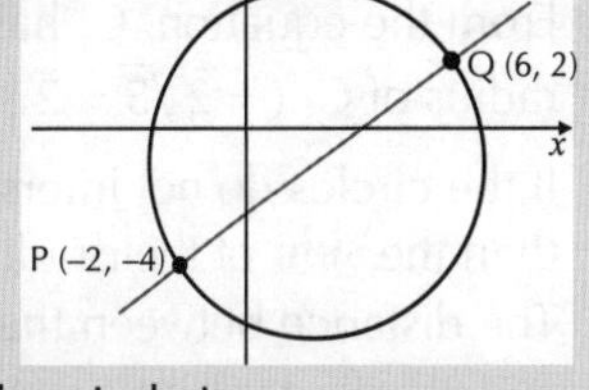

The **radius** of the circle is the **distance** from the centre to either point, which you can find using **Pythagoras' theorem**:

radius $= \sqrt{(6-2)^2 + (2-(-1))^2} = \sqrt{4^2 + 3^2} = \mathbf{5}$

The centre is at the point (2, –1) and the radius is 5, so the equation of the circle is:
$\mathbf{(x-2)^2 + (y+1)^2 = 25}$

EXAMPLE:

Two points P (–3, –4) and Q (5, 0) lie on the circumference of a circle.

a) Find the equation of the perpendicular bisector of PQ.

Another point R (2, 1) is also on the circumference of the circle.
The line joining the centre of the circle, C, with point R is parallel to the y-axis.

b) Find the coordinates of C.

c) Find the equation of the circle with centre C that goes through P and Q.

a) Find the **gradient** of PQ: $m_{PQ} = \frac{-4-0}{-3-5} = \frac{1}{2}$

So the gradient of a line perpendicular to PQ is $-1 \div \frac{1}{2} = -2$.

The **midpoint** of PQ is $\left(\frac{-3+5}{2}, \frac{-4+0}{2}\right) = (1, -2)$

So the equation of the **perpendicular bisector** of PQ is

$y - (-2) = -2(x-1) \Rightarrow \mathbf{y = -2x}$

b) The **perpendicular bisector** of a chord passes through the **centre** of the circle, so the centre lies at the **intersection** of the lines $x = 2$ (as it must have the same x-coordinate as R) and $y = -2x$ — these lines meet at **(2, –4)**.

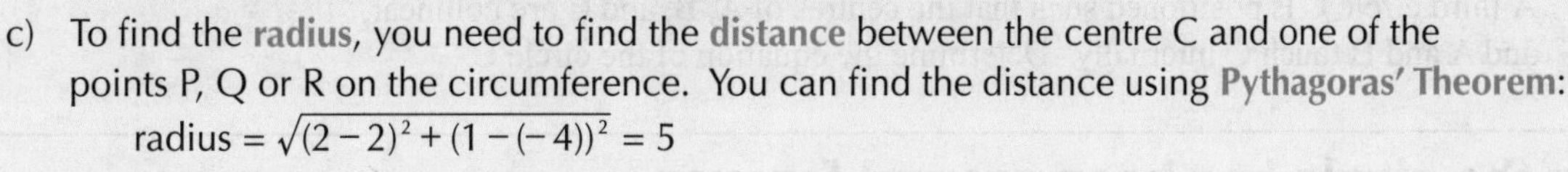

c) To find the **radius**, you need to find the **distance** between the centre C and one of the points P, Q or R on the circumference. You can find the distance using **Pythagoras' Theorem**:

radius $= \sqrt{(2-2)^2 + (1-(-4))^2} = 5$

So the equation of the circle is $\mathbf{(x-2)^2 + (y+4)^2 = 25}$.

Circle Geometry

Circles can be **Positioned** in **Different Ways**

Circles can be...

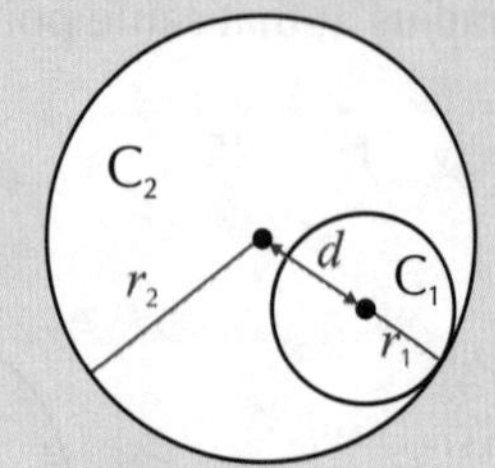

... touching **internally**: they touch at **one point** and one circle is **inside** the other.

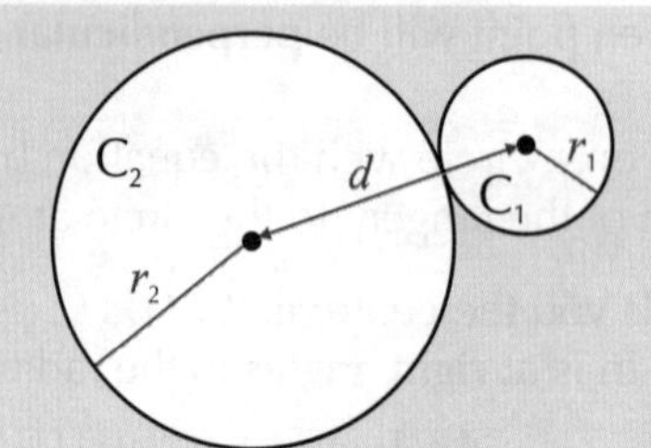

... touching **externally**: they touch at **one point** and are positioned **next to each other**.

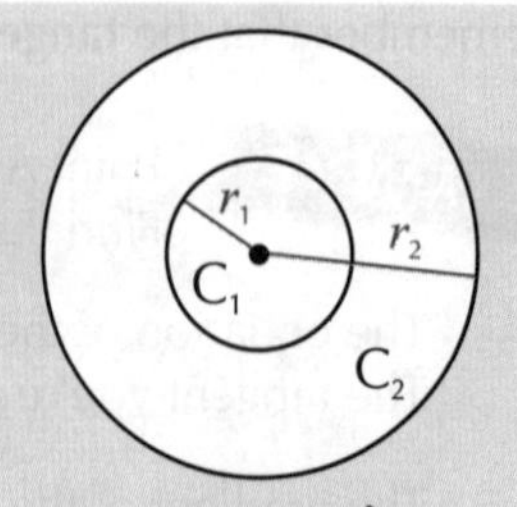

... **concentric**: one circle is **inside** the other and they have the **same centre**.

- Two circles are touching **internally** if the distance between their centres, d, is the **difference between the two radii** — so $d = r_2 - r_1$, where r_1 and r_2 are the radii of C_1 and C_2 respectively.
- Similarly, if two circles touch **externally**, the distance, d, will be the **sum of the two radii** — $d = r_1 + r_2$.
- Circles can also **not touch at all** (so $d > r_1 + r_2$), **overlap** so that they intersect **twice** (so $r_2 - r_1 < d < r_1 + r_2$) or one circle could be completely **inside the other**, but **not** concentric (so $d < r_2 - r_1$).
- **Concentric** circles have the **same centre**, so $d = 0$.

Two circles C_1 and C_2 are arranged as shown. C_1 has the equation $(x + 1)^2 + (y - 3)^2 = 20$ and C_2 is centred at $(-5, 5)$. The radius of C_1 is twice the radius of C_2.

a) Write down the equation of C_2.

b) Another circle C_3 has equation $(x + 6)^2 + (y + 9)^2 = 45$. Verify that C_1 and C_3 do not intersect.

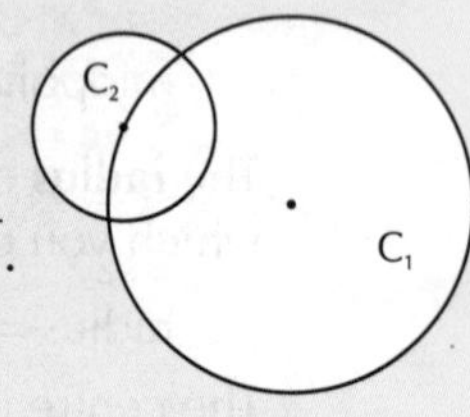

a) From the equation, C_1 has radius $\sqrt{20} = 2\sqrt{5}$. The radius of C_2 is half the radius of C_1 ($= 2\sqrt{5} \div 2 = \sqrt{5}$), so the equation of C_2 is: $(x + 5)^2 + (y - 5)^2 = 5$

b) If the circles do not intersect, the distance between their centres must be **greater** than the **sum** of their radii. The radius of C_1 is $2\sqrt{5}$ and the radius of C_3 is $\sqrt{45} = 3\sqrt{5}$. The distance between the centre of C_1 $(-1, 3)$ and the centre of C_3 $(-6, -9)$ is:

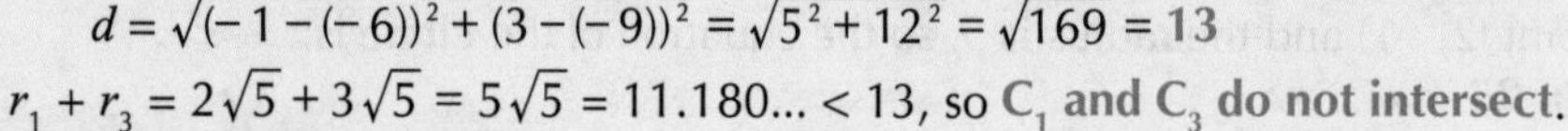

$$d = \sqrt{(-1-(-6))^2 + (3-(-9))^2} = \sqrt{5^2 + 12^2} = \sqrt{169} = \mathbf{13}$$

$r_1 + r_3 = 2\sqrt{5} + 3\sqrt{5} = 5\sqrt{5} = 11.180... < 13$, so **$C_1$ and C_3 do not intersect.**

Warm-Up Questions

PRACTICE QUESTIONS

Q1 Write down the equation of the circle with centre $(3, -1)$ and radius 7 in both forms.

Q2 Give the radius and the coordinates of the centre of the circles with the following equations:
a) $x^2 + y^2 = 9$ b) $(x - 2)^2 + (y + 4)^2 = 4$ c) $x(x + 6) = y(8 - y)$

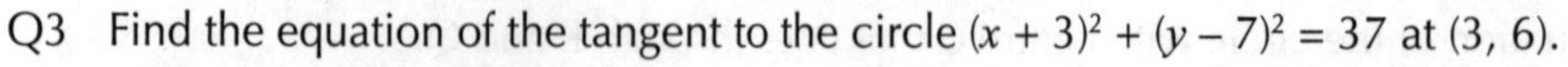

Q3 Find the equation of the tangent to the circle $(x + 3)^2 + (y - 7)^2 = 37$ at $(3, 6)$.

Q4 Write down the equation of a circle with radius 4 that is concentric with the circle $(x - 5)^2 + (y + 4)^2 = 18$.

Exam Questions

Q1 Find the equation of the tangent to the circle $x^2 + y^2 - 4x + 10y + 19 = 0$ at the point P $(1, -8)$. [4 marks]

Q2 The points J $(2, 3)$ and K $(8, -7)$ lie on a circle, and JK is a diameter. Find the equation of the circle. [3 marks]

Q3 Two circles A and B touch externally at the point P. The equation of circle A is $(x + 2)^2 + (y - 9)^2 = 100$ and the equation of circle B is $(x - 10)^2 + y^2 = 25$.

a) A line l joins the centres of the circles. Find the ratio into which P divides the line l. [3 marks]

b) Hence, or otherwise, find the coordinates of the point P. [2 marks]

c) A third circle C is positioned such that the centres of A, B, and C are collinear, and A and B touch C internally. Determine the equation of the circle C. [4 marks]

They say the circle has been around forever...

This circle geometry stuff is a lot easier if you use information from the question to draw yourself a quick sketch.

Solving Geometrical Problems

At National 5, you saw how to use simultaneous equations to find the point of intersection of two straight lines. Now it's time to extend that to finding the points of intersection of lines and curves. Exciting stuff...

Number of **Solutions** = number of **Intersections**

Geometrically, a **point of intersection** between two lines, circles or curves represents a **solution** that satisfies **both** equations — i.e. a solution to the simultaneous equations that produce the lines, circles or curves.

Two Solutions

The graphs meet in **two places**.

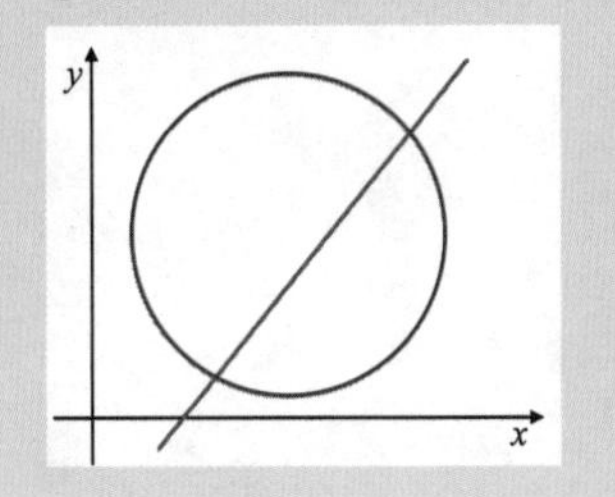

One Solution

The graphs meet in **one place** — the straight line is a **tangent** to the curve.

No Solutions

The graphs **never meet**.

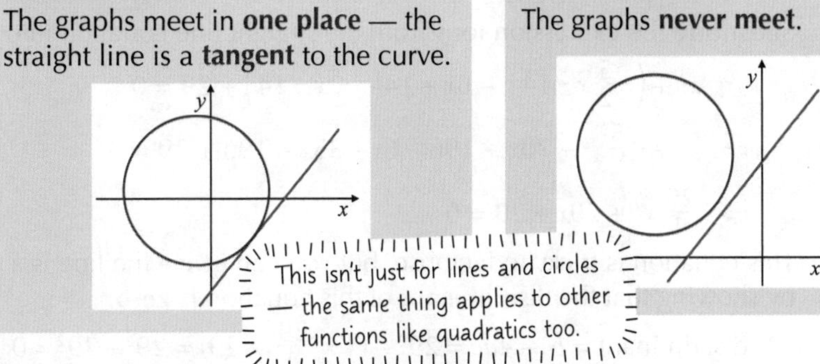

Solve Equations to find where **Lines** and **Curves Intersect**

To find the **points of intersection** of two lines or curves, you have to find **solutions** that are true for **both** equations. In some cases, you can do this by setting the two equations **equal** to each other, **rearranging**, and solving for x.

EXAMPLE: Find the points of intersection between the line $y = 5 - 2x$ and the curve $y = x^3 - 4x^2 + x + 5$.

Set the two equations **equal** to each other and **solve** the resulting cubic:

$$5 - 2x = x^3 - 4x^2 + x + 5 \Rightarrow x^3 - 4x^2 + 3x = 0$$
$$\Rightarrow x(x^2 - 4x + 3) = 0$$
$$\Rightarrow x(x - 1)(x - 3) = 0$$

So the **points of intersection** are at $\mathbf{x = 0}$, $\mathbf{x = 1}$ and $\mathbf{x = 3}$.

Using $y = 5 - 2x$ to find the y-coordinates gives the points of intersection as **(0, 5)**, **(1, 3)** and **(3, –1)**.

Three solutions mean there are three points of intersection.

When you're dealing with **circles**, the circle equation will have x^2 and y^2 terms as well as x's and y's. You can't set the equations equal to each other because the circle equation isn't a function of **only** x or y. Instead, you can solve them **simultaneously** using the **substitution** method:

EXAMPLE: Find the points where the circle $x^2 + y^2 + 6x - 14y = 15$ and the line $y = x - 1$ intersect.

Substitute $y = x - 1$ into the circle equation:

$$x^2 + (x - 1)^2 + 6x - 14(x - 1) = 15$$
$$\Rightarrow x^2 + x^2 - 2x + 1 + 6x - 14x + 14 = 15$$
$$\Rightarrow 2x^2 - 10x = 0 \Rightarrow \mathbf{x = 0} \text{ and } \mathbf{x = 5}$$

If the equation isn't in the form 'y = ', you have to rearrange to get one variable on its own (like in the example below).

When $x = 0$, $y = -1$, and when $x = 5$, $y = 4$, so the **points of intersection** are **(0, –1)** and **(5, 4)**.

EXAMPLE: Determine the points of intersection between $2y - x + 26 = 0$ and $(x - 1)^2 + (y + 5)^2 = 45$.

Rearrange the line equation to get **one variable** on its own: $2y - x + 26 = 0 \Rightarrow x = 2y + 26$.

Then **substitute** the expression for x into the circle equation:

$$((2y + 26) - 1)^2 + (y + 5)^2 = 45$$
$$\Rightarrow (2y + 25)^2 + (y + 5)^2 = 45$$
$$\Rightarrow 4y^2 + 100y + 625 + y^2 + 10y + 25 = 45$$
$$\Rightarrow 5y^2 + 110y + 605 = 0$$
$$\Rightarrow 5(y^2 + 22y + 121) = 0$$
$$\Rightarrow 5(y + 11)^2 = 0 \Rightarrow \mathbf{y = -11}$$

It's easier to use x = 2y + 26 instead of 'y = ' so you don't have to deal with a fraction.

Showing that there are equal roots proves the line is a tangent, but you must state this clearly in your working.

When $y = -11$, $x = 4$, so **(4, –11)** is the **only** solution. This means that the line is **tangent** to the circle at (4, –11).

Solving Geometrical Problems

Use the **Discriminant** if an equation is **Hard To Factorise**

If you're left with a quadratic that's hard to factorise, you can find out how many solutions it has by looking at its **discriminant** (see p.4). You can use this to show that a line is a **tangent** to a curve — in that case, the discriminant will be **zero**. You can also use the discriminant to show that the equation has **no solutions**, which means that the lines or curves **don't intersect** at all — this happens when the discriminant is **less than zero.**

EXAMPLE: Show that $y = -\frac{5}{2}x - 14$ is a tangent to the circle given by $x^2 + y^2 - 6x + 14y + 29 = 0$.

Substitute the expression for y from the straight line equation into the circle equation:

$$x^2 + \left(-\frac{5}{2}x - 14\right)^2 - 6x + 14\left(-\frac{5}{2}x - 14\right) + 29 = 0$$

$$\Rightarrow x^2 + \frac{25}{4}x^2 + 70x + 196 - 6x - 35x - 196 + 29 = 0$$

$$\Rightarrow \frac{29}{4}x^2 + 29x + 29 = 0$$

This equation is tricky to factorise, but you can **prove** the line is a **tangent** by showing that the **discriminant** of this equation is **zero**.

$$\text{discriminant} = b^2 - 4ac = 29^2 - (4 \times \frac{29}{4} \times 29) = 29^2 - 29^2 = 0$$

So the line $y = -\frac{5}{2}x - 14$ is a **tangent** to the circle.

EXAMPLE: Show that the line $y - 6x + 12 = 0$ and the circle $x^2 + y^2 + 2x - 8y + 11 = 0$ do not intersect.

Rearrange the line equation to get $y = 6x - 12$ and **substitute** this into the circle equation:

$$x^2 + (6x - 12)^2 + 2x - 8(6x - 12) + 11 = 0$$

$$\Rightarrow x^2 + 36x^2 - 144x + 144 + 2x - 48x + 96 + 11 = 0$$

$$\Rightarrow 37x^2 - 190x + 251 = 0$$

This is impossible to factorise, but you can find its **discriminant:**

$$\text{discriminant} = b^2 - 4ac = (-190)^2 - (4 \times 37 \times 251) = -1048$$

Since this is **less than zero**, there are no solutions, so **the line and the circle do not intersect.**

Warm-Up Questions

PRACTICE QUESTIONS

Q1 Find the points of intersection for:
a) $y = 4x - 1$ and $y = x^2 - 6$
b) $y = x^2 - 7x + 8$ and $y = 2x - 10$

Q2 Find the coordinates of the points where the following lines and circles intersect:
a) $(x - 4)^2 + (y + 3)^2 = 17$ and $y = 4x - 19$
b) $x^2 + y^2 + 6x - 4y - 13 = 0$ and $2y - 3x = 26$

Q3 Show that $2y + x = 0$ is tangent to the circle $(x + 2)^2 + (y - 6)^2 = 20$ and find the point where the line and the circle meet.

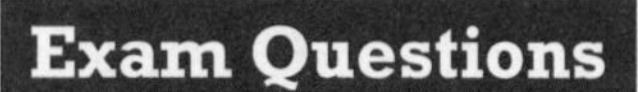

Exam Questions

Q1 Find the points where the curve $y = 16 + 10x - x^3$ and the line $y = 4 - 3x$ intersect. [5 marks]

Q2 Show that the line $y = 2x + 13$ is tangent to the circle $(x + 1)^2 + (y - 6)^2 = 5$ and find the coordinates of the point where the line and the circle touch. [5 marks]

Q3 A circle C has the equation $x^2 + y^2 - 8x + 12y + 27 = 0$. Find the coordinates of the points of intersection of the circle C and the line $y = 1 - 3x$. [5 marks]

If only all of my problems could be solved simultaneously...

If you're asked to show that a line is tangent to a curve, make sure you actually give a reason. You can either find the discriminant like in the example above, or if the quadratic equation is easy to factorise, show that it has a repeated root — this means it only has one unique solution, so the line and curve only meet in one place. And that's that.

Vectors

You'll have seen vectors at National 5 — they're used to represent positions and movements in space. Adding, subtracting and finding the magnitude of vectors should be familiar — but it's all recapped here.

Vectors have Magnitude and Direction — Scalars Don't

1) **Vectors** have both a **size** and a **direction** — e.g. a velocity of 2 m/s on a bearing of 050°. **Scalars** are quantities **without a direction** — e.g. a speed of 2 m/s, a distance of 3 m.
2) Vectors are drawn as lines with arrowheads on them.
   - The **length** of the line represents the **magnitude** (size) of the vector (e.g. the speed component of velocity).
   - The **direction** of the arrowhead shows the **direction** of the vector.
3) Vectors can be written in **component** form. You'll learn all about this on the next page.

There are two ways of **writing** vectors:

1) Using a lower case, bold letter:

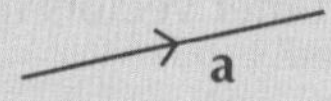

When you're handwriting a vector like this, you should underline the letter, i.e. a.

2) Putting an arrow over the endpoints:

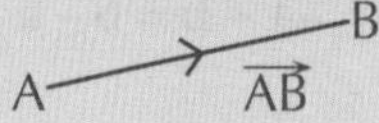

This means the vector from point A to point B.

Find the Resultant by Drawing Vectors Nose to Tail

You can **add** vectors together by drawing the arrows **nose to tail.**
The single vector that goes from the start to the end of the vectors is called the **resultant** vector.

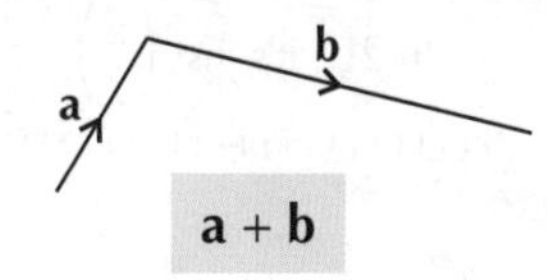

$\mathbf{a} + \mathbf{b}$

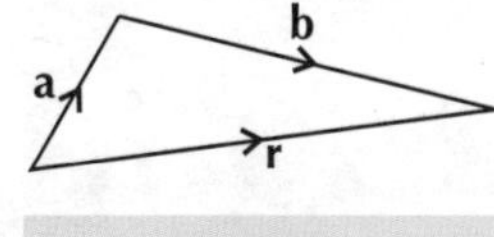

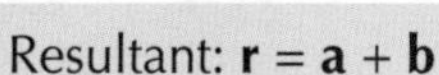

Resultant: $\mathbf{r} = \mathbf{a} + \mathbf{b}$

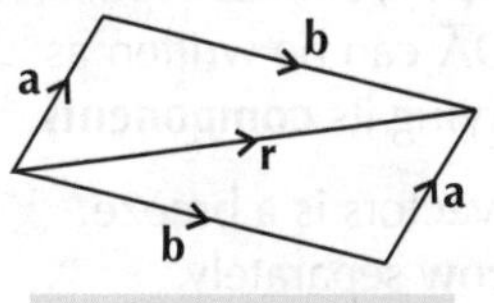

$\mathbf{a} + \mathbf{b} = \mathbf{r} = \mathbf{b} + \mathbf{a}$

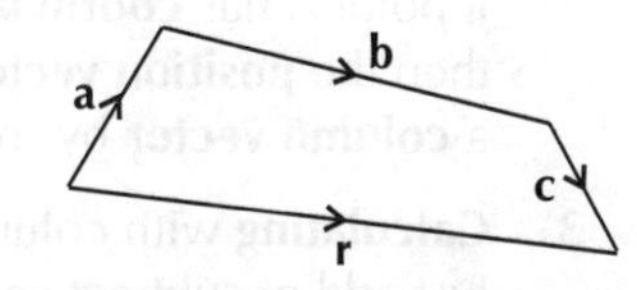

Resultant: $\mathbf{r} = \mathbf{a} + \mathbf{b} + \mathbf{c}$

Resultant vectors work the same way in 3D.

The diagram shows a cube ABCD,EFGH with $\overrightarrow{AB} = \mathbf{s}$, $\overrightarrow{AD} = \mathbf{t}$ and $\overrightarrow{AE} = \mathbf{u}$. Write $\overrightarrow{AG}$ in terms of **s**, **t** and **u**.

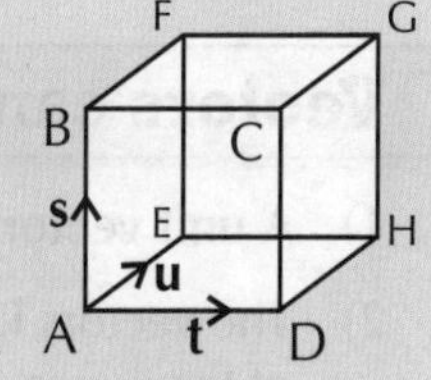

To determine an **unknown** vector like $\overrightarrow{AG}$, you need to find a **pathway** from A to G: $\overrightarrow{AG} = \overrightarrow{AD} + \overrightarrow{DH} + \overrightarrow{HG}$

There's more than one pathway but they'll all give the same answer.

The **path** from D to H has the same **size** and **direction** as the path from A to E, so: $\overrightarrow{DH} = \overrightarrow{AE} = \mathbf{u}$

The **path** from H to G has the same **size** and **direction** as the path from A to B, so: $\overrightarrow{HG} = \overrightarrow{AB} = \mathbf{s}$

The vectors $\overrightarrow{DH}$ and $\overrightarrow{HG}$ aren't given, but you can work them out using vectors you do know and the symmetry of the cube.

Putting this all together gives the answer: $\overrightarrow{AG} = \overrightarrow{AD} + \overrightarrow{DH} + \overrightarrow{HG} = \mathbf{t} + \mathbf{u} + \mathbf{s}$

Subtracting a Vector is the Same as Adding a Negative Vector

1) The vector **–a** is in the **opposite direction** to the vector **a**. They're both the **same size.**

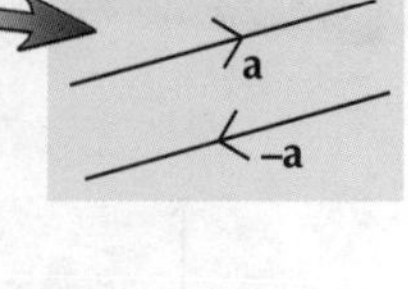

2) So **subtracting a vector** is the same as **adding the negative vector.**

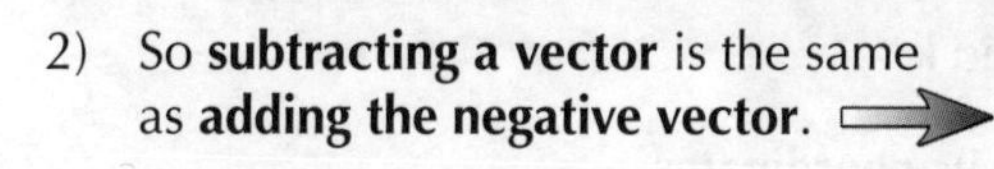

$\mathbf{b} - \mathbf{a} = \mathbf{b} + (-\mathbf{a})$

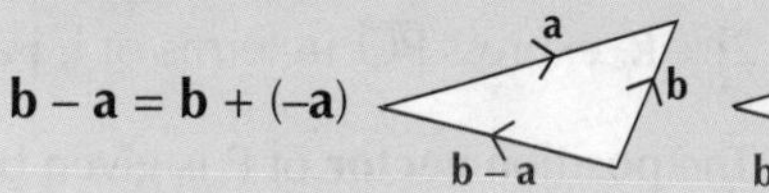

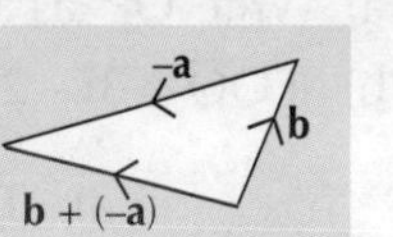

3) You can use the adding and subtracting rules to find a vector **in terms of other vectors.**

EXAMPLE: Write $\overrightarrow{WZ}$ and $\overrightarrow{ZX}$ in terms of **p**, **q** and **r**.

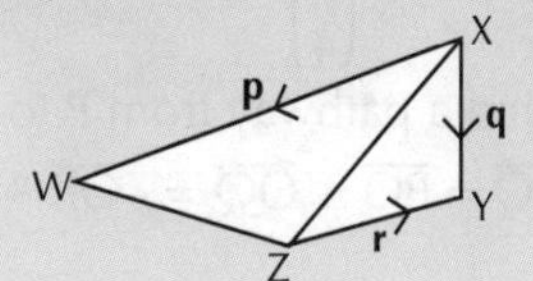

$\overrightarrow{WZ} = -\mathbf{p} + \mathbf{q} - \mathbf{r}$

$\overrightarrow{ZX} = \mathbf{r} - \mathbf{q}$

4) Vectors can **cancel** each other out, e.g. $\mathbf{a} + (-\mathbf{a}) = \mathbf{0}$ — the **zero vector**. See p.50 for more on this.

Vectors

Position Vectors Describe Where a Point Lies

You can use a vector to describe the **position of a point** in relation to the **origin, O**.

> The position vector of point A is $\overrightarrow{OA}$. It's usually called vector **a**.
> The position vector of point B is $\overrightarrow{OB}$. It's usually called vector **b**.

The position vector of your current location will point to somewhere around here — probably.

You can write other vectors in terms of position vectors:

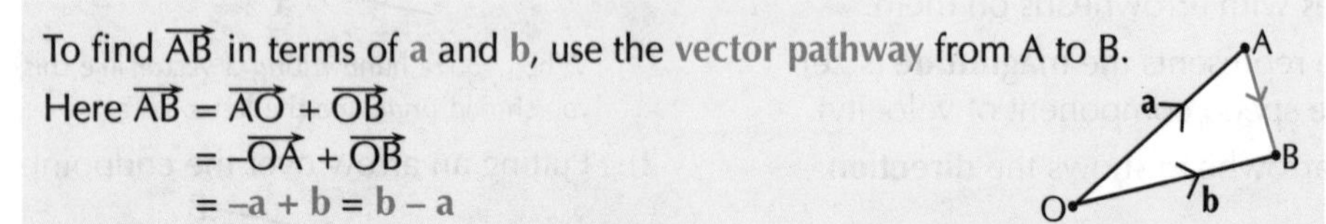

To find $\overrightarrow{AB}$ in terms of **a** and **b**, use the vector pathway from A to B.
Here $\overrightarrow{AB} = \overrightarrow{AO} + \overrightarrow{OB}$
$= -\overrightarrow{OA} + \overrightarrow{OB}$
$= -\mathbf{a} + \mathbf{b} = \mathbf{b} - \mathbf{a}$

Column Vectors are Vectors written in Component Form

Column vectors are a really easy way of writing out vectors.

1) Imagine that the x- and y-axes lie **flat** on the page. Then imagine a **third axis** sticking **straight through** the page at right angles to it — this is the **z-axis**.
2) If point A has **coordinates** (x, y, z) in 3D space, then the **position vector** $\overrightarrow{OA}$ can be written as a **column vector** by specifying its **components**.

$$\overrightarrow{OA} = \begin{pmatrix} x \\ y \\ z \end{pmatrix}$$
x ← the x-component
y ← the y-component
z ← the z-component

In 2D, it's just $\begin{pmatrix} x \\ y \end{pmatrix}$.

3) **Calculating** with column vectors is a breeze. Just add or subtract each **row** separately.
4) When you're **multiplying** a column vector by a **scalar**, you multiply **each number** in the column vector by the scalar. There's more about multiplying by scalars on p.50.

$$2\begin{pmatrix} 4 \\ 1 \\ 2 \end{pmatrix} - 3\begin{pmatrix} 5 \\ 7 \\ -1 \end{pmatrix} = \begin{pmatrix} 8 \\ 2 \\ 4 \end{pmatrix} - \begin{pmatrix} 15 \\ 21 \\ -3 \end{pmatrix} = \begin{pmatrix} -7 \\ -19 \\ 7 \end{pmatrix}$$

Vectors can be described using i, j and k Unit Vectors

1) A **unit vector** is any vector with a **magnitude** of **1 unit**.
2) The vectors **i**, **j** and **k** are the **standard unit vectors**. **i** is in the direction of the x-axis, **j** is in the direction of the y-axis, and **k** is in the direction of the z-axis. In 2D, you only need **i** and **j** as there's no z-axis.
3) You can write any vector in terms of scalar multiples of **i**, **j** and **k**.

2D unit vectors

$$\mathbf{i} = \begin{pmatrix} 1 \\ 0 \end{pmatrix} \quad \mathbf{j} = \begin{pmatrix} 0 \\ 1 \end{pmatrix}$$

3D unit vectors

$$\mathbf{i} = \begin{pmatrix} 1 \\ 0 \\ 0 \end{pmatrix} \quad \mathbf{j} = \begin{pmatrix} 0 \\ 1 \\ 0 \end{pmatrix} \quad \mathbf{k} = \begin{pmatrix} 0 \\ 0 \\ 1 \end{pmatrix}$$

$$a\mathbf{i} + b\mathbf{j} + c\mathbf{k} = \begin{pmatrix} a \\ b \\ c \end{pmatrix}$$

Both notations specify exactly 'a' units along the x-axis, 'b' units along the y-axis, and 'c' units along the z-axis.

EXAMPLE: The point P has coordinates (2, 5, 4).
a) Write $\overrightarrow{OP}$ as a column vector and in terms of **i**, **j** and **k**.
b) If $\overrightarrow{OQ} = 3\mathbf{i} - 2\mathbf{j} + \mathbf{k}$, express $\overrightarrow{PQ}$ in terms of **i**, **j** and **k**.

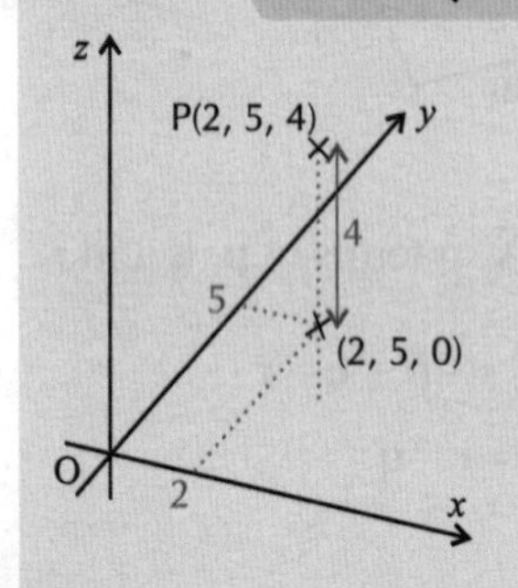

a) The **position vector** of P is given by its **coordinates**.
It's 2 in the x-direction, 5 in the y-direction and 4 in the z-direction.

So $\overrightarrow{OP} = \begin{pmatrix} 2 \\ 5 \\ 4 \end{pmatrix} = 2\mathbf{i} + 5\mathbf{j} + 4\mathbf{k}$

b) Find a pathway from P to Q, using your answer from part a):
$\overrightarrow{PQ} = \overrightarrow{PO} + \overrightarrow{OQ} = -\overrightarrow{OP} + \overrightarrow{OQ} = -(2\mathbf{i} + 5\mathbf{j} + 4\mathbf{k}) + (3\mathbf{i} - 2\mathbf{j} + \mathbf{k})$
$= (-2 + 3)\mathbf{i} + (-5 - 2)\mathbf{j} + (-4 + 1)\mathbf{k} = \mathbf{i} - 7\mathbf{j} - 3\mathbf{k}$

Vectors

Use **Pythagoras' Theorem** to Find Vector **Magnitudes**

1) The **magnitude** of vector **a** is written as $|\mathbf{a}|$ and the magnitude of $\overrightarrow{AB}$ is written as $|\overrightarrow{AB}|$.
2) You can use a variation of **Pythagoras' theorem** to find the distance of any point from the **origin, O**.

The **distance** of point (x, y, z) from the **origin** is $\sqrt{x^2 + y^2 + z^2}$ ⟵ In 2D, it's $\sqrt{x^2 + y^2}$.

3) This means that you can use Pythagoras' theorem to find the magnitude of any vector.

EXAMPLE: Find $|\overrightarrow{OQ}|$ for the point Q (2, 5, 4).

$|\overrightarrow{OQ}| = \sqrt{x^2 + y^2 + z^2} = \sqrt{2^2 + 5^2 + 4^2}$
$= \sqrt{45} =$ **6.7 units** (1 d.p.)

EXAMPLE: Find the magnitude of the vector $\mathbf{r} = 5\mathbf{i} + 7\mathbf{j} + 3\mathbf{k}$.

$|\mathbf{r}| = \sqrt{5^2 + 7^2 + 3^2} = \sqrt{83} =$ **9.1 units** (1 d.p.)

4) There's also a Pythagoras-based formula for finding the **distance** between any **two points**.

The **distance between** points (x_1, y_1, z_1) and (x_2, y_2, z_2) is $\sqrt{(x_1 - x_2)^2 + (y_1 - y_2)^2 + (z_1 - z_2)^2}$

In 2D, it's $\sqrt{(x_1 - x_2)^2 + (y_1 - y_2)^2}$.

5) You can change the **magnitude** of a vector without changing its **direction**.

The **unit vector** in the **direction** of vector **a** is $\frac{\mathbf{a}}{|\mathbf{a}|}$

Remember — a unit vector has a magnitude of 1. **a** has a magnitude of 5, so you need to divide **a** by 5.

EXAMPLE: Find the unit vector in the direction of $\mathbf{a} = 4\mathbf{i} + 3\mathbf{j}$.

First find the **magnitude** of **a**:
$|\mathbf{a}| = \sqrt{4^2 + 3^2} = \sqrt{25} = 5$
So, the **unit vector** is:
$\frac{\mathbf{a}}{|\mathbf{a}|} = \frac{1}{5}\mathbf{a} = \frac{1}{5}(4\mathbf{i} + 3\mathbf{j}) = \frac{4}{5}\mathbf{i} + \frac{3}{5}\mathbf{j}$

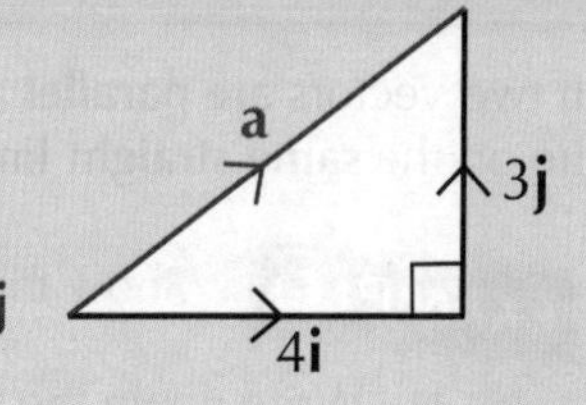

Warm-Up Questions

Q1 Using the diagram on the right, find these vectors in terms of vectors **a**, **b** and **c**:
a) $\overrightarrow{AB}$ b) $\overrightarrow{BA}$ c) $\overrightarrow{CB}$ d) $\overrightarrow{AC}$

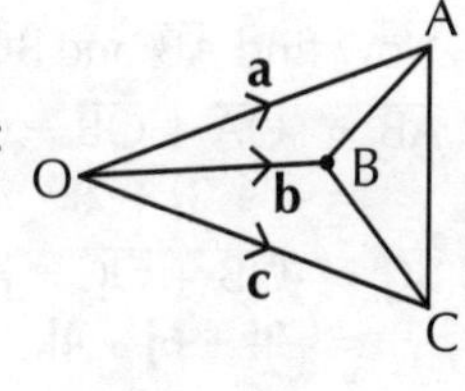

Q2 For each of the following points, give its position vector in terms of **i**, **j** and **k**.
a) P(2, –4) b) Q(–1, 4, –2) c) R(0, –1, 0)

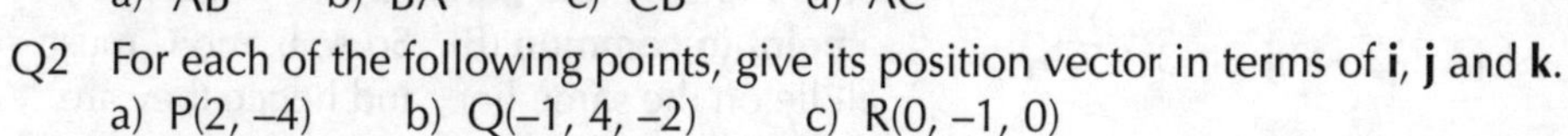

Q3 Let $\mathbf{a} = \begin{pmatrix} 3 \\ -4 \end{pmatrix}$ and $\mathbf{b} = \begin{pmatrix} -2 \\ -1 \end{pmatrix}$.
a) Express $3\mathbf{a} - 2\mathbf{b}$ in component form. b) Calculate $|3\mathbf{a} - 2\mathbf{b}|$ to 2 d.p.

Q4 If A = (1, 2, 1) and B = (3, –1, 2), find: a) $|\overrightarrow{OA}|$ b) $|\overrightarrow{OB}|$ c) $|\overrightarrow{AB}|$

Exam Questions

Q1 The diagram on the right shows a triangle ABC.
M is the midpoint of line BC.
Given that $\overrightarrow{AB} = \begin{pmatrix} -5 \\ 2 \end{pmatrix}$ and $\overrightarrow{AC} = \begin{pmatrix} -2 \\ 4 \end{pmatrix}$, find the exact value of $|\overrightarrow{AM}|$. [3 marks]

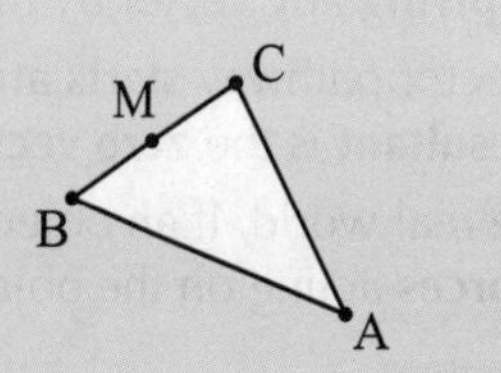

Q2 Consider the vectors $\mathbf{a} = \mathbf{i} + 3\mathbf{j} - 4\mathbf{k}$ and $\mathbf{b} = p\mathbf{i} + 2\mathbf{j} + \sqrt{12}\mathbf{k}$.
a) For $p = 1$, express $\mathbf{a} - \mathbf{b}$ in component form. [1 mark]
b) Find the values of p for which $|\mathbf{b}| = 5$. [3 marks]

Q3 $\overrightarrow{PQ} = 6\mathbf{i} + 2\mathbf{j} - 2\mathbf{k}$ and $\overrightarrow{QR} = -4\mathbf{i} + \mathbf{j} + 8\mathbf{k}$.
a) Express $\overrightarrow{PR}$ in terms of **i**, **j** and **k**. [2 marks]
b) Find the unit vector in the direction of $\overrightarrow{RP}$. Give your answer in component form. [2 marks]

A topic of this magnitude isn't easily scaled into such a tidy unit...

*There are lots of ways to write vectors — so make sure you know your x, y and z's from your **i**, **j** and **k**'s. Both 'x, y, z' and '**i**, **j**, **k**' are in alphabetical order, so it's easy to remember that **i** goes along the x-axis, **j** goes along the y-axis, etc...*

More Vectors

It's time to put vectors to work. Read on to find out all about parallel vectors, collinear points and the zero vector...

Vectors a, 2a and 3a are all Parallel

You can **multiply** a vector by a **scalar** (just a number, see p.47). If the scalar is **non-zero**, the result of the multiplication is a vector **parallel** to the one you started with. Parallel vectors can have **different magnitudes** but they always point in the **same** or **opposite direction**.

All these vectors are parallel: $9\mathbf{a} + 15\mathbf{b}$ $\quad -18\mathbf{a} - 30\mathbf{b}$ $\quad 6\mathbf{a} + 10\mathbf{b}$

This is $-2(9\mathbf{a} + 15\mathbf{b})$.

This is $\frac{2}{3}(9\mathbf{a} + 15\mathbf{b})$.

To show that two vectors are **parallel**, you just need to show that they are **scalar multiples** of each other.

In the diagram on the right, $\overrightarrow{CA} = \mathbf{v}$ and $\overrightarrow{CB} = \mathbf{u}$. Point P divides $\overrightarrow{CA}$ in the ratio 1 : 2 and Q divides $\overrightarrow{CB}$ in the ratio 1 : 2. Show that $\overrightarrow{PQ}$ is parallel to $\overrightarrow{AB}$.

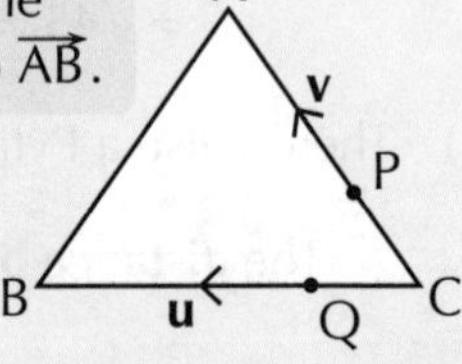

$\overrightarrow{AB} = -\mathbf{v} + \mathbf{u}$. P divides $\overrightarrow{CA}$ in the ratio 1 : 2, so P is one third of the way along $\overrightarrow{CA}$.

This means $\overrightarrow{CP} = \frac{1}{3}\mathbf{v}$, so $\overrightarrow{PC} = -\frac{1}{3}\mathbf{v}$. Similarly, $\overrightarrow{CQ} = \frac{1}{3}\mathbf{u}$.

So, $\overrightarrow{PQ} = -\frac{1}{3}\mathbf{v} + \frac{1}{3}\mathbf{u} = \frac{1}{3}(-\mathbf{v} + \mathbf{u}) = \frac{1}{3}\overrightarrow{AB}$. This shows that $\overrightarrow{PQ}$ is parallel to $\overrightarrow{AB}$.

There's more about ratios on the next page.

You can use Vectors to show Points are Collinear

If two vectors are **parallel** and also have a **point in common**, then they must lie on the **same straight line**. You say that the points on the line are **collinear**.

You can do your working in component form if you prefer.

EXAMPLE: Show that the points A(2, −1, 1), B(1, 2, 3) and C(−1, 8, 7) are collinear.

1) Write down the **position vectors** of the points:
   $\overrightarrow{OA} = 2\mathbf{i} - \mathbf{j} + \mathbf{k}$, $\overrightarrow{OB} = \mathbf{i} + 2\mathbf{j} + 3\mathbf{k}$, $\overrightarrow{OC} = -\mathbf{i} + 8\mathbf{j} + 7\mathbf{k}$
2) Now find $\overrightarrow{AB}$ and $\overrightarrow{BC}$:
   $\overrightarrow{AB} = -\overrightarrow{OA} + \overrightarrow{OB} = (-2 + 1)\mathbf{i} + (1 + 2)\mathbf{j} + (-1 + 3)\mathbf{k}$
   $= -\mathbf{i} + 3\mathbf{j} + 2\mathbf{k}$
   $\overrightarrow{BC} = -\overrightarrow{OB} + \overrightarrow{OC} = (-1 - 1)\mathbf{i} + (-2 + 8)\mathbf{j} + (-3 + 7)\mathbf{k}$
   $= -2\mathbf{i} + 6\mathbf{j} + 4\mathbf{k}$
3) Show that $\overrightarrow{AB}$ and $\overrightarrow{BC}$ are **parallel** by showing one is a **scalar multiple** of the other:
   $\overrightarrow{BC} = -2\mathbf{i} + 6\mathbf{j} + 4\mathbf{k}$
   $= 2(-\mathbf{i} + 3\mathbf{j} + 2\mathbf{k}) = 2\overrightarrow{AB}$
4) So $\overrightarrow{AB}$ and $\overrightarrow{BC}$ are **parallel**. They also have a **point in common** (B). So A, B and C must all lie on the same line, and hence they are **collinear**.

In your answer, you must say the vectors are parallel and have a point in common.

Multiplying a Vector by 0 gives the Zero Vector

1) The **zero vector**, **0**, is the vector with all components **equal to 0**, so $\mathbf{0} = 0\mathbf{i} + 0\mathbf{j} + 0\mathbf{k}$. Its magnitude is $|\mathbf{0}| = 0$.
2) **Multiplying** any vector by the **zero scalar** results in the **zero vector**.
3) If a vector pathway **starts** and **ends** at the **same point**, the **resultant** is the **zero vector**.
4) In the real world, if an object is **stationary**, then the **sum** of all the **forces** acting on the object is the **zero vector**.

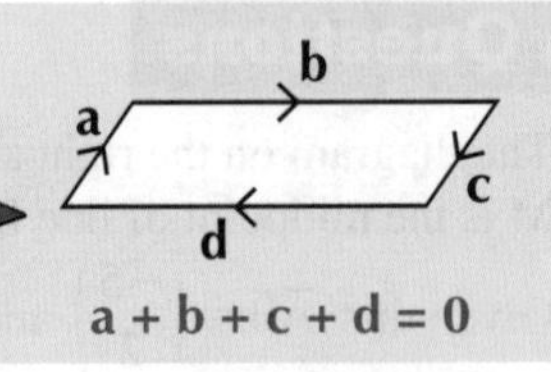

The diagram shows the three forces acting on a kite:
$\mathbf{u} = \mathbf{i} + 3\mathbf{j} + 8\mathbf{k}$ (uplift), $\mathbf{p} = -2\mathbf{i} - \mathbf{j} - 3\mathbf{k}$ (pull) and $\mathbf{w}$ (weight).
If the kite is stationary in the air, calculate $\mathbf{w}$.

Write $\mathbf{w}$ in component form: $\mathbf{w} = a\mathbf{i} + b\mathbf{j} + c\mathbf{k}$ for scalars a, b and c.
For the kite to be stationary, the forces must sum to the zero vector:

$\mathbf{u} + \mathbf{p} + \mathbf{w} = \mathbf{0} \Rightarrow (1 - 2 + a)\mathbf{i} + (3 - 1 + b)\mathbf{j} + (8 - 3 + c)\mathbf{k} = \mathbf{0}$

$\Rightarrow (a - 1)\mathbf{i} + (b + 2)\mathbf{j} + (c + 5)\mathbf{k} = 0\mathbf{i} + 0\mathbf{j} + 0\mathbf{k}$

$\Rightarrow a = 1, b = -2$ and $c = -5$

$\Rightarrow \mathbf{w} = \mathbf{i} - 2\mathbf{j} - 5\mathbf{k}$

To find a, b and c, set each component equal to 0 and solve — you want to end up with $0\mathbf{i} + 0\mathbf{j} + 0\mathbf{k}$.

More Vectors

You can use Vectors to Divide Lines in a given Ratio

To divide a line in the **ratio** $a:b$, you need to find the **division point** that **splits** the line into ***a* parts** on one side and ***b* parts** on the other — giving $a + b$ parts in total. This division point is $\frac{a}{a+b}$ of the way along the line.

Points P and Q have position vectors $\mathbf{i} - 2\mathbf{j} + 3\mathbf{k}$ and $-\mathbf{i} + 3\mathbf{j} + 2\mathbf{k}$. R divides the line PQ in the ratio 3 : 1. Find the coordinates of R.

First you need to find the vector $\overrightarrow{PQ}$:

$$\overrightarrow{PQ} = \overrightarrow{OQ} - \overrightarrow{OP} = \begin{pmatrix}-1\\3\\2\end{pmatrix} - \begin{pmatrix}1\\-2\\3\end{pmatrix} = \begin{pmatrix}-2\\5\\-1\end{pmatrix}$$

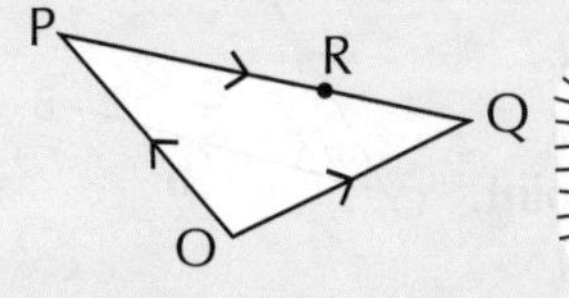

Visualising 3D vector problems can be quite hard. Break it down and draw simple 2D diagrams.

R divides $\overrightarrow{PQ}$ in the ratio 3 : 1, so R is $\frac{3}{3+1} = \frac{3}{4}$ of the way along $\overrightarrow{PQ}$.

P R Q — R divides $\overrightarrow{PQ}$ into $3 + 1 = 4$ parts.

This means $\overrightarrow{PR} = \frac{3}{4}\overrightarrow{PQ} = \frac{3}{4}\begin{pmatrix}-2\\5\\-1\end{pmatrix} = \begin{pmatrix}-\frac{3}{2}\\\frac{15}{4}\\-\frac{3}{4}\end{pmatrix}$

Calculate the **position vector** of R: $\overrightarrow{OR} = \overrightarrow{OP} + \overrightarrow{PR} = \begin{pmatrix}1\\-2\\3\end{pmatrix} + \begin{pmatrix}-\frac{3}{2}\\\frac{15}{4}\\-\frac{3}{4}\end{pmatrix} = \begin{pmatrix}-\frac{1}{2}\\\frac{7}{4}\\\frac{9}{4}\end{pmatrix}$

You could also do $\overrightarrow{OR} = \overrightarrow{OQ} + \overrightarrow{QR}$.

So the **coordinates** of R are $\left(-\frac{1}{2}, \frac{7}{4}, \frac{9}{4}\right)$.

Warm-Up Questions

Q1 Pair up each of the following vectors with one that it is parallel to.
$2\mathbf{i}$ $-3\mathbf{i} + 2\mathbf{j} - 4\mathbf{k}$ $-7\mathbf{i}$ $10\mathbf{j} + 12\mathbf{k}$ $3\mathbf{i} - 2\mathbf{j} + 4\mathbf{k}$ $5\mathbf{j} + 6\mathbf{k}$

Q2 Point P has coordinates (3, –5, 12). $\overrightarrow{PQ} = 2\mathbf{i} + 6\mathbf{j} - 3\mathbf{k}$ and $\overrightarrow{QR} = 4\overrightarrow{PQ}$.
a) Give the ratio in which Q divides PR. b) Find the coordinates of R.

Q3 The vectors $\mathbf{s} = a\mathbf{i} - \mathbf{k}$, $\mathbf{b} = 5\mathbf{i} + b\mathbf{j} + 3\mathbf{k}$ and $\mathbf{u} = 2\mathbf{i} + 2\mathbf{j} + c\mathbf{k}$ represent the forces acting on a ball. Find the values of a, b and c when the ball is stationary.

Q4 The points A, B and C are collinear. $\overrightarrow{AB} = 5\mathbf{i} + 2\mathbf{j} - 4\mathbf{k}$ and $\overrightarrow{BC} = -10\mathbf{i} - b\mathbf{j} + 8\mathbf{k}$.
a) Find the value of b. b) A has coordinates (0, –2, 3). Find the coordinates of B and C.

Exam Questions

Q1 The diagram on the right shows three parallel chords of an ellipse. Their midpoints are A (3, –5, 7), B (1, –4, 4) and C(–5, –1, –5). Determine whether A, B and C are collinear. Justify your answer. [3 marks]

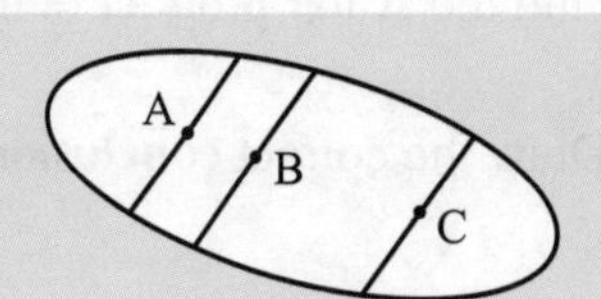

Q2 The points K(1, –5, 7), L(–7, p, 9) and M(–19, 5, q) are collinear.
a) State the ratio in which L divides the line KM in its simplest form. [2 mark]
b) Given that $\overrightarrow{KM} = -20\mathbf{i} + 10\mathbf{j} + 5\mathbf{k}$, find the value of q. [1 mark]
c) Find the value of p. [2 marks]

Q3 The points P and Q are defined by $\begin{pmatrix}1\\0\\3\end{pmatrix}$ and $\begin{pmatrix}11\\5\\18\end{pmatrix}$ respectively. Point R divides the line PQ in the ratio 4 : 1.
Find the position vector of R, giving your answer in component form. [3 marks]

Q4 The vectors $\mathbf{d} = a\mathbf{i} + b\mathbf{j} + c\mathbf{k}$, $\mathbf{f} = \mathbf{i} + 6\mathbf{j} - 2\mathbf{k}$ and $\mathbf{w} = -6\mathbf{j}$ represent forces acting on a car. The resultant force vector is parallel to $\mathbf{i} + \mathbf{j} + \mathbf{k}$ and has a magnitude of $\sqrt{12}$. If $b > 0$, determine the values of a, b and c. [5 marks]

The zero vector has no direction, you'll just have to accept it...

Remember, vectors can be parallel and points can be collinear. To show three points are collinear, calculate two vectors between them and show they're parallel — it's important to state the common point of the two vectors.

The Scalar Product

The scalar product of two vectors is kind of what it says on the tin — two vectors multiplied together to give a scalar.

The Scalar Product is a way of Multiplying Vectors

The scalar product is often called the dot product.

1) The **scalar product** of two vectors **a** and **b** is written **a.b** (you read this as 'a dot b').

The definition of the scalar product is:

$$\mathbf{a.b} = |\mathbf{a}||\mathbf{b}|\cos\theta$$

where θ is the angle between the two vectors when they're both directed away from the same point. (It's given on the formula sheet.)

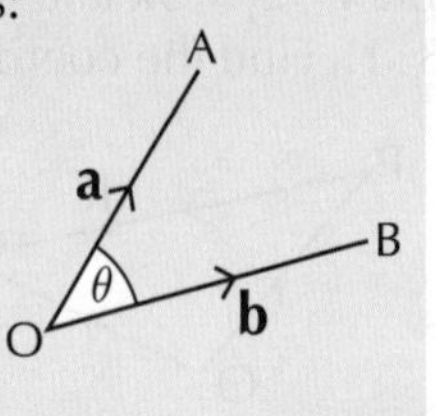

Watch out — the **correct angle** might not always be obvious.

θ is the angle in the definition.

Here you have to continue **b** on so that it's also **directed away** from the intersection point, O.

2) The scalar product of two vectors is always a **scalar quantity** — it's **never** a vector.
3) It's really, really important to put the dot in, as it shows you mean the **scalar product**.
4) Like normal multiplication, scalar products follow the **commutative law** (i.e. **a.b** = **b.a**) and the **distributive law** (i.e. **a.(b + c)** = **a.b** + **a.c**).
5) The **scalar product** can be used to calculate the **angle** between two vectors (see p.53).

To work out the scalar product you can use this formula:

$$\mathbf{a.b} = a_1b_1 + a_2b_2 + a_3b_3$$

← For 2D vectors, just remove a_3b_3.

where $\mathbf{a} = \begin{pmatrix} a_1 \\ a_2 \\ a_3 \end{pmatrix}$ and $\mathbf{b} = \begin{pmatrix} b_1 \\ b_2 \\ b_3 \end{pmatrix}$.

This formula is derived from the definition of the scalar product — and it's also on the formula sheet.

Perpendicular Vectors have a Scalar Product of Zero

The unit vectors **i**, **j** and **k** are all perpendicular to each other.

1) Perpendicular vectors are at **90°** to each other, and **cos 90° = 0**. This means that if **a** and **b** are perpendicular, then the scalar product **a.b** = |**a**| |**b**| cos 90° = |**a**| |**b**| × 0 = 0.
2) So for two **non-zero** vectors **a** and **b**: **a.b** = 0 ⇔ **a** and **b** are **perpendicular**
3) This **non-zero** bit is really important — if either vector is **0**, you'd always get a scalar product of 0.

The ⇔ symbol means 'if and only if' — one side of the equation is true if and only if the other side is also true.

Show that the vectors $\begin{pmatrix} 1 \\ 2 \\ 2 \end{pmatrix}$ and $\begin{pmatrix} 4 \\ -3 \\ 1 \end{pmatrix}$ are perpendicular.

1) Find the **scalar product** of the vectors: $\begin{pmatrix} 1 \\ 2 \\ 2 \end{pmatrix} \cdot \begin{pmatrix} 4 \\ -3 \\ 1 \end{pmatrix} = (1 \times 4) + (2 \times -3) + (2 \times 1) = 4 - 6 + 2 = 0$

2) Draw the correct **conclusion**: The scalar product is 0 so the vectors are **perpendicular**.

Vectors in the Same Direction have a Scalar Product of |a| |b|

Parallel vectors pointing in the **same direction** have an angle of 0° between them. And **cos 0° = 1**, so...

If vectors **a** and **b** have the **same direction**:

a.b = |**a**| |**b**| cos 0° = |**a**| |**b**|

Vectors **s** and **t** are parallel and in the same direction, and **u** is perpendicular to both **s** and **t**. Given |**s**| = 3 and |**t**| = 4, calculate the value of the scalar product **s.(t + u)**.

First, use the distributive law: **s.(t + u) = s.t + s.u**

As **s** and **t** have the same direction: **s.t** = |**s**||**t**|

As **s** and **u** are perpendicular vectors: **s.u** = 0

Use the information given in the question.

...and so: **s.(t + u)** = |**s**||**t**| + 0 = 3 × 4 = **12**

The Scalar Product

Use the **Scalar Product** to find the **Angle** between two **Vectors**

Rearranging the scalar product formula gives you a formula for working out the **angle between** two vectors, θ.

The Angle Formula

$$\cos\theta = \frac{\mathbf{a}.\mathbf{b}}{|\mathbf{a}||\mathbf{b}|}$$

This will always give you an angle in the range $0° \leq \theta \leq 180°$.

EXAMPLE: Find the angle between the vectors $4\mathbf{i} - 6\mathbf{j} + 3\mathbf{k}$ and $-\mathbf{i} - 2\mathbf{j} - 7\mathbf{k}$, giving your answer in degrees to 1 d.p.

1) Call the vectors **a** and **b**. Find the **scalar product** of the vectors:
$$\mathbf{a}.\mathbf{b} = a_1b_1 + a_2b_2 + a_3b_3 = -4 + 12 - 21 = -13$$
2) Find the **magnitude** of each vector:
$$|\mathbf{a}| = \sqrt{16+36+9} = \sqrt{61} \qquad |\mathbf{b}| = \sqrt{1+4+49} = \sqrt{54}$$
Use Pythagoras to find the magnitude of each vector.
3) Now plug these values into the equation and find the **angle**:
$$\cos\theta = \frac{\mathbf{a}.\mathbf{b}}{|\mathbf{a}||\mathbf{b}|} = \frac{-13}{\sqrt{61}\sqrt{54}} = -0.2265... \Rightarrow \theta = \cos^{-1}(-0.2265...) = \mathbf{103.1° \text{ (1 d.p.)}}$$

You might be asked to complete a vector when an angle has been given.

EXAMPLE: The angle between the vectors $\mathbf{a} = p\mathbf{i} - 6\mathbf{j} + 3\mathbf{k}$ and $\mathbf{b} = \mathbf{i} + \mathbf{k}$ is 45°. Find the value of p.

1) Use the **angle formula**: $\frac{\mathbf{a}.\mathbf{b}}{|\mathbf{a}||\mathbf{b}|} = \cos 45° \Rightarrow \frac{\mathbf{a}.\mathbf{b}}{|\mathbf{a}||\mathbf{b}|} = \frac{1}{\sqrt{2}} \Rightarrow \sqrt{2}\,\mathbf{a}.\mathbf{b} = |\mathbf{a}||\mathbf{b}|$
2) Calculate the **scalar product**: $\mathbf{a}.\mathbf{b} = p \times 1 + (-6) \times 0 + 3 \times 1 = p + 3$
3) Calculate the **magnitudes**: $|\mathbf{a}| = \sqrt{p^2 + (-6)^2 + 3^2} = \sqrt{p^2 + 45}$ and $|\mathbf{b}| = \sqrt{1^2 + 0^2 + 1^2} = \sqrt{2}$
4) **Plug in** these values to **find** p: $\sqrt{2}\,\mathbf{a}.\mathbf{b} = |\mathbf{a}||\mathbf{b}| \Rightarrow \sqrt{2}(p+3) = \sqrt{p^2+45}\sqrt{2}$
$\Rightarrow (p+3)^2 = p^2 + 45$
$\Rightarrow p^2 + 6p + 9 = p^2 + 45$
$\Rightarrow 6p = 36 \Rightarrow p = 6$

Cancel $\sqrt{2}$, then square both sides.

Warm-Up Questions

PRACTICE QUESTIONS

Q1 Find **a.b** when: a) $\mathbf{a} = 3\mathbf{i} + 4\mathbf{j}$, $\mathbf{b} = \mathbf{i} - 2\mathbf{j} + 3\mathbf{k}$ b) $\mathbf{a} = 4\mathbf{i} + 2\mathbf{j} + \mathbf{k}$, $\mathbf{b} = 3\mathbf{i} - 4\mathbf{j} - 3\mathbf{k}$

Q2 Find the angle, in degrees to 1 d.p., between the vectors $\mathbf{a} = -4\mathbf{i} + 6\mathbf{j} - 9\mathbf{k}$ and $\mathbf{b} = -\mathbf{i} - 3\mathbf{j}$.

Q3 The vector $4\mathbf{i} - 2\mathbf{j} + t\mathbf{k}$ is perpendicular to $3\mathbf{i} + 4\mathbf{j} - 2\mathbf{k}$. Find the value of t.

Q4 The angle between **i** and a vector **u** is 45° and $\mathbf{i}.\mathbf{u} = 3$. Find the magnitude of **u**.

Exam Questions

Q1 The points A(1, 0, 5), B(6, –1, 3), C(t, 6, 3) and D(2, 1, –2) are such that $\overrightarrow{AB}$ is perpendicular to $\overrightarrow{CD}$. Find the value of t. [4 marks]

Q2 The vector **w** makes an angle of 120° with **u**. $\mathbf{u} = -5\mathbf{i} + \sqrt{8}\mathbf{j} + 4\mathbf{k}$ and $|\mathbf{w}| = 6$. Find the exact value of **u.w**. [3 marks]

Q3 In the diagram on the right, $\overrightarrow{PQ} = \mathbf{i} + 2\mathbf{j} - 4\mathbf{k}$ and $\overrightarrow{PS} = 3\mathbf{i} - 4\mathbf{j} + \mathbf{k}$. The line SR is parallel to PQ.

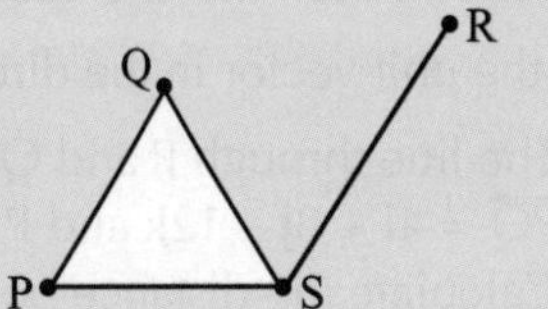

a) Express $\overrightarrow{SQ}$ in terms of **i**, **j** and **k**. [1 mark]
b) Find the angle QSR in degrees to 1 d.p. [5 marks]

Q4 The vectors **p** and **q** are unit vectors, both perpendicular to a vector **r**. The angle between **p** and **q** is 60°. Calculate the value of $\mathbf{p}.(\mathbf{q} + \mathbf{r})$. [3 marks]

Scalar products? No thanks — snakeskin isn't really my thing...

Don't expect vector diagrams to be drawn to scale — a vector or angle may look a certain size on paper but, if it's not written down, you need to calculate the size yourself. The key thing here is the formula for the scalar product — it'll be given on the formula sheet in your exams, but make sure that you can rearrange it into the angle formula above.

Revision Summary for Section Three

Phew — you made it to the end of Section Three. But before you start celebrating, give these questions a go.

- Try these questions and tick off each one when you get it right.
- When you've done all the questions for a topic and are completely happy with it, tick off the topic.

Linear Coordinate Geometry (p.39-41)

1) Write the following equations in the form: (i) $y = mx + c$ (ii) $ax + by + c = 0$ (for integers a, b and c)
   a) $y - 3 = 4(x + 7)$ b) $y + \frac{3}{2} = -6(x - \frac{7}{2})$ c) $y - 4 = -\frac{1}{2}(x + \frac{3}{4})$
2) Find the equation of the line parallel to $y = 7x - 11$ that goes through the point (2, 12).
3) Show that the points A (1, –7), B (–2, –3) and C (–5, 1) are collinear.
4) a) Determine the equation of the line l through (5, –2) that is perpendicular to $y = 3 - 5x$.
   b) Find the angle that l makes with the positive x-axis.
5) Define the terms: a) altitude b) median c) perpendicular bisector

Circle Geometry (p.42-44)

6) a) Write $(x - 1)^2 + (y + 3)^2 = 17$ in $x^2 + y^2 + 2gx + 2fy + c = 0$ form and state the radius and centre.
   b) Write $x^2 + y^2 - 6x + 10y + 22 = 0$ in $(x - a)^2 + (y - b)^2 = r^2$ form and state the radius and centre.
7) Find the equation of the tangent to the circle with equation $(x + 6)^2 + (y - 2)^2 = 5$ at the point (–8, 3).
8) A (–9, 9) and B (3, –7) are points on the circumference of a circle such that AB is a diameter. Find the equation of this circle.
9) Two circles C_1 and C_2, which have the same radius, touch externally. A third circle, C_3, touches C_1 and C_2 internally, as shown. C_1 has the equation $(x + 4)^2 + (y - 1)^2 = 4$, and the line joining the centres of C_1 and C_2 is parallel to the x-axis. Find the equation of the circle C_3.

Solving Geometrical Problems (p.45-46)

10) Find the points of intersection of $y = 3x - 3$ and $y = x^3 - 6x^2 + 8x - 3$.
11) Find the points of intersection for the circle $x^2 + y^2 - 4x + 6y + 8 = 0$ and the line $y - 3x + 14 = 0$.
12) When finding points of intersection between a line and a circle, what does it mean if the discriminant of the resulting quadratic equation is zero?
13) Show that the line $y = 8 - x$ is tangent to $x^2 + y^2 + 8x - 12y + 34 = 0$.

Vectors (p.47-51)

14) Find a vector pathway from B to C and give the resultant vector in terms of **s**, **t**, **u** and **v**.
15) a) Give the position vector of the point A(2, 6, –3) in component form.
    b) The point B is such that $\overrightarrow{AB} = 8\mathbf{i} + 2\mathbf{j} - 4\mathbf{k}$. Find the coordinates of B.
    c) The point C is such that B divides the line AC in the ratio 2 : 1. Give the position vector of the point C in terms of **i**, **j** and **k**.
    d) Write down the exact value of $|\overrightarrow{BC}|$.
16) How can you tell that the vectors $\mathbf{u} = 12\mathbf{i} + 21\mathbf{j} + 15\mathbf{k}$ and $\mathbf{v} = -4\mathbf{i} - 7\mathbf{j} - 5\mathbf{k}$ are parallel?
17) Give the unit vector in the direction of $2\mathbf{i} + 6\mathbf{j} + 9\mathbf{k}$.
18) a) The line through P and Q passes through the origin. $\overrightarrow{PQ} = 4\mathbf{i} + 8\mathbf{j} - 12\mathbf{k}$ and P has coordinates $(1, p, -3)$. What is the value of p?
    b) Calculate the distance between P and Q to 2 d.p.

The Scalar Product (p.52-53)

19) Calculate the scalar product $(2\mathbf{i} - 7\mathbf{j} + \mathbf{k}).(-8\mathbf{i} - 3\mathbf{j} + 5\mathbf{k})$.
20) The vector $\mathbf{w} = -6\mathbf{i} + 2\mathbf{j} - t\mathbf{k}$ is perpendicular to $\mathbf{i} + 3\mathbf{j} - \mathbf{k}$. Find the value of t.
21) a) State the exact angle in degrees between each of the following pairs of vectors.
    (i) **i** and **i** (ii) **i** and –**i** (iii) **i** and **j** (iv) $2\mathbf{i} + \mathbf{j}$ and **k**
    b) Find the angle between the vectors $-2\mathbf{i} + \sqrt{3}\mathbf{j} - \mathbf{k}$ and $4\mathbf{i} - \sqrt{3}\mathbf{j} + 2\mathbf{k}$, in degrees to 1 d.p.

Differentiation

Differentiation is a great way to work out gradients of graphs. You take a function, differentiate it, and you can quickly tell how steep a graph is. It's magic. No, wait, the other thing — it's calculus.

Use this **Formula** to **Differentiate Powers of x**

For a function $f(x) = x^n$, the **derivative** $f'(x)$ can be found using this formula:

'Derivative' just means 'the thing you get when you differentiate something'.

$\frac{d}{dx}$ just means 'the derivative of the thing in the brackets with respect to x'.

$$f'(x) = \frac{d}{dx}(x^n) = nx^{n-1}$$

If you have y = (some function of x), its derivative is written $\frac{dy}{dx}$, which means 'the rate of change of y with respect to x'.

Functions are much easier to **differentiate** when they're written as **powers of** x — like writing $\sqrt{x}$ as $x^{\frac{1}{2}}$.
You'll have seen this at National 5, so have a flick back over your notes if you're unsure.
When you're happy with powers notation, you can use the formula in the box above to differentiate the function.

Use the differentiation formula:

For **positive** powers:
E.g. $f(x) = x^2$ ← n is just the power of x.
Here, $n = 2$, so:
$f'(x) = nx^{n-1} = 2x^1 = \mathbf{2x}$

For **negative** powers:
E.g. $f(x) = \frac{1}{x^2} = x^{-2}$ ← Always rewrite the function as a power of x.
Here $n = -2$, so:
$f'(x) = nx^{n-1} = -2x^{-3} = -\frac{2}{x^3}$

For **fractional** powers:
E.g. $f(x) = \sqrt{x} = x^{\frac{1}{2}}$ ← Write the square root as a power of x.
Here, $n = \frac{1}{2}$, so:
$f'(x) = \frac{1}{2}x^{-\frac{1}{2}} = \frac{1}{2\sqrt{x}}$

Differentiate each term **Separately**

Even if there are loads of terms in the function, it doesn't matter. Differentiate each bit **separately** and you'll be fine.

EXAMPLE: Differentiate $y = 3\sqrt{x} = 3x^{\frac{1}{2}}$

If the function is being multiplied by a constant (3 in this case)... ...multiply the derivative by the same number.

$$\frac{dy}{dx} = 3\left(\frac{1}{2}x^{-\frac{1}{2}}\right) = \frac{3}{2} \times x^{-\frac{1}{2}} = \frac{3}{2\sqrt{x}}$$

EXAMPLE: Differentiate $y = 6x^2 + 4x\sqrt{x} - \frac{2}{x^2} + 1$

This looks a bit funny, but if you rewrite it in powers of x, you get $4x\sqrt{x} = 4x^1x^{\frac{1}{2}} = 4x^{\frac{3}{2}}$.

Write each term as a **power of** x, including the **constants**: $1 = x^0$

$$y = 6x^2 + 4x^{\frac{3}{2}} - 2x^{-2} + x^0$$

Differentiate each bit **separately** and add or subtract the results.

$$\frac{dy}{dx} = 6(2x) + 4\left(\frac{3}{2}x^{\frac{1}{2}}\right) - 2(-2x^{-3}) + 0x^{-1} = \mathbf{12x + 6\sqrt{x} + \frac{4}{x^3}}$$

A constant always differentiates to 0.

You can **Differentiate** to find **Gradients**

Differentiating tells you the **gradient** of a curve at any given point, which is the same as the gradient of the **tangent** to the curve at that point. Tangents will become a lot more important on the next page, so stay tuned...

EXAMPLE: Find the gradient of the graph $y = x^2$ at $x = 1$ and $x = -2$.

You need the **gradient** of the graph of: $y = x^2$

So **differentiate** this function to get: $\frac{dy}{dx} = 2x$

When $x = 1$, $\frac{dy}{dx} = 2(1) = 2$, so the gradient at $x = 1$ is **2**.

When $x = -2$, $\frac{dy}{dx} = 2(-2) = -4$, so the gradient at $x = -2$ is **−4**.

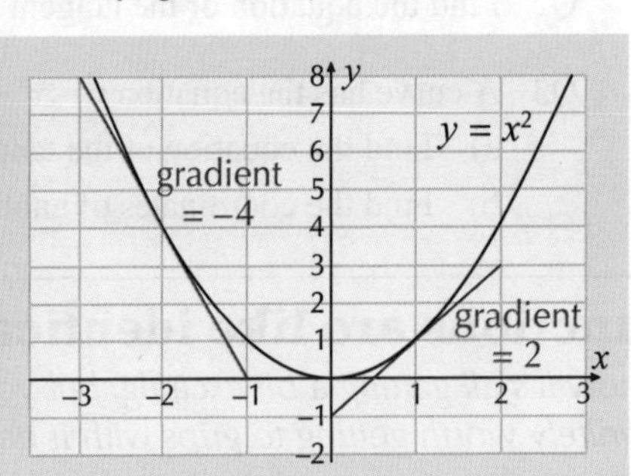

Differentiation

You can find the **Equation** of a **Tangent** to a curve

Tangents

A **tangent** just touches the curve but doesn't go through it — it has the **same gradient** as the curve.

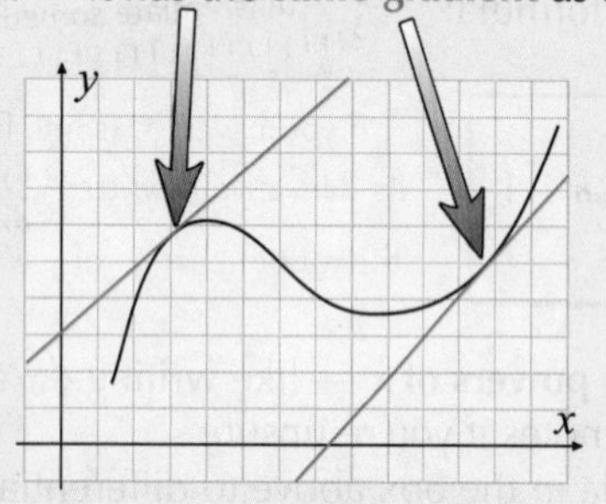

Finding Tangents

1) **Differentiate** the function.
2) Find the **gradient** of the **tangent** at a given point. This is the **same** as the gradient of the **curve** at that point.
3) Write the **equation** of the tangent in the form $y - b = m(x - a)$ or $y = mx + c$.
4) Use the **coordinates** of the point (a, b) on the tangent to complete the equation of the tangent.

EXAMPLE: Find the equation of the tangent to the curve $y = (4 - x)(x + 2)$ at the point (2, 8).

To find the **gradient** of the curve (and the tangent), first write the equation in a **form** you can differentiate:

$$y = (4 - x)(x + 2) = 8 + 2x - x^2$$

Then **differentiate** it: $\frac{dy}{dx} = 2 - 2x$

The **gradient** of the tangent at (2, 8) will be the gradient of the curve at $x = 2$.

At $x = 2$, $\frac{dy}{dx} = -2$

So the tangent has equation $y - b = -2(x - a)$, ← You could also use $y = mx + c$ here.

and since it passes through the point (2, 8), this becomes:

$$y - 8 = -2(x - 2) \Rightarrow \mathbf{y = 12 - 2x}$$

Typical Steve, off on a tangent again...

Warm-Up Questions

PRACTICE QUESTIONS

Q1 Differentiate these functions with respect to x:
a) $y = x^2 + 2$
b) $y = x^4 + \sqrt{x}$
c) $y = \frac{7}{x^2} - \frac{3}{\sqrt{x}} + 12x^3$

Q2 Find the gradient of the graph of $y = x^3 - 7x^2 - 1$ at $x = 2$.

Q3 Find the equation of the tangent to the curve $y = \sqrt{x^3} - 3x - 10$ at $x = 16$.

Exam Questions

Q1 Find the gradient of the curve $y = \frac{1}{x} + 2x\sqrt{x}$ at $x = 4$. [4 marks]

Q2 Find the equation of the tangent to the curve $y = \frac{4x^5 - 10x^2}{2x^2}$ at the point where $x = 2$. [4 marks]

Q3 A curve has the equation $y = x^3 - 4x + 2$.
a) Find the equation of the tangent to the curve at the point A, where $x = -1$. [4 marks]
b) Find the coordinates of another point, B, where the tangent meets the curve again. [4 marks]

Functions are like identical twins — it can be hard to differentiate them...

I know it's all getting a bit exciting, but you're going to be using this stuff over and over again in this section, so it's definitely worth getting to grips with it now. Rewriting any functions with fractions or roots as powers of x makes them much easier to differentiate, but you should change them back when you write down your final answer.

Stationary Points

Ah, the magical stationary point, where the gradient is zero and there's a pot of g- oh no, wait. It's just the gradient thing.

Stationary Points occur when the gradient is Zero

Stationary points are points on a graph where the curve **flattens out** — i.e. the **gradient** is **zero**.

A stationary point could be...

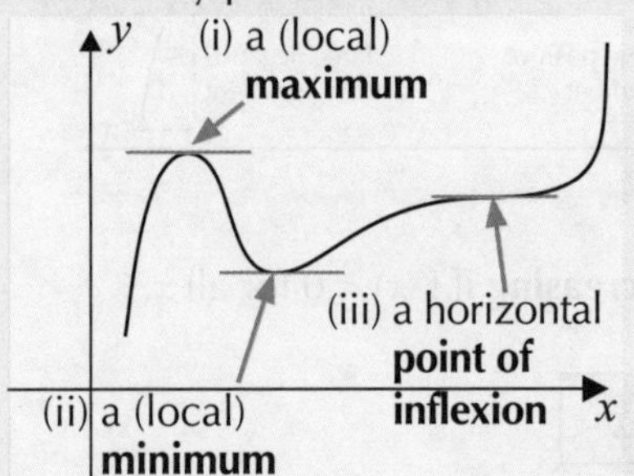

EXAMPLE: Find the coordinates of the stationary points of the curve $y = 2x^3 - 3x^2 - 12x + 5$, and determine the nature of each.

You need to find where $\frac{dy}{dx} = 0$. So first, **differentiate** the function.

$$y = 2x^3 - 3x^2 - 12x + 5 \Rightarrow \frac{dy}{dx} = 6x^2 - 6x - 12$$

Then set this derivative equal to **zero** and solve for x:

$$6x^2 - 6x - 12 = 0 \Rightarrow x^2 - x - 2 = 0$$
$$\Rightarrow (x + 1)(x - 2) = 0 \Rightarrow x = -1 \text{ or } x = 2$$

So the graph has **two** stationary points, at $x = -1$ and $x = 2$.

When $x = -1$, $y = 2(-1)^3 - 3(-1)^2 - 12(-1) + 5 = 12$

When $x = 2$, $y = 2(2)^3 - 3(2)^2 - 12(2) + 5 = -15$

So the stationary points are at **(–1, 12)** and **(2, –15)**. *To be continued...*

Decide if it's a Maximum or a Minimum using Nature Tables...

Once you've found the stationary points, you have to decide what their **nature** is. This just means figuring out whether each one is a **maximum**, a **minimum** or a **point of inflexion**. Going back to the example above...

You've just found that the stationary points are at (–1, 12) and (2, –15), and $\frac{dy}{dx} = 6x^2 - 6x - 12$.

You can use **nature tables** to decide if each one is a **maximum**, a **minimum**, or a **point of inflexion**. You need to consider the **gradient** either side of each **stationary point** — just pick two x values and find $\frac{dy}{dx}$ at those points. This tells you if the gradient is **positive** or **negative**, so you can work out what the slope looks like.

x	–2	–1	0
$\frac{dy}{dx}$	24	0	–12
slope	/	—	\

The gradient is positive before the stationary point and negative after, so **(–1, 12) is a maximum.**

x	1	2	3
$\frac{dy}{dx}$	–12	0	24
slope	\	—	/

Here the gradient is negative, and then becomes positive, so **(2, –15) is a minimum.**

Your nature table might also look like this: ⁄—⁄ if the stationary point is a **rising point of inflexion**, or like this: \—\ if it's a **falling point of inflexion.**

...or by Differentiating the equation Again

Another way to decide whether a stationary point is a **maximum** or a **minimum** is to differentiate again to find $\frac{d^2y}{dx^2}$, or $f''(x)$. $f''(x)$ is called the **second order derivative**, and is the **rate of change** of the gradient.

If $f''(x) > 0$, it's a **minimum**.

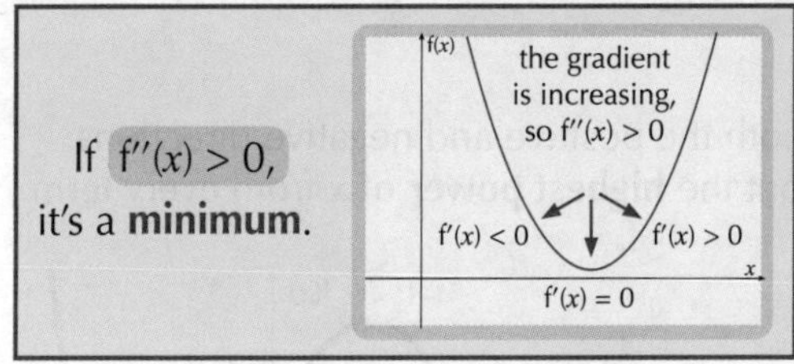

If $f''(x) < 0$, it's a **maximum**.

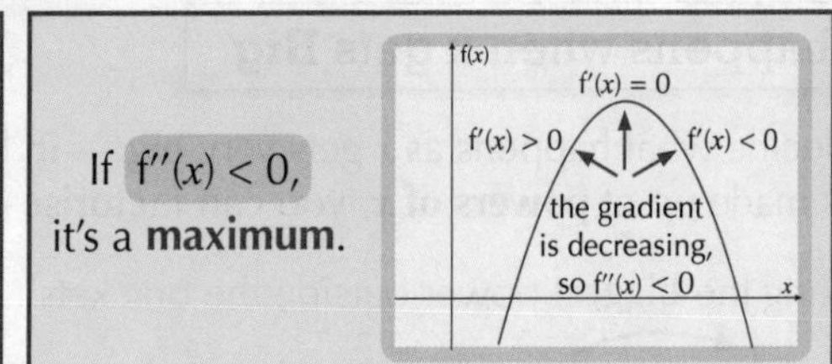

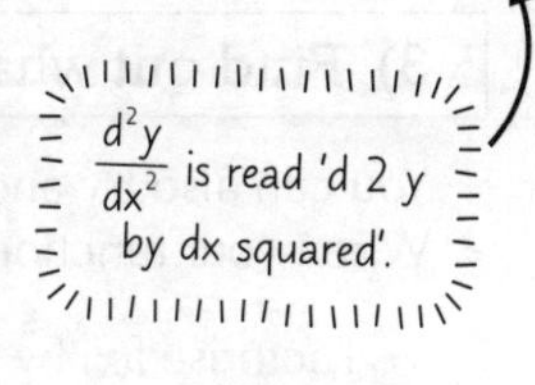

For the example above, $\frac{dy}{dx} = 6x^2 - 6x - 12$, so **differentiate again:** $\frac{d^2y}{dx^2} = 12x - 6$

At $x = -1$, $\frac{d^2y}{dx^2} = -18$ This is **negative**, so **(–1, 12) is a maximum.**

At $x = 2$, $\frac{d^2y}{dx^2} = 18$ This is **positive**, so **(2, –15) is a minimum.**

If $\frac{d^2y}{dx^2} = 0$, you can't tell what type of stationary point it is — you'll have to use a nature table.

Stationary Points

Find out if a function is **Increasing** or **Decreasing**

You can use differentiation to work out exactly where a function is **increasing** or **decreasing** — and how quickly.

A function is **increasing** if the gradient is **positive**.

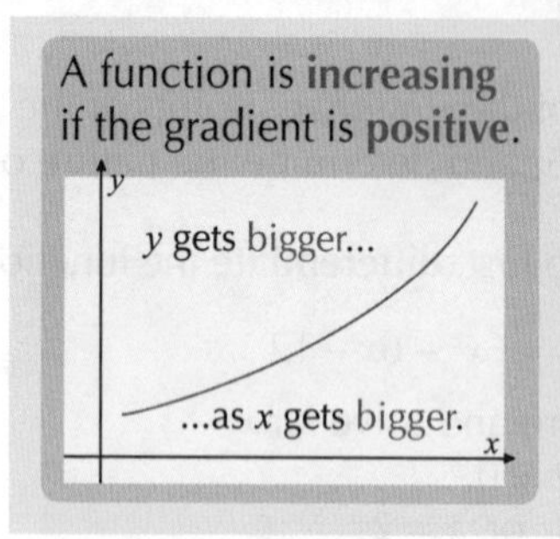

A function is **decreasing** if the gradient is **negative**.

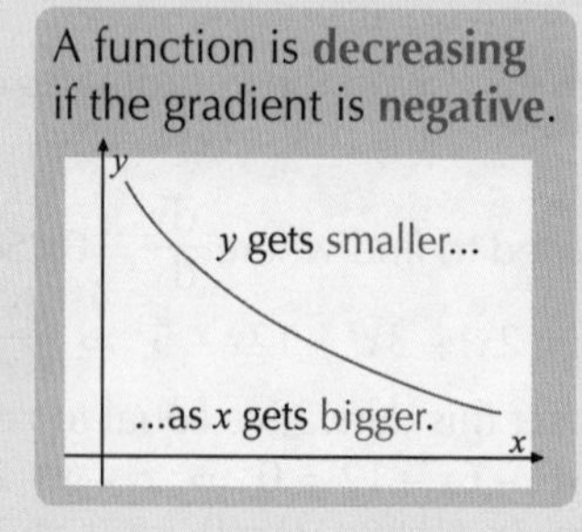

The **bigger** the gradient, the **quicker** y changes as x changes.

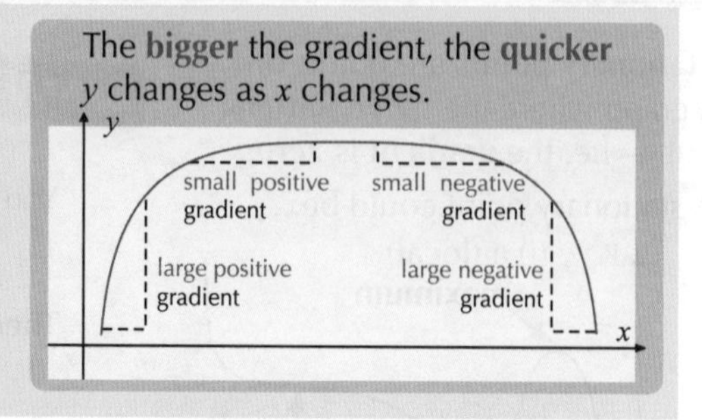

A function is said to be **strictly increasing** if $f'(x) > 0$ for all x, and **strictly decreasing** if $f'(x) < 0$ for all x.

Use differentiation to make **Curve Sketching** easier

You've seen curve sketching already on pages 11-12, but all of this stuff about increasing functions, stationary points and gradients helps you to make a more accurate sketch of a complicated function.

1) Find where the curve crosses the **Axes**

EXAMPLE: Sketch the graph of $f(x) = x^3 - 3x + 2$.

The curve crosses the **y-axis** when $x = 0$ — so put $x = 0$ in the expression for $f(x)$.

When $x = 0$, $f(x) = 0^3 - 3(0) + 2 = 2$ — so the curve goes through **(0, 2)**.

The curve crosses the **x-axis** when $f(x) = 0$. So solve:

$x^3 - 3x + 2 = 0 \Rightarrow (x - 1)^2(x + 2) = 0 \Rightarrow x = 1, x = 1, x = -2$

So the curve **crosses** the x-axis when $x = -2$ and **touches** the x-axis when $x = 1$.

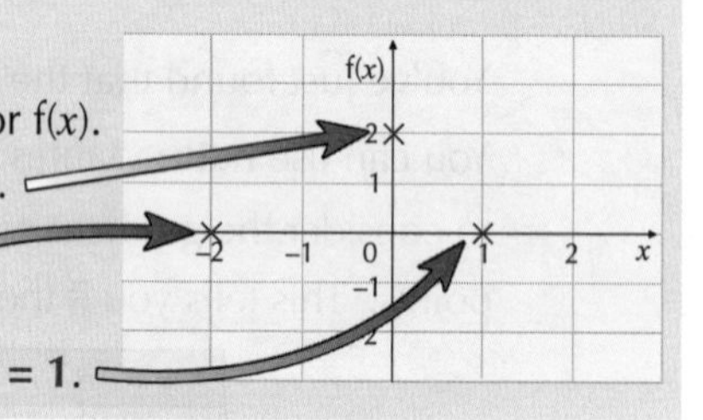

2) **Differentiate** to find information about the **Gradient** and **Stationary Points**

Differentiating the function gives: $f'(x) = 3x^2 - 3 = 3(x^2 - 1) = 3(x + 1)(x - 1)$

Find any **stationary points**: $3(x + 1)(x - 1) = 0 \Rightarrow x = -1$ and $x = 1$

$f(1) = 1^3 - 3(1) + 2 = 0$ so **(1, 0)** is a stationary point.

$f(-1) = (-1)^3 - 3(-1) + 2 = 4$ so **(–1, 4)** is a stationary point.

Fill in your **nature table**. The gradient is **positive** for $x < -1$ (so the function is increasing), **negative** for $-1 < x < 1$ (so the function is decreasing), and **positive** for $x > 1$ (so it's increasing again).

So (–1, 4) is a **maximum** and (1, 0) is a **minimum**.

x	–2	–1	0	1	2
$\frac{dy}{dx}$	9	0	–3	0	9
slope	/	—	\	—	/

3) Find out what happens when x gets **Big**

You can also try and decide what happens as x gets very **big** — in both the positive and negative directions. When your function is made up of **powers of x**, you can **factorise** out the **highest power of x** from every term.

Factorise $f(x)$ by taking the **biggest** power outside the brackets:

$f(x) = x^3\left(1 - \frac{3}{x^2} + \frac{2}{x^3}\right)$

As x gets large, the $-\frac{3}{x^2} + \frac{2}{x^3}$ gets smaller and smaller — so the bit in brackets gets closer to 1.

So as x gets **large** in both the **positive** and **negative** directions, $f(x)$ gets closer and closer to x^3.

When x is **large** and **positive**, x^3 is **large** and **positive**, and when x is **large** and **negative**, x^3 is **large** and **negative**.

Now you can put all this information together and **sketch** the graph.

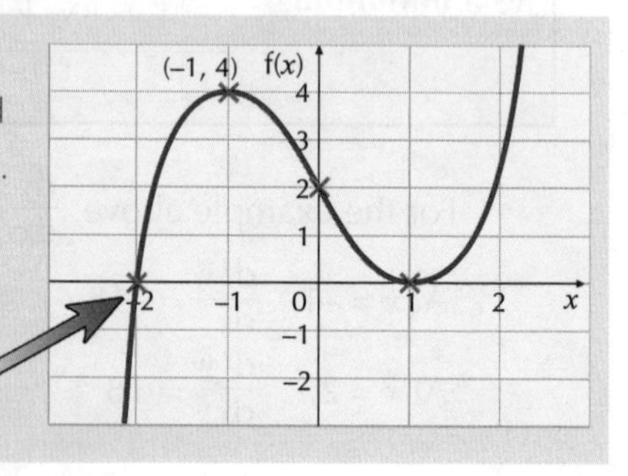

Stationary Points

You can Sketch f′(x) using the Graph of f(x) (and vice versa)

You might be given the **graph** of a function $y = f(x)$ and asked to **sketch f′(x)**, or maybe given the **graph of f′(x)** and asked to **sketch f(x)**. Everything you'll need is on the graph — it's just a matter of **finding** the information you want.

Sketching f′(x) from f(x)

1) Identify the **stationary points** of f(x). This is where $f'(x) = 0$, so it's where the graph of f′(x) crosses the **x-axis**.
2) Look at how the **gradient changes** around each stationary point. When the gradient of f(x) is **positive**, $f'(x) > 0$ so the graph of f′(x) is **above** the x-axis. When the gradient of f(x) is **negative**, $f'(x) < 0$, so the graph of f′(x) is **below** the x-axis.
3) When you differentiate a polynomial, its **degree** decreases by one. So if f(x) is cubic, f′(x) will be quadratic, if f(x) is quadratic, f′(x) will be linear, etc. This gives you an idea of the **shape** of the graph.

EXAMPLE: The graph of $y = f(x)$ is shown on the right. Use this to sketch f′(x).

1) Identify the stationary points on the graph:
   $x = -2$ and $x = 3$
2) Look at the gradient of $y = f(x)$ around the stationary points.
   For $-2 < x < 3$, the gradient is positive, so $f'(x) > 0$.
   For $x < -2$ and $x > 3$, the gradient is negative, so $f'(x) < 0$.
3) You can tell that $y = f(x)$ is cubic from its shape (see p.11), so you know f′(x) will be a quadratic function.

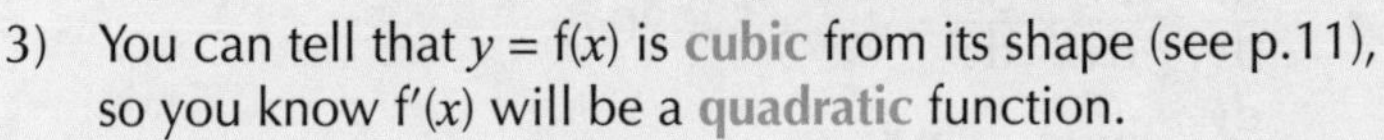

4) Putting these bits together, you should get something like this...

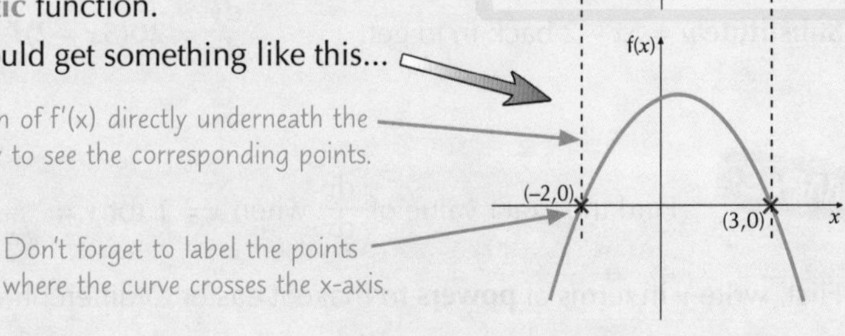

If you're given the graph of f′(x), you can **reverse** the process above to sketch the graph of f(x). A few things to note:

1) The points where the graph of f′(x) **crosses** the x-axis become the **stationary points** of f(x).
2) In the regions where the graph of f′(x) is **above** the x-axis, the gradient of f(x) is **increasing**. In any sections where f′(x) is **below** the x-axis, the gradient of f(x) is **decreasing**.
3) Going from f′(x) to f(x) means the **degree** of the polynomial **increases** by one — so a **quadratic** f′(x) gives a **cubic** f(x), and a **linear** f′(x) means the graph of f(x) is **quadratic**.

Warm-Up Questions

Q1 Find the x-values of the stationary points of the graph of $y = x^3 - 2x^2 - 15x + 7$. Determine whether each stationary point is a minimum, a maximum or a point of inflexion.

Q2 For which values of x are these functions increasing and decreasing?
a) $f(x) = 6(x + 2)(x - 3)$ b) $f(x) = 2x^3 + 4x^2 + 4$

Q3 Sketch the graph of $y = x^2 - 4x$, clearly showing the coordinates of any turning points.

Exam Questions

Q1 Given $f(x) = 3 - 7x - 2x^3$, find $f'(x)$, and explain why $y = f(x)$ is strictly decreasing for all x. [3 marks]

Q2 a) Find the coordinates of the stationary points of the curve $f(x) = x^3 + 4x^2 - 3x + 2$. [5 marks]
b) Determine whether each of these points is a maximum, minimum or a point of inflexion. [3 marks]
c) Sketch the graph of $f'(x)$. [2 marks]

I always eat food off the floor — it's nature's table...

You don't have to write the values of the derivative in your nature tables — you can just write + or – in the table instead.

Chain Rule

Hold on to your hats — it's time to upgrade your differentiation with some exciting new features...

The Chain Rule is used for Functions of Functions

The **chain rule** is a nifty little tool that allows you to differentiate complicated functions by **splitting them up** into easier ones. The trick is spotting **how** to split them up, and choosing the right bit to **substitute**.

If $y = f(u)$ and $u = g(x)$ then:

$$\frac{dy}{dx} = \frac{dy}{du} \times \frac{du}{dx}$$

Chain Rule Method

- Pick a suitable function of x for 'u' and rewrite y in terms of u.
- Differentiate u (with respect to x) to get $\frac{du}{dx}$, and differentiate y (with respect to u) to get $\frac{dy}{du}$.
- Stick it all in the formula.

Another way of thinking of the chain rule is: if $h(x) = f(g(x))$, then $h'(x) = f'(g(x)) \times g'(x)$

EXAMPLE: Find $\frac{dy}{dx}$ for the curve with the equation $y = (5x - 2)^4$.

First, identify which bit of the equation to call 'u', and **rewrite** y — here, let $u = 5x - 2$, so $y = u^4$

Now **differentiate** both parts: $u = 5x - 2 \Rightarrow \frac{du}{dx} = 5$ and $y = u^4 \Rightarrow \frac{dy}{du} = 4u^3$

Use the **chain rule** to find $\frac{dy}{dx}$: $\frac{dy}{dx} = \frac{dy}{du} \times \frac{du}{dx} = 4u^3 \times 5 = 20u^3$

Substitute $u = 5x - 2$ back in to get: $\frac{dy}{dx} = 20(5x - 2)^3$

'Exact' means leave in surd form — you might need to rationalise the denominator (look back over your N5 notes if you can't remember how).

EXAMPLE: Find the exact value of $\frac{dy}{dx}$ when $x = 1$ for $y = \frac{1}{\sqrt{x^2 + 4x}}$.

First, write y in terms of **powers** to make it easier to differentiate: $y = (x^2 + 4x)^{-\frac{1}{2}}$.

Pick a chunk of the equation to call 'u', and rewrite **y in terms of u** — in this case let $u = x^2 + 4x$, so $y = u^{-\frac{1}{2}}$.

Now differentiate both bits **separately**: $u = x^2 + 4x \Rightarrow \frac{du}{dx} = 2x + 4$ and $y = u^{-\frac{1}{2}} \Rightarrow \frac{dy}{du} = -\frac{1}{2}u^{-\frac{3}{2}}$

Use the **chain rule** to find $\frac{dy}{dx}$: $\frac{dy}{dx} = \frac{dy}{du} \times \frac{du}{dx} = -\frac{1}{2}u^{-\frac{3}{2}} \times (2x + 4)$

Substitute in $u = x^2 + 4x$ and **rearrange**: $\frac{dy}{dx} = -\frac{1}{2}(x^2 + 4x)^{-\frac{3}{2}} \times (2x + 4) = -\frac{x + 2}{(\sqrt{x^2 + 4x})^3}$

Finally, put in $x = 1$ to get the answer: $\frac{dy}{dx} = -\frac{1 + 2}{(\sqrt{1^2 + 4})^3} = -\frac{3}{5\sqrt{5}}$ or $-\frac{3\sqrt{5}}{25}$

Warm-Up Question

Q1 Differentiate with respect to x: a) $y = (3x - 7)^{12}$ b) $y = \sqrt{2x^2 + 6}$ c) $y = \frac{1}{\sqrt{3x^3 - 2x}}$

Exam Questions

Q1 a) Find $\frac{dy}{dx}$ for the curve given by the equation $y = \sqrt{x^2 - 8x}$. [3 marks]

b) Hence find the equation of the tangent to the curve at $(-1, 3)$. [2 marks]

Q2 A function f is defined on a suitable domain by $f(x) = \frac{2}{\sqrt{x^3 - 5x}}$. Find $f'(-1)$. [4 marks]

Don't get tied down by the chain rule...

Figuring out which bit of the equation to make 'u' is the hardest bit here. As a general rule, if you've got a tricky expression inside some brackets or under a square root, that's a pretty good starting point for what to use as u.

Differentiating sin and cos

So you think you know all there is to know about trigonometry. Well think again, 'cos here it comes again. (You see what I did there with the 'cos'? Pun #27 from 'Ye Olde Booke of Maths Punnes'...)

The **Rules** for differentiating **sin** and **cos** only work in **Radians**

For **trigonometric functions**, where the angle is measured in **radians** (see p.26), the following rules apply:

If $y =$	$\frac{dy}{dx} =$
$\sin x$	$\cos x$
$\cos x$	$-\sin x$

You can use the chain rule to show that, if k is a constant:
$\sin kx \longrightarrow k\cos kx$
$\cos kx \longrightarrow -k\sin kx$
They're given in this form on the formula sheet.

Use the **Chain Rule** with **sin (f(x))** or **cos (f(x))**

EXAMPLE: Differentiate $y = \cos x^2 + \sin(x+1)$ with respect to x.

It's the chain rule (again) for both parts of this equation:

1) Differentiate $y = \cos x^2$: $y = \cos u$, $u = x^2$,
so $\frac{dy}{du} = -\sin u$ (see above) and $\frac{du}{dx} = 2x \Rightarrow \frac{dy}{dx} = -2x\sin x^2$
2) Differentiate $y = \sin(x+1)$: $y = \sin u$, $u = x + 1$,
so $\frac{dy}{du} = \cos u$ (see above) and $\frac{du}{dx} = 1 \Rightarrow \frac{dy}{dx} = \cos(x+1)$
3) Put it all together to get: $\frac{dy}{dx} = \mathbf{-2x\sin x^2 + \cos(x+1)}$

Remember to use **Trig Identities** where **Necessary**

EXAMPLE: For $y = 2\cos^2 x + \sin 2x$, show that $\frac{dy}{dx} = 2(\cos 2x - \sin 2x)$.

1) Writing out the equation in a **slightly different way** helps with the chain rule: $y = 2(\cos x)^2 + \sin 2x$.
2) For the first bit, $y = 2u^2$, $u = \cos x$, so $\frac{dy}{du} = 4u$ and $\frac{du}{dx} = -\sin x$.
For the second bit, $y = \sin u$, $u = 2x$, so $\frac{dy}{du} = \cos u$ and $\frac{du}{dx} = 2$.
3) Putting it all in the chain rule formula gives $\frac{dy}{dx} = -4\sin x\cos x + 2\cos 2x$.
4) From the target answer in the question it looks like we need a $\sin 2x$ from somewhere, so use the **double angle formula** (see p.35) $\sin 2x \equiv 2\sin x\cos x$:
$\frac{dy}{dx} = -2\sin 2x + 2\cos 2x$, which **rearranges** nicely to give $\frac{dy}{dx} = \mathbf{2(\cos 2x - \sin 2x)}$.

You could also use the identity $\cos 2x \equiv 2\cos^2 x - 1$ before differentiating. You'll get the same answer.

Warm-Up Question

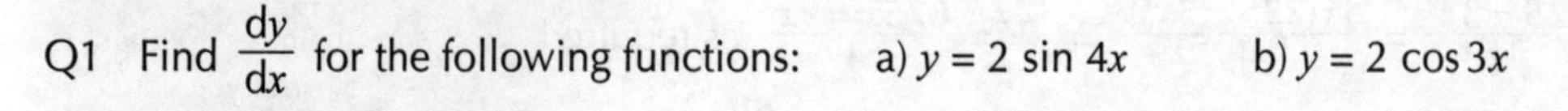

Q1 Find $\frac{dy}{dx}$ for the following functions: a) $y = 2\sin 4x$ b) $y = 2\cos 3x$ c) $y = \cos x^3$

Exam Question

Q1 a) Show that $\frac{\sin 2x}{2\sin x} - \cos x\sin^2 x = \cos^3 x$, where $0 < x < \frac{\pi}{2}$. [3 marks]

b) Hence, differentiate $\frac{\sin 2x}{2\sin x} - \cos x\sin^2 x$, where $0 < x < \frac{\pi}{2}$. [3 marks]

I'm having an identity crisis — I can't differentiate between sin and cos...

Don't get tied down by the chain rule (pun #28...). After a bit of practice you'll be able to do it a lot quicker in one step — just say in your working 'using the chain rule...' so the examiner can see how clever you are.

Using Differentiation

Differentiation isn't just mathematical daydreaming. It can be applied to real-life problems. For instance, you can use differentiation to find out the maximum possible volume of a box, given a limited amount of cardboard. Thrilling.

You can find the **Greatest** and **Least** values of a function on an **Interval...**

To find the **biggest** and **smallest values** a function reaches on an **interval**, you need to consider the value of the function at the **end points** of the interval, and at any **stationary points** to find the **local** minimum or maximum.

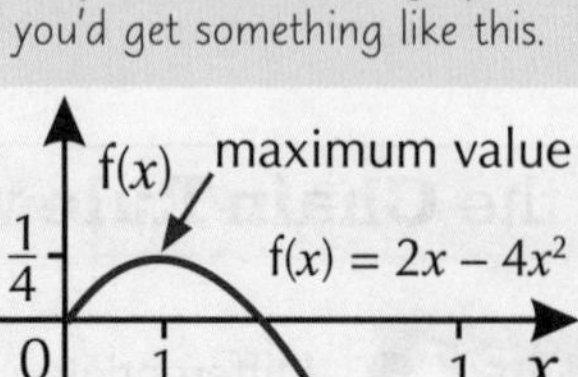

Find the greatest and least value of $y = f(x)$ for the curve $f(x) = 2x - 4x^2$ on the interval $0 \le x \le 1$.

If you sketched the graph, you'd get something like this.

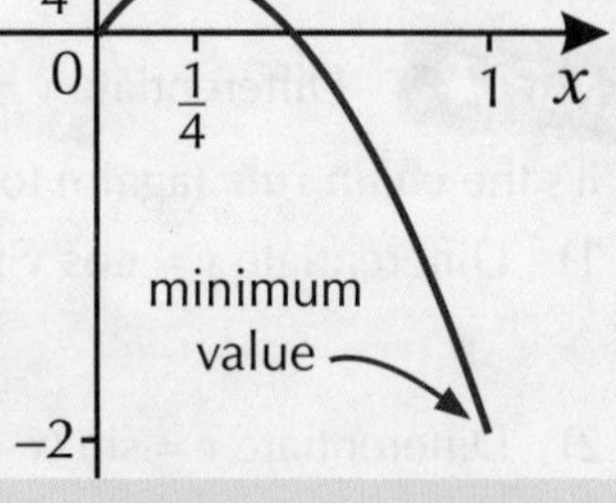

1) Identify any **stationary points** and determine their **nature**:

$f'(x) = 2 - 8x$, so $f'(x) = 0 \Rightarrow 2 - 8x = 0 \Rightarrow x = \frac{1}{4}$

$f\left(\frac{1}{4}\right) = 2 \times \frac{1}{4} - 4 \times \left(\frac{1}{4}\right)^2 = \frac{1}{4}$, so $\left(\frac{1}{4}, \frac{1}{4}\right)$ is a stationary point.

$f''(x) = -8$ so the stationary point $\left(\frac{1}{4}, \frac{1}{4}\right)$ **is a maximum.**

2) Find the **value** of the function at the **ends of the interval**:

$f(0) = 2(0) - 4(0)^2 = 0$ and $f(1) = 2(1) - 4(1)^2 = -2$

3) So the **greatest value** of f on the interval $0 \le x \le 1$ is $\mathbf{f\left(\frac{1}{4}\right) = \frac{1}{4}}$, and the **least value** is $\mathbf{f(1) = -2}$.

...and the **Maximum** or **Minimum Values** for **Volume** and **Area**

To find the maximum for a shape's volume (or area), all you need is an equation for the volume (or area) **in terms of only one variable** — then just **differentiate as normal**. But examiners don't hand it to you on a plate — there's usually one too many variables chucked in. So you need to know how to manipulate the information to get rid of that unwanted variable.

A jewellery box with a lid has dimensions $3x$ cm by x cm by y cm and is made using a total of 450 cm² of wood.

a) Show that the volume of the box can be expressed as: $V = \frac{675x - 9x^3}{4}$.

b) Use calculus to find the maximum possible volume.

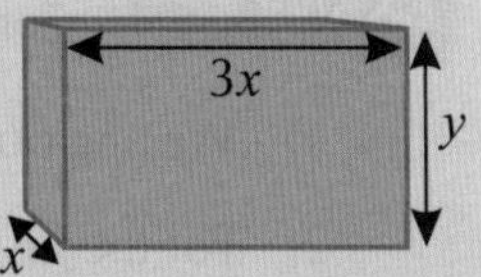

a) You know the basic equation for **volume**: V = width × depth × height $= 3x \times x \times y = 3x^2y$

But the question asks for volume in terms of **x only** — you don't want that pesky y in there. So you need to find **y in terms of x** and substitute that in.

Write an expression for the **surface area**:

$A = 2[(3x \times x) + (3x \times y) + (x \times y)] = 450 \Rightarrow 3x^2 + 4xy = 225$

Be careful when finding the surface area — here there's a lid so there are two of each side, but sometimes you'll get an open-topped shape.

Then rearrange to find an expression for y:

$4xy = 225 - 3x^2 \Rightarrow y = \frac{225 - 3x^2}{4x}$

Finally, **substitute** this into the equation for the volume:

$V = 3x^2y = 3x^2 \times \frac{225 - 3x^2}{4x} = \frac{3x(225 - 3x^2)}{4} \Rightarrow \mathbf{V = \frac{675x - 9x^3}{4}}$ as required

b) You want to find the **maximum** value of V, so **differentiate** and set $\frac{dV}{dx} = 0$:

$\frac{dV}{dx} = \frac{675 - 27x^2}{4}$, $\frac{dV}{dx} = 0 \Rightarrow \frac{675 - 27x^2}{4} = 0 \Rightarrow 675 = 27x^2 \Rightarrow x^2 = 25 \Rightarrow \mathbf{x = 5}$

Ignore the other solution, $x = -5$, since you can't have a negative length.

You can check that this is a maximum using a nature table:

x	4	5	6
$\frac{dV}{dx}$	$\frac{243}{4}$	0	$-\frac{297}{4}$
slope	/	—	\

From the slopes either side of the stationary point, you can see that $x = 5$ is a maximum.

So the maximum volume is: $V = \frac{(675 \times 5) - (9 \times 5^3)}{4} = \mathbf{562.5\ cm^3}$

You could find the second derivative here instead.

Using Differentiation

Another example? Coming right up. You want pie in this one? No probl- oh hang on — do you mean pie, or pi? I'll use both, just to make sure — I wouldn't want you to be disappointed. I really spoil you, don't I...

Tamal uses a circular tin to bake his pies in. The tin is h cm high with a d cm diameter. The volume of the pie tin is 1000 cm³.

a) Prove that the surface area of the tin, $A = \frac{\pi}{4}d^2 + \frac{4000}{d}$.

b) Find the minimum surface area.

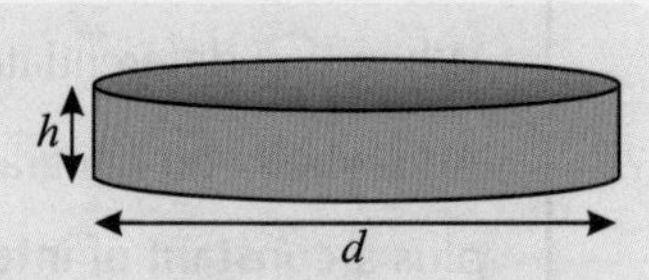

a) A = area of tin's base + area of tin's curved face $= \pi\left(\frac{d}{2}\right)^2 + (\pi d \times h) = \frac{\pi}{4}d^2 + \pi dh$

This shape is open-topped, so only count the area of the circle once.

You want to get rid of the h, so use the given value of volume to find an expression for h in terms of d:

$$V = \pi\left(\frac{d}{2}\right)^2 h = 1000 \Rightarrow \pi d^2 h = 4000 \Rightarrow h = \frac{4000}{\pi d^2}$$

Substitute your expression for h into the equation for surface area:

$$A = \frac{\pi}{4}d^2 + \left(\pi d \times \frac{4000}{\pi d^2}\right) \Rightarrow \boldsymbol{A = \frac{\pi}{4}d^2 + \frac{4000}{d}} \text{ as required.}$$

b) Differentiate and find the stationary point:

$$\frac{dA}{dd} = \frac{\pi}{2}d - \frac{4000}{d^2}, \quad \frac{\pi}{2}d - \frac{4000}{d^2} = 0 \Rightarrow d^3 = \frac{8000}{\pi} \Rightarrow d = \frac{20}{\sqrt[3]{\pi}} = 13.655...$$

Check it's a minimum:

d	13	$\frac{20}{\sqrt[3]{\pi}}$	14
$\frac{dA}{dd}$	−3.24...	0	1.58...
slope	\	—	/

You could use different values either side of d here, but it's best to keep them as close to the stationary point as possible. From the slope, you can see that it's a minimum.

Calculate the surface area for this value of d: $A = \frac{\pi}{4}\left(\frac{20}{\sqrt[3]{\pi}}\right)^2 + \left(\frac{4000}{\left(\frac{20}{\sqrt[3]{\pi}}\right)}\right) = \mathbf{439\ cm^2}$ (3 s.f.)

Warm-Up Questions

Q1 Find the greatest and least values of y on the curve $y = 3x - 6x^{\frac{3}{2}}$ in the interval $0 \le x \le 4$.

Q2 The height (h m) a firework can reach is related to the mass (m g) of fuel it carries by: $h = \frac{m^2}{10} - \frac{m^3}{800}$
Find the mass of fuel required to achieve the maximum height and calculate the maximum height.

Exam Questions

Q1 a) Find $\frac{dy}{dx}$ for the curve with the equation $y = (2x + 1)(x + 3)(x - 1)$. [3 marks]

b) Hence, or otherwise, find the maximum and minimum values of y on the interval $-3 \le x \le -1$. [4 marks]

Q2 A steam train travels between Fort William and Glenfinnan at a speed of x miles per hour and burns y units of coal, where y is modelled by: $2\sqrt{x} + \frac{27}{x}$, for $x > 2$.

a) Find the speed that gives the minimum coal consumption, and verify that it is a minimum. [5 marks]

b) Calculate the minimum coal consumption. [1 mark]

Q3 Catriona is building a shed with a flat roof. She uses a total of 72 m² of wood to build the walls and roof (the floor is not included). The shed is x metres long, $\frac{x}{2}$ metres wide and d metres high.

a) Show that the full capacity of the shed is given by: $V = 12x - \frac{x^3}{12}$. [4 marks]

b) Find the value of x for which V is maximised or minimised. Leave your answer in surd form. [3 marks]

c) Show that this is a maximum value and hence calculate the maximum value of V. [3 marks]

All this page has done is maximise my hunger for pie...

I hope I've managed to convince you that differentiation can pop up pretty much anywhere — those cheeky examiners can make a whole question about it without so much as a single 'd'. Don't fall for their evil schemes.

Integrating $f(x) = x^n$

Integration is the 'opposite' of differentiation — and so if you can differentiate, you can be pretty confident you'll be able to integrate too. There's just one extra thing you have to remember — the constant of integration...

When you differentiate y, you get $\frac{dy}{dx}$.
And when you integrate $\frac{dy}{dx}$, you get y plus a **constant of integration**.

$$y\ (+\ C) \xrightarrow{\text{Differentiate}} \frac{dy}{dx}, \quad \frac{dy}{dx} \xrightarrow{\text{Integrate}} y\ (+\ C)$$

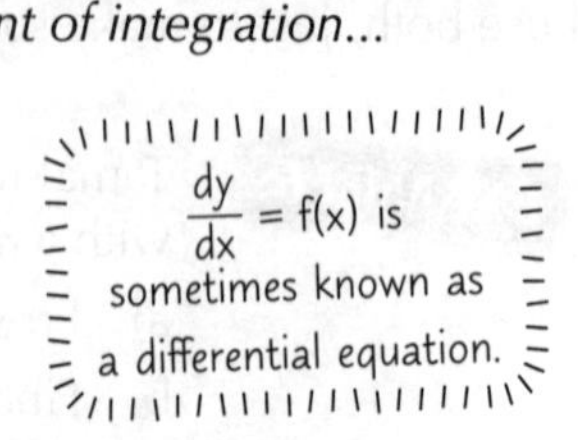

You need the constant because there's **More Than One** right answer

When you **integrate** something, you're trying to find a function that differentiates to give what you started with. You add the **constant of integration** to allow for the fact that there's **more than one** possible function that does this...

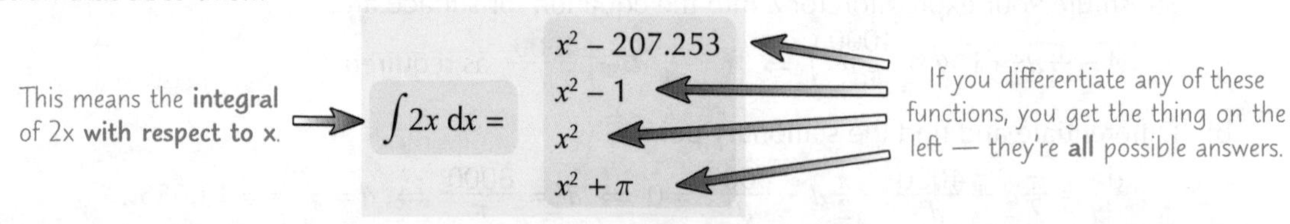

So the answer to this integral is actually...

$$\int 2x\,dx = x^2 + C$$

The 'C' just means 'any number'. This is the constant of integration.

You only need to add a constant of integration to **indefinite integrals** like these ones.
Definite integrals are just integrals with **limits** (or little numbers) next to the integral sign (see p.69).

Increase the power by **One** — then **Divide** by it

The formula below tells you how to integrate **any** power of x (except x^{-1}).

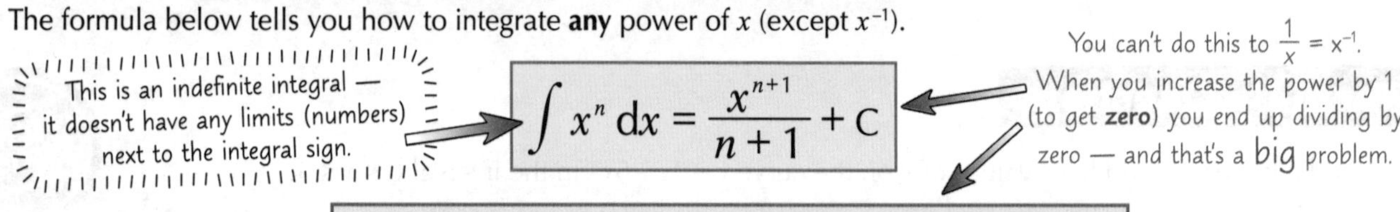

In a nutshell, this says:

> To integrate a power of x: (i) increase the power by one — then divide by the new power,
> and (ii) stick a constant on the end.

EXAMPLES: Use the integration formula...

1 For positive powers

$$\int x^3\,dx = \frac{x^4}{4} + C$$

Increase the power to 4... ...and then divide by 4.

2 For negative powers

$$\int \frac{1}{x^3}\,dx = \int x^{-3}\,dx = \frac{x^{-2}}{-2} + C = -\frac{1}{2x^2} + C$$

Increase the power by 1 to −2... ...and then divide by −2.

3 For fractional powers

$$\int \sqrt[3]{x^4}\,dx = \int x^{\frac{4}{3}}\,dx = \frac{x^{\frac{7}{3}}}{(7/3)} + C = \frac{3\sqrt[3]{x^7}}{7} + C$$

Add 1 to the power... ...then divide by this new power.

4 And for complicated looking stuff...

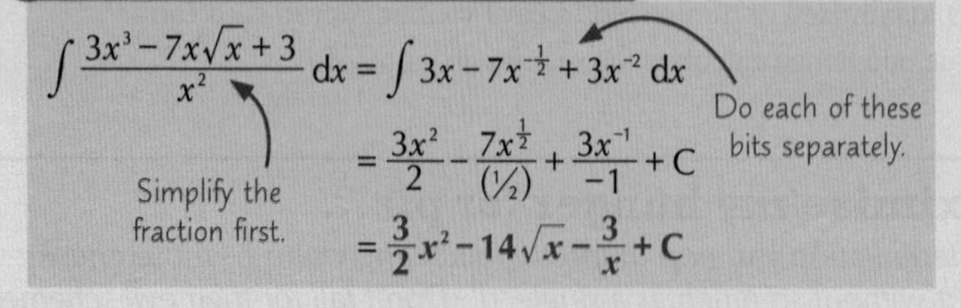

CHECK YOUR ANSWERS:
You can check you've integrated properly by **differentiating** the **answer** — you should end up with the thing you started with.

Integrating $f(x) = x^n$

You sometimes need to find the **Value** of the **Constant of Integration**

When the examiners tell you something else about the curve as well as its derivative, you can work out the value of that **constant of integration**. Usually the 'something' is the **coordinates** of one of the points the curve goes through.

EXAMPLE: The curve $y = f(x)$ goes through the point (2, 8) and $\frac{dy}{dx} = 6x(x - 1)$. Find y in terms of x.

You know the derivative $\frac{dy}{dx}$ and need to find the function y — so **integrate**.

$$\frac{dy}{dx} = 6x(x-1) = 6x^2 - 6x$$

So integrating both sides gives...

$$y = \int (6x^2 - 6x)\,dx$$

$$\Rightarrow y = 6\int (x^2 - x)\,dx$$

6 is a constant factor of both terms, so you can take it outside the integral.

$$\Rightarrow y = 6\left(\frac{x^3}{3} - \frac{x^2}{2} + C\right)$$

$$\Rightarrow y = 2x^3 - 3x^2 + C$$

You don't need to write 6C here, as C is just 'some unknown number'.

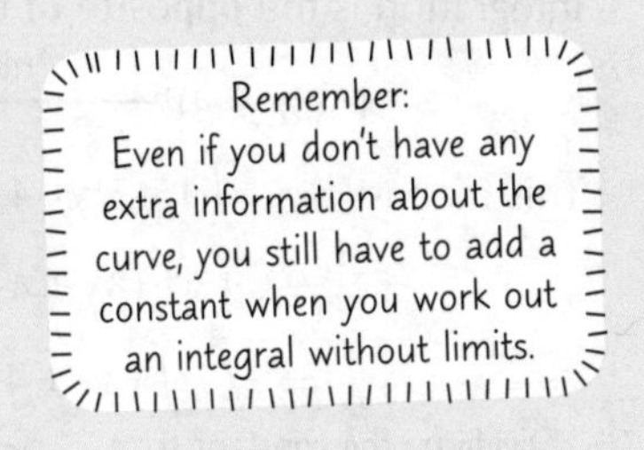

Check this is correct by **differentiating** it and making sure you get what you started with.

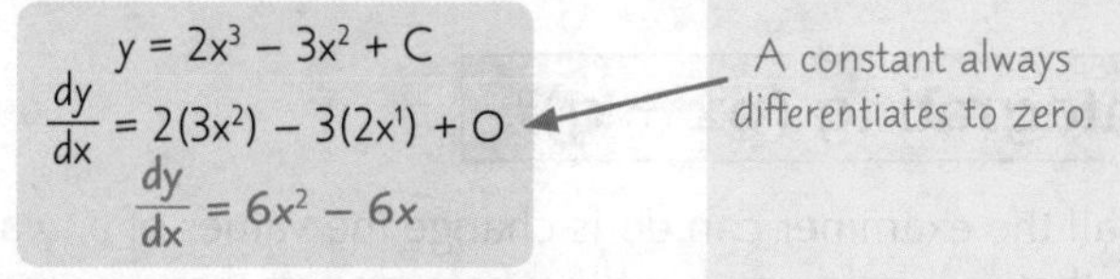

A constant always differentiates to zero.

So this function has the **correct derivative** — but you now need to **find C.**

You do this using the fact that the curve goes through (2, 8).
Putting $x = 2$ and $y = 8$ into the equation above gives:

$$8 = (2 \times 2^3) - (3 \times 2^2) + C$$

$$\Rightarrow 8 = 16 - 12 + C$$

$$\Rightarrow C = 4$$

So the answer you need is: $f(x) = 2x^3 - 3x^2 + 4$

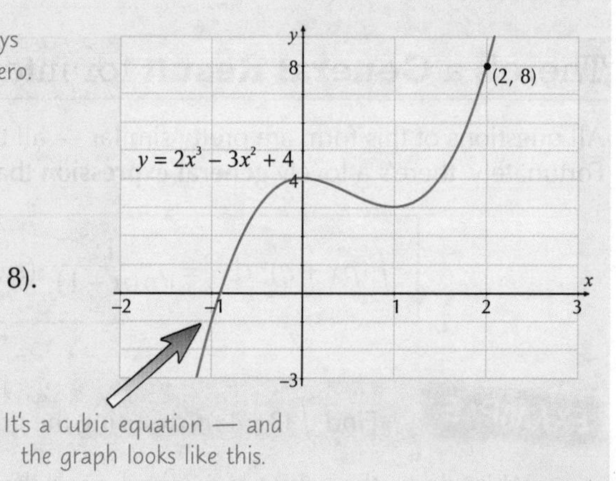

It's a cubic equation — and the graph looks like this.

Warm-Up Questions

Q1 Integrate: a) $\int 10x^4\,dx$ b) $\int 3x + 5x^2\,dx$ c) $\int \frac{3x^3 - 7}{x^2}\,dx$

Q2 Find the equation of the curve that has derivative $\frac{dy}{dx} = 6x - 11$ and goes through the point (1, 0).

Q3 $f(x)$ passes through (1, 0) and $f'(x) = 3x^3 + 2$. Work out the equation of $f(x)$.

Exam Questions

Q1 a) Show that $(5 + 2\sqrt{x})^2$ can be written in the form $a + b\sqrt{x} + cx$, stating the values of the constants a, b and c. [3 marks]

b) Hence find $\int (5 + 2\sqrt{x})^2\,dx$. [3 marks]

Q2 Curve C has equation $y = f(x)$, $x \neq 0$, where the derivative is given by $f'(x) = \frac{x^5 - 2}{x^2}$. The point P (1, 2) lies on C.

a) Find an equation for the tangent to C at the point P, giving your answer in the form $y = mx + c$, where m and c are integers. [4 marks]

b) Find $f(x)$. [5 marks]

Indefinite integrals — joy without limits...

This integration lark isn't too bad, but that constant of integration catches loads of people out — it's so easy to forget, and you'll definitely lose marks if you miss it out. You have been warned. Other than that, there's not much to it.

Integrating f(x) = (x + q)ⁿ and (px + q)ⁿ

The ones on this page are a bit more complicated than your standard x^n, but it's nothing the ***chain rule*** *can't handle...*

You can Integrate (px + q)ⁿ using the Chain Rule in Reverse

You can **differentiate** functions in the form $(px + q)^n$ using the chain rule (see p.60) — so you can **integrate** them too.

EXAMPLE: Differentiate $(3x + 4)^5$ with respect to x, and use this to find $\int (3x+4)^4$.

Using the **chain rule**, $\frac{d}{dx}(3x + 4)^5 = 5(3x + 4)^4 \times 3 = 15(3x + 4)^4$.

Integration is the **opposite of differentiation**, so

$$15(3x + 4)^4 \xrightarrow{\text{Integration}} (3x + 4)^5 + C$$

This means: $\int 15(3x+4)^4\,dx = (3x + 4)^5 + C$

$\Rightarrow 15\int (3x+4)^4\,dx = (3x + 4)^5 + C$

$\Rightarrow \int (3x+4)^4\,dx = \frac{1}{15}((3x + 4)^5 + C)$

$= \frac{1}{15}(3x + 4)^5 + C$

Divide by the constant term to get the integral you're after.

You can always differentiate your answer to check it — you should get back to what you started with.

There's a General Result for integrating (px + q)ⁿ

All questions of this form are pretty similar — all the examiner can do is change the values of p, q and n. Fortunately, there's a lovely **general expression** that will help you handle whatever gets thrown your way.

$$\int (px+q)^n\,dx = \frac{1}{p(n+1)}(px + q)^{n+1} + C \quad \text{for } n \neq -1, p \neq 0$$

This doesn't work for n = –1 because you'd end up having to divide by n + 1 = 0.

EXAMPLE: Find $\int (3-4x)^2\,dx$, using the general expression for $\int (px+q)^n\,dx$.

Write down the values of p, q and n and then **substitute** them into the **formula.**

Here $p = -4$, $q = 3$ and $n = 2$, so $\int (3-4x)^2\,dx = \frac{1}{-4 \times 3}(3 - 4x)^3 + C = -\frac{1}{12}(3 - 4x)^3 + C$

p = –4   n + 1 = 3

Warm-Up Questions

Q1 Integrate with respect to x: a) $(x + 8)^4$ b) $(3x - 2)^{-3}$ c) $(12-7x)^{-\frac{1}{2}}$

Q2 Given that a curve y has the derivative $\frac{dy}{dx} = (7 - 2x)^4$, find an expression for y in terms of x.

Exam Questions

Q1 Find $\int \frac{1}{(4x+3)^{\frac{1}{3}}}\,dx,\ x > -\frac{3}{4}$. [4 marks]

Q2 Find the equation of the curve y that goes through the point (1, –6), where $\frac{dy}{dx} = (2 - 5x)^3$. [4 marks]

My mum always told me to mind my Ps and Qs...

... and that's actually pretty good advice here. If you get a question where the expression is in the form $(x + q)^n$, there's no need to panic. It's just a special case of $(px + q)^n$ where $p = 1$, and you know how to handle them (it's even easier when $p = 1$). Just stick it all in the formula and there's no stopping the train leaving the integration station. (Choo choo.)

Integrating sin and cos

You thought you'd killed off the dragon that is trigonometry back in Section Two, but it rears its ugly head again now — you need to know how to integrate trig functions. Grab your trustiest dragon-slaying sword and read on...

Sin and Cos are Easy to integrate

On page 61, you saw that **sin x** differentiates to give **cos x** and **cos x** differentiates to give **–sin x** (where the angle x is in **radians**). Since integration is the **opposite** of differentiation, it's pretty obvious that:

$$\int \sin x\,dx = -\cos x + C \quad \text{and} \quad \int \cos x\,dx = \sin x + C$$

EXAMPLE: Find $\int 5\cos x - 2\sin x\,dx$.

Integrate each term **individually**:

$5\int \cos x\,dx = 5\sin x + C$

$-2\int \sin x\,dx = -(-2\cos x) + C$

Putting the terms together gives:

$\int 5\cos x - 2\sin x\,dx = \mathbf{5\sin x + 2\cos x + C}$

EXAMPLE: Find $\int \frac{3}{2}\sin x - 7\cos x\,dx$.

Integrate each term **individually**:

$\frac{3}{2}\int \sin x\,dx = -\frac{3}{2}\cos x + C$

$-7\int \cos x\,dx = -7\sin x + C$

Putting the terms together gives:

$\int \frac{3}{2}\sin x - 7\cos x\,dx = \mathbf{-\frac{3}{2}\cos x - 7\sin x + C}$

You can integrate p sin (qx + r) and p cos (qx + r)

You've seen how to handle multiples of sin and cos above. Now consider what happens if x has a **coefficient** that **isn't 1** (e.g. sin $3x$)... Well, you just **divide** by the **coefficient** when you integrate — just like on the last page.

EXAMPLE: Find $\int \cos 4x - 2\sin 2x\,dx$.

Integrate each term separately using the results from above:

$\int \cos 4x\,dx = \frac{1}{4}\sin 4x + C \qquad \int -2\sin 2x\,dx = -2\left(-\frac{1}{2}\cos 2x\right) + C = \cos 2x + C$

Putting the terms together gives:

$\int (\cos 4x - 2\sin 2x)\,dx = \mathbf{\frac{1}{4}\sin 4x + \cos 2x + C}$

Sadly, Boris' personality wasn't making it any easier to integrate at all.

You can integrate **transformations** of sin x and cos x of the form $p\sin(qx + r)$ and $p\cos(qx + r)$. **Differentiating** $\sin(qx + r)$ using the **chain rule** gives $q\cos(qx + r)$, so when **integrating** $\cos(qx + r)$, you need to **divide** by q, giving $\frac{1}{q}\sin(qx + r)$. The same can be done when integrating $\sin(qx + r)$, which gives:

$$\int \sin(qx+r)\,dx = -\frac{1}{q}\cos(qx+r) + C$$
$$\int \cos(qx+r)\,dx = \frac{1}{q}\sin(qx+r) + C$$

$$\int p\sin(qx+r)\,dx = -\frac{p}{q}\cos(qx+r) + C$$
$$\int p\cos(qx+r)\,dx = \frac{p}{q}\sin(qx+r) + C$$

EXAMPLE: Find $\int 3\sin(1-6x) - 5\cos 2x\,dx$.

Integrate each term separately using the **general formulas**:

$\int 3\sin(1-6x)\,dx = -\frac{3}{-6} \times \cos(1-6x) + C = \mathbf{\frac{1}{2}\cos(1-6x) + C}$ ($p = 3$, $q = -6$)

$\int -5\cos 2x\,dx = \frac{-5}{2} \times \sin 2x + C = \mathbf{-\frac{5}{2}\sin 2x + C}$ ($p = -5$, $q = 2$)

Putting the terms together gives:

$\int 3\sin(1-6x) - 5\cos 2x\,dx = \mathbf{\frac{1}{2}\cos(1-6x) - \frac{5}{2}\sin 2x + C}$

Integrating sin and cos

Double Angle Formulas are useful for **Integration**

If you're given a tricky **trig function** to integrate, see if you can **simplify** it using one of the **double angle formulas**. They're especially useful for things like $\cos^2 x$, $\sin^2 x$ and $\sin x \cos x$. Here are the double angle formulas (see p.35):

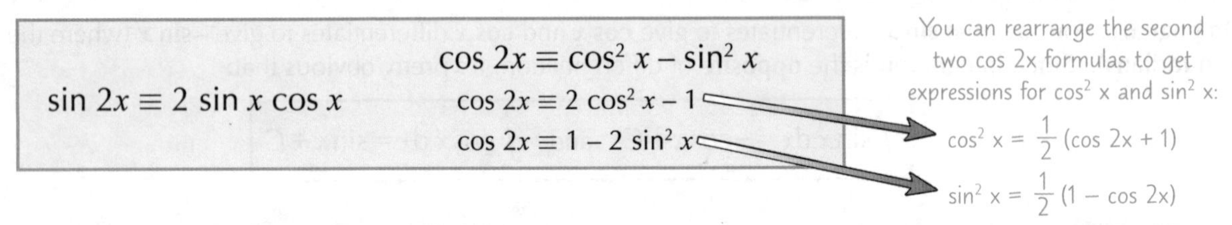

$$\sin 2x \equiv 2 \sin x \cos x$$

$$\cos 2x \equiv \cos^2 x - \sin^2 x$$

$$\cos 2x \equiv 2\cos^2 x - 1$$

$$\cos 2x \equiv 1 - 2\sin^2 x$$

Once you've **replaced** the **original function** with one of the **double angle formulas**, you can **integrate** as normal.

EXAMPLE: Find $\int \sin x \cos x \, dx$.

Using the double angle formula for sin 2x, write $\sin x \cos x$ as $\frac{1}{2}\sin 2x$, then integrate.

$$\int \sin x \cos x \, dx = \int \frac{1}{2}\sin 2x \, dx = \frac{1}{2}\left(-\frac{1}{2}\cos 2x\right) + C = \mathbf{-\frac{1}{4}\cos 2x + C}$$

$\cos^2 x + \sin^2 x \equiv 1$ might also come in handy.

EXAMPLE: Find $\int \sin^2 x \, dx$.

Using the double angle formulas for cos 2x, write $\sin^2 x$ as $\frac{1}{2}(1 - \cos 2x)$, then integrate.

$$\int \sin^2 x \, dx = \int \frac{1}{2}(1 - \cos 2x) = \frac{1}{2}\left(x - \frac{1}{2}\sin 2x\right) + C = \mathbf{\frac{1}{2}x - \frac{1}{4}\sin 2x + C}$$

EXAMPLE: Find $\int \cos^2 5x \, dx$.

Using the double angle formula above, write $\cos^2 5x$ as $\frac{1}{2}(\cos 10x + 1)$, then integrate.

Don't forget to double the coefficient of x here. You'll also need to divide by 10 when you integrate.

$$\int \cos^2 5x \, dx = \int \frac{1}{2}(\cos 10x + 1) = \frac{1}{2}\left(\frac{1}{10}\sin 10x + x\right) + C = \mathbf{\frac{1}{20}\sin 10x + \frac{1}{2}x + C}$$

Warm-Up Questions

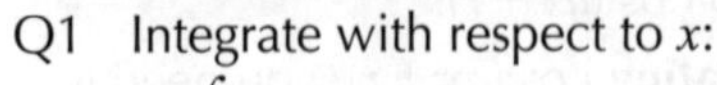

Q1 Integrate with respect to x:

a) $\int 6 \cos 3x \, dx$ b) $\int 3 \sin (2x + 1) \, dx$ c) $\int 4 \cos 6x - 2 \sin (3x + 4) \, dx$

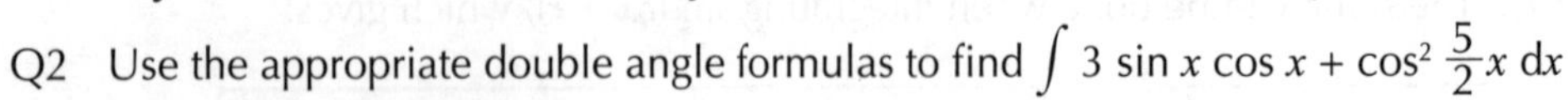

Q2 Use the appropriate double angle formulas to find $\int 3 \sin x \cos x + \cos^2 \frac{5}{2}x \, dx$

Exam Questions

Q1 Find $\int 7 \sin (3x - 4) \, dx$. [2 marks]

Q2 a) Show that $1 - \cos^2 2x \equiv 4\sin^2 x - 4\sin^4 x$. [3 marks]

b) Hence, or otherwise, find $\int (8\sin^4 x - 8\sin^2 x) \, dx$. [3 marks]

Q3 A curve $y = f(x)$ has a gradient given by $\frac{dy}{dx} = 6 \sin 4x$ and goes through the point $(\frac{\pi}{4}, -2)$.
Find the equation of the curve y in terms of x. [4 marks]

Double the angle formula, double the fun...

This little trick for integrating $\cos^2 x$ and $\sin^2 x$ is pretty handy. You'll be pleased to hear that the double angle formulas are on your formula sheet, but you need to know how to rearrange them to get expressions for $\cos^2 x$ and $\sin^2 x$ that you can integrate. The standard derivatives and integrals for sin x and cos x are on the formula sheet too, so there's no need to worry about remembering it all — as long as you know what to do with them, you'll be laughing.

Definite Integrals

Some integrals have limits (little numbers) next to the integral sign. For these, you don't need a constant of integration.

Definite Integrals are like regular integrals, but with **Limits**

Definite integrals are ones that have little numbers on the top and bottom called **limits**. These are the values of x that you're 'integrating between'.

Finding a definite integral isn't really any harder than an indefinite one — there's just an **extra** stage you have to do. After you've integrated the function, you have to work out the value of this new function by **sticking in** the limits, and **subtracting** what the **bottom** limit gave you from what the **top** limit gave you.

Evaluate $\int_1^3 (x^2 + 2)\,dx$.

This is the integral of $x^2 + 2$ "from 1 to 3".

You don't need a constant of integration with a **definite** integral.

Find the integral in the normal way, then use the limits:

$$\int_1^3 (x^2 + 2)\,dx = \left[\frac{x^3}{3} + 2x\right]_1^3 = \left(\frac{(3)^3}{3} + 2(3)\right) - \left(\frac{(1)^3}{3} + 2(1)\right) = 15 - \frac{7}{3} = \frac{\mathbf{38}}{\mathbf{3}}$$

Put the integrated function in **square brackets** and rewrite the limits on the right-hand side.

Do '**top limit** minus **bottom limit**'.

EXAMPLE:

Evaluate $\int_0^{\frac{\pi}{4}} (8\sin 4x + 6\cos 2x)\,dx$.

$$\int_0^{\frac{\pi}{4}} (8\sin 4x + 6\cos 2x)\,dx = [-2\cos 4x + 3\sin 2x]_0^{\frac{\pi}{4}} = \left(-2\cos\pi + 3\sin\frac{\pi}{2}\right) - (-2\cos 0 - 3\sin 0)$$

$$= (-2(-1) + 3(1)) - (-2(1) - 3(0)) = 7$$

Integrate each term separately.

See p.27 for common angles of trig functions.

A **Definite Integral** finds the **Area Under a Curve**

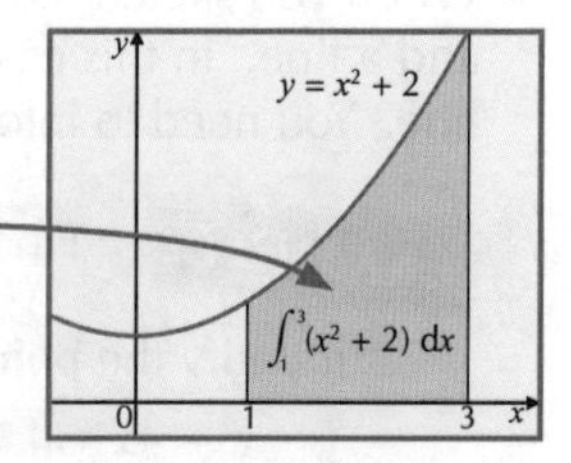

1) Definite integrals give you the **area under the graph** of the function you're integrating. For instance, the integral in the first example above gives this area:
2) However, parts of the graph that are **below the x-axis** will give a **negative answer**, so you might need to split the integral up into bits. For example, if you wanted to find the area between the graph of $y = x^3$ and the x-axis between $x = -2$ and $x = 2$:

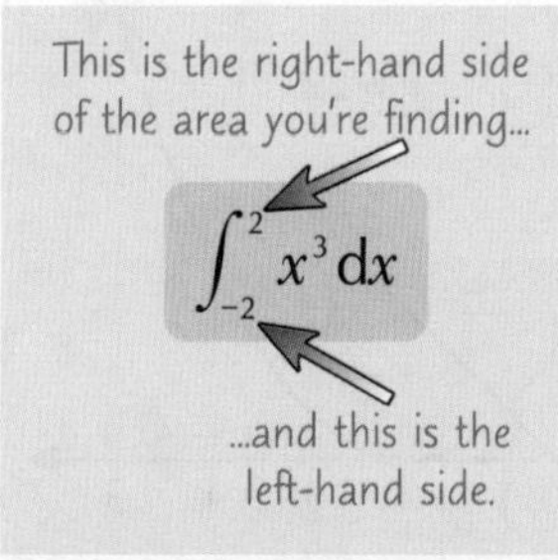

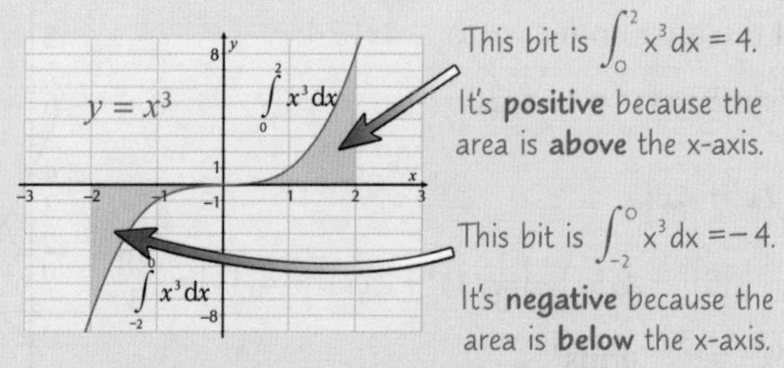

This bit is $\int_0^2 x^3\,dx = 4$. It's **positive** because the area is **above** the x-axis.

This bit is $\int_{-2}^0 x^3\,dx = -4$. It's **negative** because the area is **below** the x-axis.

The **value** of the integral $\int_{-2}^{2} x^3\,dx$ is **zero**, because the area below the x-axis '**cancels out**' the area above. To find the **area**, you need to work out the two parts **separately** and **subtract** the negative from the positive. In this example, **area = 4 − (−4) = 8 units²**.

EXAMPLE:

The graph of $y = x(x - 2)(x + 1)$ is shown below. Calculate the area of the shaded region.

The shaded region is partly **above** and partly **below** the x-axis, so **integrate** each bit **separately**. The roots $x = -1$, $x = 0$ and $x = 2$ give you the **limits** for integration.

A: $\int_{-1}^0 x(x-2)(x+1)\,dx = \int_{-1}^0 (x^3 - x^2 - 2x)\,dx = \left[\frac{x^4}{4} - \frac{x^3}{3} - x^2\right]_{-1}^0 = 0 - \left(\frac{1}{4} + \frac{1}{3} - 1\right) = \frac{\mathbf{5}}{\mathbf{12}}$

B: $\int_0^2 x(x-2)(x+1)\,dx = \int_0^2 (x^3 - x^2 - 2x)\,dx = \left[\frac{x^4}{4} - \frac{x^3}{3} - x^2\right]_0^2 = \left(\frac{16}{4} - \frac{8}{3} - 4\right) - 0 = -\frac{\mathbf{8}}{\mathbf{3}}$

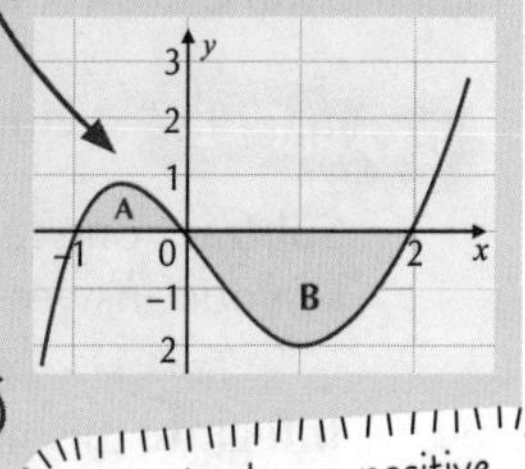

So the total area is $\frac{5}{12} - \left(-\frac{8}{3}\right) = \frac{\mathbf{37}}{\mathbf{12}}$ **units²**

If the integral is negative (because it's below the x-axis), you **subtract** the negative bit.

Area is always positive, even though integrals are sometimes negative.

Definite Integrals

Sometimes you have to **Add** or **Subtract** integrals

This looks pretty hard — until you draw a picture and see what it's all about. To find the **limits** for each integration, you might have to **solve** an equation to find out where lines and curves **intersect** (see p.45).

EXAMPLE: Find the area A enclosed by the curve $y = x^2$, the line $y = 2 - x$ and the x-axis.

1) Do a **sketch** — from this, you can see that you need to calculate the area in **two bits**: first, the area under $y = x^2$ and then the area under $y = 2 - x$.
2) You need to know the **point** where $y = x^2$ and $y = 2 - x$ **cross**, which gives you the **limits** for each integration. Set the equations **equal** to each other and **solve**:

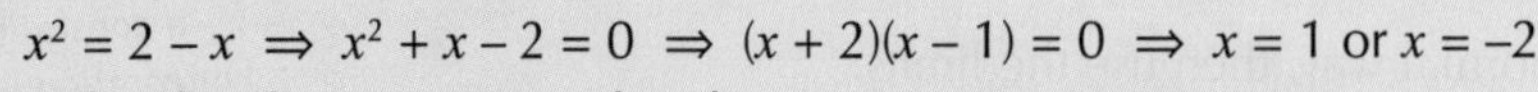

$x^2 = 2 - x \Rightarrow x^2 + x - 2 = 0 \Rightarrow (x + 2)(x - 1) = 0 \Rightarrow x = 1$ or $x = -2$

From the sketch, you can see that the point you want is $x = 1$.

3) So the two bits to integrate are $y = x^2$ with **limits 0** and **1** (A_1) and $y = 2 - x$ with **limits 1** and **2** (A_2).
4) Find each area separately:

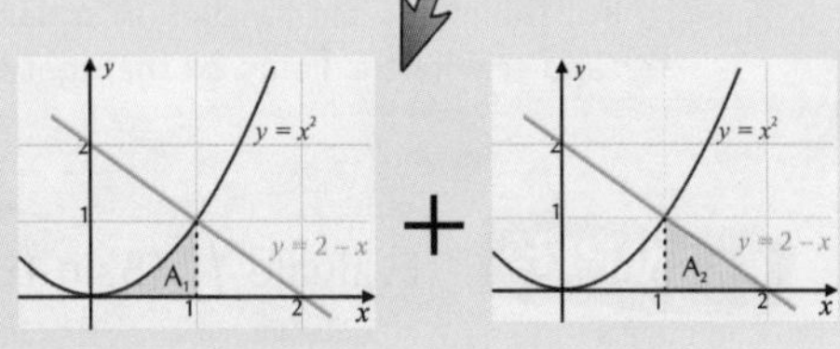

$$A_1 = \int_0^1 x^2 dx = \left[\frac{1}{3}x^3\right]_0^1 = \left(\frac{1}{3} - 0\right) = \mathbf{\frac{1}{3}}$$

A_2 is just a triangle with base length $2 - 1 = 1$ and height $= 1$

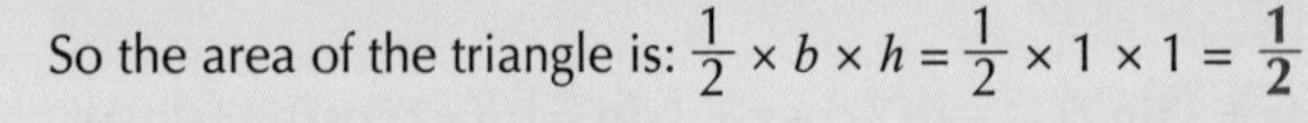

So the area of the triangle is: $\frac{1}{2} \times b \times h = \frac{1}{2} \times 1 \times 1 = \mathbf{\frac{1}{2}}$

5) Adding them up, the total area is $A_1 + A_2 = \frac{1}{3} + \frac{1}{2} = \mathbf{\frac{5}{6}}$ **units²**

You might need to find the **Area Between Curves** and **Lines**

When you sketch the graph, you might find that the area you want lies **between** two curves, or between a curve and a line. In this case, **subtract** the area under the **lower curve** or **line** from the area under the **upper curve** or **line**. You need to integrate between the **same limits** — and you might have to **find** these first.

EXAMPLE: Find the shaded area enclosed by the curves $y = x^2 - 4x + 4$ and $y = 2x - 1$.

Identify the **points** where the line and curve **cross** to find the limits:

$x^2 - 4x + 4 = 2x - 1 \Rightarrow x^2 - 6x + 5 = 0 \Rightarrow (x - 1)(x - 5) = 0$, so the lines cross at $\mathbf{x = 1}$ and $\mathbf{x = 5}$.

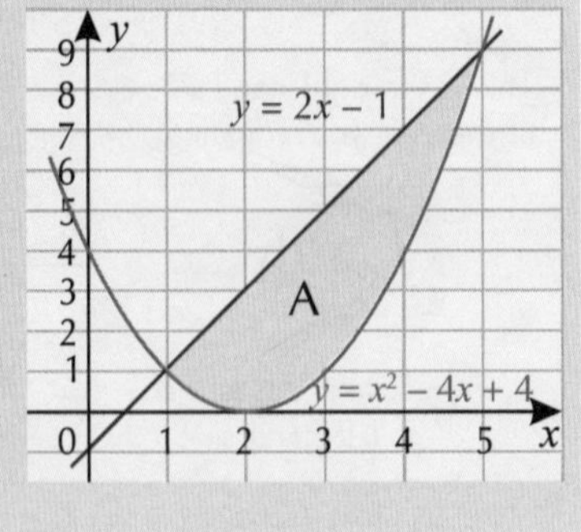

To find the shaded area, calculate the area under $y = 2x - 1$ between these limits, and then **subtract** the area under $y = x^2 - 4x + 4$:

$$\int_1^5 2x - 1\, dx = [x^2 - x]_1^5 = (5^2 - 5) - (1^2 - 1) = \mathbf{20}$$

$$\int_1^5 x^2 - 4x + 4\, dx = \left[\frac{1}{3}x^3 - 2x^2 + 4x\right]_1^5$$

$$= \left(\frac{1}{3}(5)^3 - 2(5)^2 + 4(5)\right) - \left(\frac{1}{3}(1)^3 - 2(1)^2 + 4(1)\right) = \mathbf{\frac{28}{3}}$$

Then the shaded area is $20 - \frac{28}{3} = \mathbf{\frac{32}{3}}$ **units²**

You can also **subtract** the two functions first, and then **integrate the resulting equation**. It's a bit less intuitive, but you get the same answer and it's much quicker — plus, you don't have to worry about if bits are above or below the x-axis.

EXAMPLE: Find the shaded area enclosed by the curves $y = x^2 - 4x + 4$ and $y = 2x - 1$.

Subtract one function from the other **first**. Make sure you get it the right way round, or your answer will be **negative** (and you know that area can't be negative...):

$(2x - 1) - (x^2 - 4x + 4) = -x^2 + 6x - 5$ — Work out the limits in the same way as above.

Integrate this new equation between the limits 1 and 5:

$$\int_1^5 -x^2 + 6x - 5\, dx = \left[-\frac{1}{3}x^3 + 3x^2 - 5x\right]_1^5 = \left(-\frac{1}{3}(5)^3 + 3(5)^2 - 5(5)\right) - \left(-\frac{1}{3}(1)^3 + 3(1)^2 - 5(1)\right) = \mathbf{\frac{32}{3}} \textbf{ units}^2$$

Same answer as above, but much quicker and easier. Lovely.

Definite Integrals

EXAMPLE: Find the area of the shaded region between the curves $y = x^3 - 2x^2 - 5x + 6$ and $y = 6 + 7x - x^2$.

1) The curves **intersect** when $x^3 - 2x^2 - 5x + 6 = 6 + 7x - x^2$
$\Rightarrow x^3 - x^2 - 12x = 0 \Rightarrow x(x - 4)(x + 3) = 0 \Rightarrow x = 0, x = 4, x = -3$
From the graph, the **limits** of integration are $x = 0$ and $x = 4$.
2) You need the area under $y = 6 + 7x - x^2$ **minus** the area under $y = x^3 - 2x^2 - 5x + 6$. **Subtracting** the functions gives:
$(6 + 7x - x^2) - (x^3 - 2x^2 - 5x + 6) = 12x + x^2 - x^3$
3) Now **integrate** this between 0 and 4:

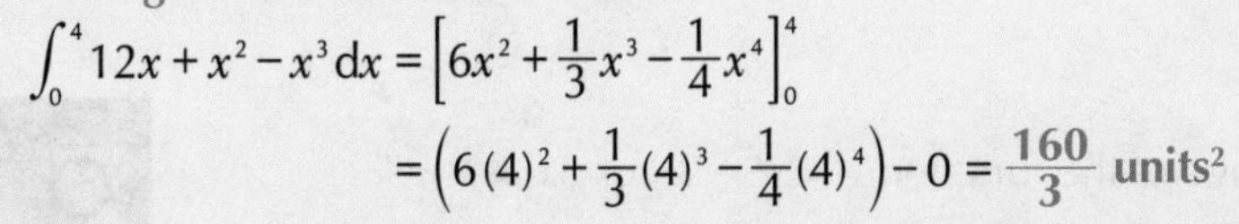

$$\int_0^4 12x + x^2 - x^3\,dx = \left[6x^2 + \frac{1}{3}x^3 - \frac{1}{4}x^4\right]_0^4$$
$$= \left(6(4)^2 + \frac{1}{3}(4)^3 - \frac{1}{4}(4)^4\right) - 0 = \frac{160}{3}\text{ units}^2$$

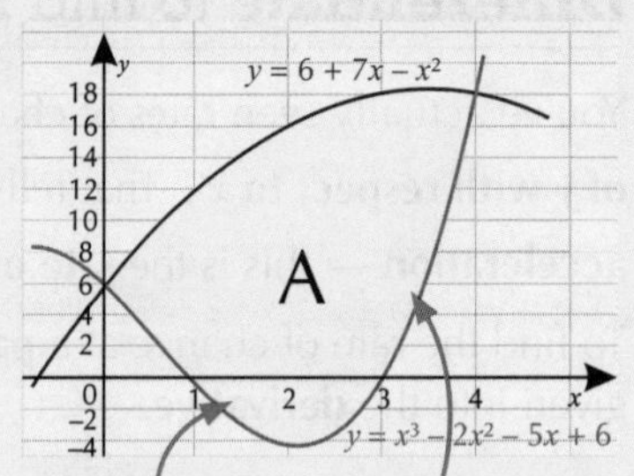

Integrating each function separately would be really awkward because the cubic lies both above and below the x-axis.

EXAMPLE: The graph shows the curves $y = \sin x + 1$ and $y = \cos x + 1$. Find the area of the shaded region.

1) The graphs **intersect** at $\sin x + 1 = \cos x + 1$
$\Rightarrow \sin x = \cos x \Rightarrow \frac{\sin x}{\cos x} = 1 \Rightarrow \tan x = 1$
$\Rightarrow x = \tan^{-1}(1) = \frac{\pi}{4}$ and $x = \frac{5\pi}{4}$.
So the **limits** are $x = \frac{\pi}{4}$ and $x = \frac{5\pi}{4}$.
2) **Subtract** the functions and **integrate** between the **limits**:
$(\sin x + 1) - (\cos x + 1) = \sin x - \cos x$

$$\int_{\frac{\pi}{4}}^{\frac{5\pi}{4}} \sin x - \cos x\,dx = [-\cos x - \sin x]_{\frac{\pi}{4}}^{\frac{5\pi}{4}} = \left(-\cos\left(\frac{5\pi}{4}\right) - \sin\left(\frac{5\pi}{4}\right)\right) - \left(-\cos\left(\frac{\pi}{4}\right) - \sin\left(\frac{\pi}{4}\right)\right)$$
$$= \left(-\left(-\frac{\sqrt{2}}{2}\right) - \left(-\frac{\sqrt{2}}{2}\right)\right) - \left(-\left(\frac{\sqrt{2}}{2}\right) - \left(\frac{\sqrt{2}}{2}\right)\right)$$
$$= \sqrt{2} - (-\sqrt{2}) = 2\sqrt{2}\text{ units}^2$$

On p.34 you saw $\cos\frac{\pi}{4}$ given as $\frac{1}{\sqrt{2}}$ but here it's written as $\frac{\sqrt{2}}{2}$. It's the same thing — you can rationalise the denominator to check.

Warm-Up Questions

Q1 Evaluate the following definite integrals:
a) $\int_0^1 (4x^3 + 3x^2 + 2x + 1)\,dx$ b) $\int_1^2 \left(\frac{8}{x^5} + \frac{3}{\sqrt{x}}\right)dx$ c) $\int_0^{\frac{\pi}{2}} 3\sin 2x + \cos 4x\,dx$

Q2 Evaluate $\int_{-3}^{3} 9 - x^2\,dx$. Sketch the area represented by this integral.

Exam Questions

Q1 Find the exact value of $\int_{\frac{\pi}{2}}^{\pi} 5\cos\left(\frac{1}{2}x + \frac{\pi}{4}\right)dx$. [4 marks]

Q2 The diagram on the right shows a sketch of the curve C, $y = (x - 3)^2(x + 1)$. Calculate the shaded area between point A, where C intersects the x-axis, and point B, where C touches the x-axis. [6 marks]

Q3 The diagram on the right shows the curve $y = (x + 1)(x - 5)$. Points J (–1, 0) and K (4, –5) lie on the curve.
a) Find the equation of the straight line joining J and K in the form $y = mx + c$. [2 marks]
b) Find the area of the shaded region. [5 marks]

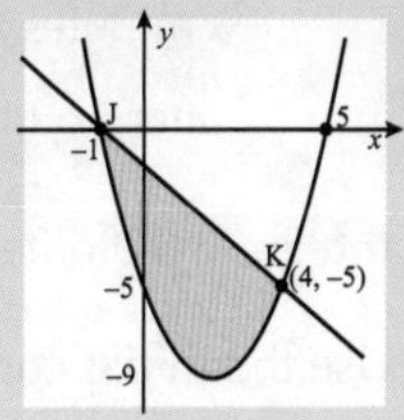

My hobbies? Well, I'm really inte grating. Especially carrots.

If one of your areas is negative (i.e. below the x-axis) make sure you subtract the negative area from the positive area. It's a small thing, but ignoring the minus sign and just adding the two areas up will lose you marks in the exam.

Rates of Change

You're probably about ready for a change from all this calculus lark, but hang on in there — just a few pages to go...

Differentiate to find Rates of Change

You've actually seen rates of change before — when you write $\frac{dy}{dx}$, what you're really saying is **'the rate of change of y with respect to x'**. That tells you about the **gradient** when y represents a curve. Now think about **acceleration** — this is the **rate of change** of **velocity** (or speed), v, over **time**, t, so you can write it as $\frac{dv}{dt}$.
To find the rate of change at a **particular point**, just **differentiate** the function and put the value you've been given into the **derivative**.

EXAMPLE: Find the rate of change of the function $y = x^2 + 3\cos 3x$ at $x = \frac{\pi}{2}$.

1) **Differentiate** the function y: $\frac{dy}{dx} = 2x - 9\sin 3x$
2) Then **evaluate** the derivative at $x = \frac{\pi}{2}$: $2\left(\frac{\pi}{2}\right) - 9\sin 3\left(\frac{\pi}{2}\right) = \boldsymbol{\pi + 9}$

Ayesha's rate of change was one of the fastest in the show.

EXAMPLE: Find the rate of change of the function $v = 3t - \frac{4}{\sqrt{t}}$ at $t = 9$.

1) Rewrite the function as **powers of t**: $v = 3t - 4t^{-\frac{1}{2}}$
2) **Differentiate** the function: $\frac{dv}{dt} = 3 + 2t^{-\frac{3}{2}}$
3) **Evaluate** the derivative at $t = 9$: $3 + \frac{2}{9^{\frac{3}{2}}} = \boldsymbol{\frac{83}{27}}$

If this equation was for velocity in m/s, it would mean that the acceleration at 9 seconds was $\frac{83}{27}$ m/s² ('metres per second per second').

Integrate a rate of change to find the Function

Rates of change questions can also involve **integration**. You might be given a function for a **rate of change** (i.e. a **differential equation** — see p.64) and some **values** for the variable involved, and asked to find the function. To do this, just **integrate**, and use the values you're given in the question to find the **constant of integration**.

Rates of change questions often have Real Life Contexts

You saw above that **acceleration** is the rate of change of **velocity** over time. Similarly, **velocity** is the rate of change of **distance travelled** (also called **displacement**) over time. Real life contexts for rates of change often involve **time**, so they use t instead of x, and a different letter instead of y (depending on what the question is about). But don't let that put you off — the maths is **exactly the same**.
When you get **extra information** to help you find the value of the constant of integration, you might be given an **'initial condition'** — this is just the value of the function at time $\boldsymbol{t = 0}$.

EXAMPLE: A radiator is switched on in a room. The rate of change of the temperature of the room, T° C, t minutes after it is switched on, is given by $\frac{dT}{dt} = kt^{-\frac{3}{4}} + \frac{1}{8}$. Initially, the room is 8° C, and after 16 minutes, the temperature has increased to 14° C. Express T as a function of t only.

This just means you need to find the value of k as well.

1) **Integrate** the differential equation: $T = \int kt^{-\frac{3}{4}} + \frac{1}{8}\,dt = 4kt^{\frac{1}{4}} + \frac{t}{8} + C$
2) Use the **initial condition** to find C: At $t = 0$, $T = 8$, so $8 = 4k(0)^{\frac{1}{4}} + \frac{0}{8} + C$, so $C = 8$
3) At $t = 16$, $T = 14$, so use this to find k: $14 = 4k(16)^{\frac{1}{4}} + \frac{16}{8} + 8 \Rightarrow 14 = 8k + 10 \Rightarrow k = \frac{1}{2}$
4) **Substitute** k and C to get the answer: $\boldsymbol{T = 2t^{\frac{1}{4}} + \frac{t}{8} + 8}$

Rates of Change

Displacement, Velocity and Acceleration are linked by Calculus

1) You can find an equation for **velocity** by **differentiating** an equation for **displacement** with respect to time. Similarly, you can find an equation for **acceleration** by **differentiating** an equation for **velocity** with respect to time.
2) Since you know integration is the **opposite** of differentiation, it follows that you can find an equation for **velocity** from an equation for **acceleration** (or an equation for **displacement** from an equation for **velocity**) by **integrating**.

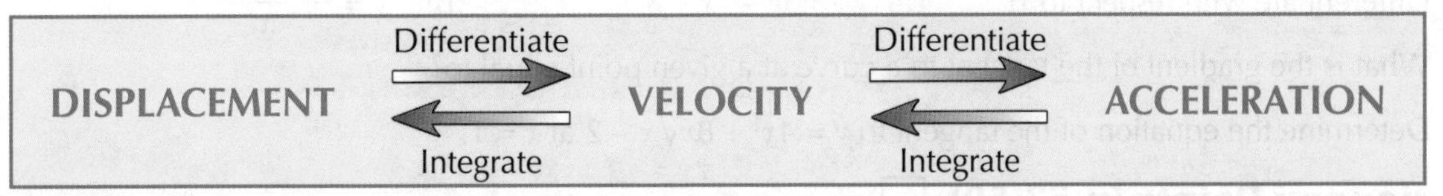

EXAMPLE: At time t seconds, a car is moving at v m/s, where $v = 15t - 6t^2$.
a) Find an expression for the car's acceleration at time t.
b) Determine whether the car is accelerating or decelerating at time $t = 3$.
c) Find an equation for the car's displacement, $s(t)$, given that $s(2) = 8$.

a) Find the **acceleration** by differentiating $v = 15t - 6t^2$: $\frac{dv}{dt} = \mathbf{15 - 12t}$

b) If the value of $\frac{dv}{dt}$ at a point is **positive**, the car is **accelerating**, and if it is **negative**, it is **decelerating**.
At $t = 3$, $\frac{dv}{dt} = 15 - 12(3) = -21$, so the car is **decelerating**.

c) You find $s(t)$ by **integrating** the equation for v: $s(t) = \int 15t - 6t^2\,dt = \frac{15}{2}t^2 - \frac{6}{3}t^3 + C$
At $t = 2$, $s(t) = 8$, so $8 = \frac{15}{2}(2)^2 - 2(2)^3 + C \Rightarrow 8 = 30 - 16 + C \Rightarrow C = -6$
Substituting this into your equation for $s(t)$ gives $\mathbf{s(t) = \frac{15}{2}t^2 - 2t^3 - 6}$

Warm-Up Questions

Q1 Find an expression for the rate of change of $y = 5\cos x - 3\sin(3x - 1)$.

Q2 Given that $\frac{dv}{dt} = 3t^2 - 4\sqrt{t} + 2$, where t is time in seconds and initially $v = 6$, find the equation for v.

Exam Questions

Q1 Calculate the rate of change of $f(x) = 4\cos^2 2x$ at $x = \frac{\pi}{8}$. [3 marks]

Q2 A population of bacteria P is decreasing at a rate of $\frac{dP}{dt} = at - \frac{3}{\sqrt{t}}$, where a is a constant and t is the time in days. Given that the initial population was 500, and that after 9 days the population had decreased to 158, express P in terms of t. [6 marks]

Q3 The acceleration in m/s² of a ball rolling along a straight, flat surface is given by the function $a(t) = 8 - 2t$, where t is the time in seconds.
a) By integrating the expression for acceleration, find the velocity, v m/s, of the ball. [2 marks]
b) Given that $v = 4$ when $t = 1$, find the velocity at time $t = 6$. [2 marks]
c) (i) By integrating the expression for velocity, find an expression for displacement. [2 marks]
(ii) Determine how far in the ball has travelled, in metres, from its initial position after 3 seconds. [2 marks]

My calculus knowledge has changed at an alarming rate...

Maths has x's and y's all over the place, so it feels a bit odd to see the rest of the alphabet suddenly turn up to the party. Don't let the different letters worry you, though — keep calm and calculus on. 'Rates of change' is just a fancy way of talking about the same old differentiation and integration business that you've been doing throughout this section. If any of it caused you any trouble, flip back a few pages, brush up on your calculus skills and then show it who's boss.

Revision Summary for Section Four

And that's a wrap on Section Four — now it's time to test out your new calculus superpowers...

- Try these questions and tick off each one when you get it right.
- When you've done all the questions for a topic and are completely happy with it, tick off the topic.

Differentiation (p.55-56)

1) Differentiate with respect to x: a) $y = x^2 - 7x + 3$ b) $y = \dfrac{4x^3 - 3\sqrt{x}}{x^2}$
2) What is the gradient of the tangent to a curve at a given point equal to?
3) Determine the equation of the tangent to $y = 4x^2 + 8x\sqrt{x} - 2$ at $x = 1$.

Stationary Points (p.57-59)

4) a) What is a stationary point?
   b) What are the three different types of stationary point?
   c) Describe one method of determining the nature of a stationary point.
5) a) Find the coordinates of the stationary point of $y = x^2 - 2x$.
   b) Determine its nature.
6) Use a nature table to determine if the stationary point at $(\sqrt{3}, -2)$ on $y = x^4 - 6x^2 + 7$ is a minimum or a maximum.
7) a) Find the range of values of x where the function $y = x^3 + 2x^2 - 15x$ is increasing and the range of values of x where the function is decreasing.
   b) Sketch the function y.
8) Using the graph of $y = f(x)$, sketch $f'(x)$.

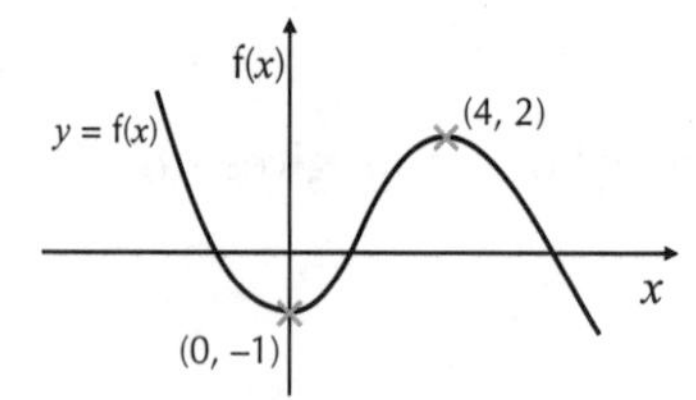

9) Using the graph of $y = g'(x)$, sketch $g(x)$.

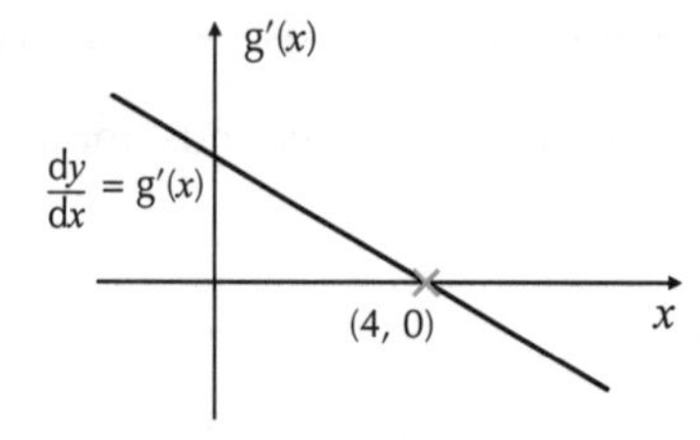

Harder Differentiation (p.60-63)

10) Use the chain rule to differentiate: a) $y = (5x + 2)^4$ b) $y = (7 - 4x)^{12}$
11) Differentiate with respect to x: a) $y = 4\cos 6x$ b) $y = -2\sin \frac{1}{2}x$
12) Find the gradient of $y = \frac{1}{2}\cos 2x$ at the point $x = \frac{\pi}{4}$.
13) Differentiate $y = \sin x \cos x$ using a trig identity.
14) Find the greatest and least values of $y = x^3 - 3x + 6$ for $0 \leq x \leq 3$.
15) Given a rectangle with sides of lengths x cm and y cm where $x \leq y$, and an area of 18 cm^2, find x and y such that the rectangle has the smallest possible perimeter.

16) A box of chocolates has width x cm, height $\frac{x}{4}$ cm and depth d cm, and a volume of 250 cm^3.
    a) Show that the surface area of the box is $A = \dfrac{x^2}{2} + \dfrac{2500}{x}$.
    b) Find the value of x that gives the smallest possible surface area for this box.

Revision Summary for Section Four

Indefinite Integrals (p.64-68)

17) Why do you need to add the constant of integration? (Other than 'to get all the marks in the exam'...)

18) Find: a) $\int 6x^2 + 4\,dx$ b) $\int \frac{1}{x^2} - 3x\,dx$ c) $\int (4x-2)^{-3}\,dx$

19) Determine the equation of the curve y with $\frac{dy}{dx} = 3x^2 - 2$ that goes through the point (1, 3).

20) Integrate with respect to x: a) $\cos\frac{3}{2}x$ b) $3\sin 4x$ c) $5\cos(1-2x)$

21) The graph of y crosses the x-axis at $x = \pi$ and $\frac{dy}{dx} = 3\cos(3x - \frac{\pi}{2}) - 6\sin 2x$. Find y in terms of x.

22) Integrate the following using trig identities: a) $\cos^2 x - \sin^2 x$ b) $\sin^2 3x$

Definite Integrals (p.69-71)

23) What is the difference between a definite and an indefinite integral?

24) What is a geometric interpretation of the integral $\int_a^b f(x)\,dx$?

25) Find: a) $\int_0^1 x^3 - 2x + 1\,dx$ b) $\int_1^4 4\sqrt{x} + x^2 - 3x\,dx$

26) Find: a) $\int_0^{\frac{\pi}{4}} 4\cos 2x\,dx$ b) $\int_0^{\pi} -6\cos\frac{1}{2}x + 1\,dx$

27) Calculate the shaded area A between $y = 2x^2 - 4x + 2$, $y = 12 - 3x$ and the x-axis.

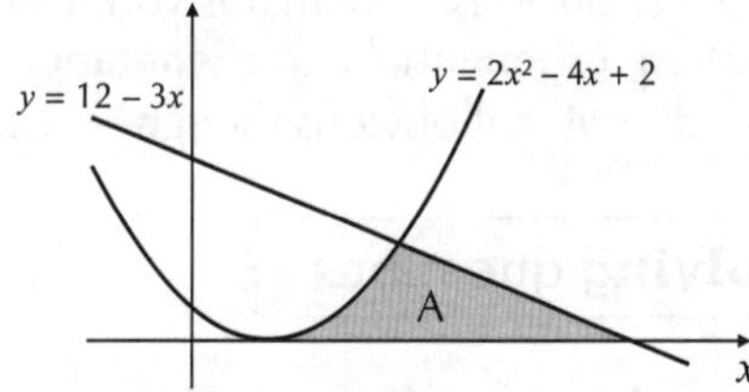

28) Determine the area enclosed between the line $y = 3x - 5$ and the curve $y = x^2 - 3$.

29) Find the shaded area A between the curves $y = (x-1)(3x+4)(x+2)$ and $y = 6 + x - 7x^2$.

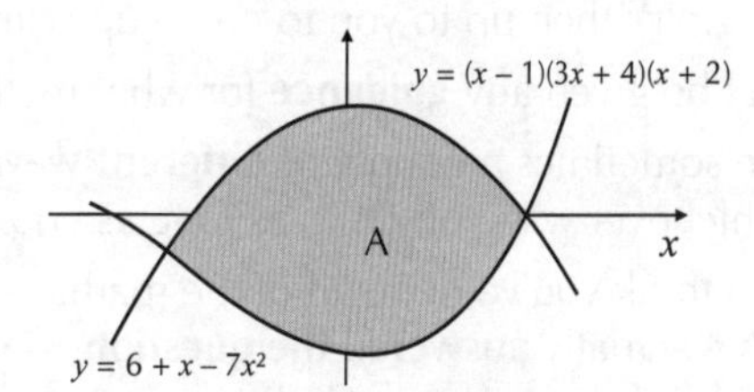

Rates of Change (p.72-73)

30) Find an expression for the rate of change of $y = \frac{4}{3t^{\frac{3}{2}}}$.

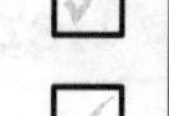

31) Determine the rate of change of $y = 3\sin 3x$ at $x = \frac{\pi}{2}$.

32) a) Given the rate of change $\frac{dx}{dt} = \frac{5t^2 - 2t + 1}{\sqrt{t}}$, find an expression for x.

b) Given that when $t = 1$, $x = \frac{2}{3}$, find x in terms of t only.

33) The rate of change of A is given by $\frac{dA}{dt} = 4t^3 - 7$, and initially $A = 4$. Express A in terms of t.

34) The velocity of a particle is given by $v = 3t^2 - 4t + 3$.

a) Differentiate the expression for velocity to find the acceleration of the particle at time $t = 2$.

b) Integrate the expression for velocity to find an expression for displacement, s, given that the initial displacement of the particle is 3.

35) The rate of change of the population of leprechauns in a forest can be modelled by $\frac{dL}{dt} = 3\sqrt{t} + \frac{1}{4}t$ where t is the time in weeks. Initially, there were 12 leprechauns. Determine how many leprechauns there will be after 4 weeks.

Reasoning Skills

Reasoning skills are all about how you tackle a mathematical problem and explain the answer. You'll have to use reasoning skills on both exam papers, so it's a good idea to know what you need to do.

There are **Two Main Types** of reasoning questions...

1) For some questions, it's **obvious** what you have to do — e.g. 'differentiate the function $f(x) = 5x^2 + 2x + 1$' is clearly a question on **differentiation**, so solve it using the usual methods (see p.55-63).
2) However, in other questions, it's **not obvious** what you have to do — you're given some **information**, and have to work out what **methods** to use to answer the question. These questions are designed to assess how you approach an **unfamiliar problem** — they test your **reasoning skills**.
3) Reasoning questions come in **two different forms** — in both cases, you have to work out what maths to do **for yourself**.

Questions with a **Real-Life Context**

1) If questions have a **real-life context**, the information you need might be **hidden** in all the wordiness. You need to read through the question and work out which bits are **relevant** to the maths, and which bits are just **setting the scene**.
2) Once you've worked this out, decide which **method(s)** you need to use to answer the question. After doing all your **calculations**, make sure you **link** your answer back to the **original context**.
3) It can be pretty obvious what maths you need to use, even with a real-life context — **differentiation**, **exponential** and **trigonometry** problems are often given in context. Sometimes it's **not** that obvious though — which leads us nicely onto...

Problem-Solving questions

Sometimes questions will be a mixture of <u>both</u> — i.e. problem-solving questions set in a real-life context.

1) In **problem-solving questions**, you'll be given a load of **mathematical information** (often including **diagrams**) and asked to **'calculate'**, **'find'** or **'determine'** something. It's then up to you to come up with a **strategy** to answer the question.
2) You won't be given any **guidance** for what method to use — you have work it out for yourself.
3) There are sometimes a couple of **different ways** you could answer the question — and you'll get the marks whichever way you do it, as long as you get the **answer right** and **show your working** clearly.
4) Once you think you've done all of the maths required, it's important that you check that you've actually **answered the question** — you might need to **explain why** your solution is the correct one, or link your answer back to the **context** of the question.

Here are some **Useful Tips** for reasoning questions

Unfortunately, there's **no** one set method for answering reasoning questions — they can be on anything the examiners fancy, so will involve **different bits** of maths. These **tips** should help you get started though.

- **Read the question** two or three times and work out what you're **trying to find**.
- Write down what you **know** — pick out any **numbers** given in the question, and add **labels** to diagrams if you can. If you're not given a diagram, it's often a good idea to **sketch one yourself**.
- See if anything **jumps out** at you — for example, a **diagram of a circle** might mean you need to use the equation of the circle $(x - a)^2 + (y - b)^2 = r^2$, or mention of **maximums / minimums** might mean you need to **differentiate** to find these values.
- **Don't rush** into a problem-solving question — **take your time** and **think it through** first. Make sure you have an **idea** of what you're going to do before diving in.
- **Show all your working** — these questions can be worth **4 or 5 marks**, so you'll get some marks for your **strategy** and **reasoning** even if you get the final answer **wrong**.
- Make sure your answer is **sensible** — look back at the **original question** and check that it seems **reasonable**.

There's an **example** of a reasoning question coming up on the **next page**.

Reasoning Skills — Worked Example

Now you know what reasoning questions are and how to tackle them, it's time to see one in the wild...

Put it into practice with a **Worked Example**

The best way to get to grips with reasoning questions is to **practise** — so here's a **worked example** to show you how it's done. Remember, all reasoning questions are **different** — but you can apply the **same skills** to tackle them.

EXAMPLE: Two circles, C_1 and C_2, with centres O and P respectively, are shown below. OXP is a straight line, with C_1 and C_2 touching externally at X. The point Q(8, 4) has the same x-coordinate as O and the same y-coordinate as P, and the triangle OPQ has an area of 9 square units. C_2 is defined by the equation $x^2 + y^2 - 4x - 8y + 15 = 0$. Determine the equation of the circle C_1.

To find the equation of C_1, you need to know its **radius** and its **centre**. It isn't immediately obvious how to obtain this information, so start by considering what you **do know**.

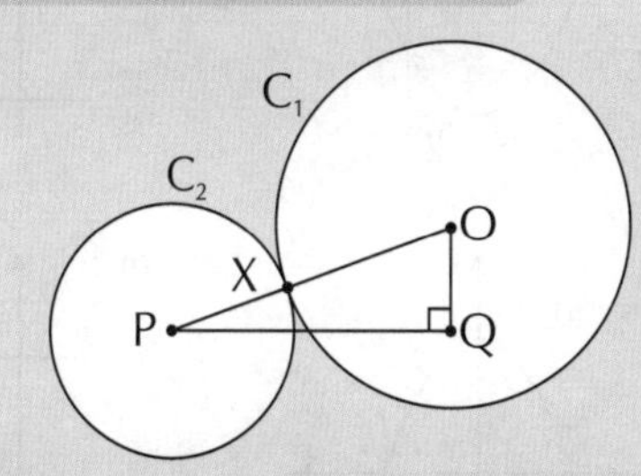

You know the equation of C_2, so **extract** all the information that you can from this — in particular, the centre of this circle and its radius. The equation is in the form $x^2 + y^2 + 2gx + 2fy + c = 0$ with $g = -2$, $f = -4$ and $c = 15$, so the centre is $(-g, -f) = \mathbf{(2, 4)}$ and the radius is $\sqrt{g^2+f^2-c} = \sqrt{4+16-15} = \sqrt{5}$.

You knew that the y-coordinate of the centre should be 4 as it had to match point Q — so this is looking good.

To find the radius of C_1, start off by finding the length of **OP**. It's the **hypotenuse** of the right-angled triangle OPQ — and you can find its length using **Pythagoras' theorem**. First, though, you'll need to find the **other two side lengths**. You're given the **area** of the triangle and you know one side length (PQ = 8 – 2 = 6), so work out the unknown side OQ:

$$\text{area} = \frac{1}{2} \times \text{base} \times \text{height} \Rightarrow 9 = \frac{1}{2} \times 6 \times OQ \Rightarrow \mathbf{OQ = 3}$$

Now that you know the lengths of the two shorter sides, you can work out the hypotenuse:

$$OP^2 = 6^2 + 3^2 = 36 + 9 = 45 \Rightarrow OP = \sqrt{45} = \mathbf{3\sqrt{5}}$$

So the radius of C_1 is $OX = OP - XP = 3\sqrt{5} - \sqrt{5} = \mathbf{2\sqrt{5}}$. XP is the radius of C_2.

You can also find both coordinates of the centre — its x-coordinate is the same as Q (**8**) and, since side OQ is 3 units long, its y-coordinate is $4 + 3 = \mathbf{7}$. ← i.e. 3 greater than the y-coordinate of Q

Then the **equation** of C_1 is $(x - 8)^2 + (y - 7)^2 = (2\sqrt{5})^2$

$$\Rightarrow \mathbf{(x - 8)^2 + (y - 7)^2 = 20}$$

In these sorts of questions, make sure you lay your working out clearly and explain what you're doing. Communication is important in reasoning questions.

In this question, you needed to know how to interpret the **equation of a circle** (see p.42), and you needed to recall the formula for the **area of a triangle** and **Pythagoras' theorem** from **National 5**. The really tricky bit was figuring out that that's what you had to do, which didn't become clear until you started working through the question.

Exam Questions

PRACTICE QUESTIONS

Q1 A car travels along a hilly road. The distance it travels is x miles and the height of the road above sea level, y metres, can be modelled by $y = -4x^3 + 10x^2 - 7x + 2$ for $x \in \{0 < x < 1.5\}$. Determine the number of miles the car drives uphill. [5 marks]

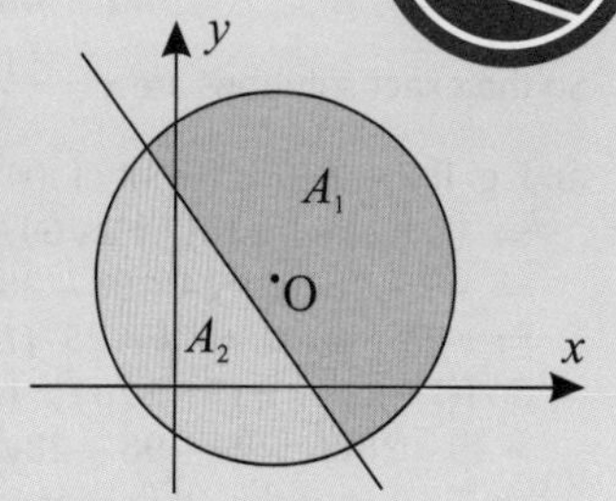

Q2 The circle, centre O, is defined by the equation $x^2 - 2x - 2y + y^2 = 1$. The circle is intersected by the line $y = mx + 2$ to create two segments, as shown on the right. The segment above the line has an area of A_1 and the segment below the line has an area of A_2. Find all values of m such that $A_1 > A_2$. [4 marks]

You think I didn't have enough problems to solve before this section?

Don't go into a panic if you come across a problem-solving question and you can't quite see how to crack it — all the maths you'll need will come from the stuff you've seen earlier in this book. If you're confident with that, your main job is working out which bits to use. Write down all you can glean from the question and it should start to become clear.

Answers

Section One — Algebraic Skills

Page 3 — Quadratic Equations

Warm-Up Questions

1 a) $(x-3)^2-4$ b) $(x+2)^2-10$
c) $2\left(x-\frac{3}{2}\right)^2-\frac{19}{2}$ d) $3\left(x-\frac{7}{6}\right)^2-\frac{13}{12}$

2 $x=-\frac{1}{4}\pm\frac{\sqrt{29}}{4}$

3 a)

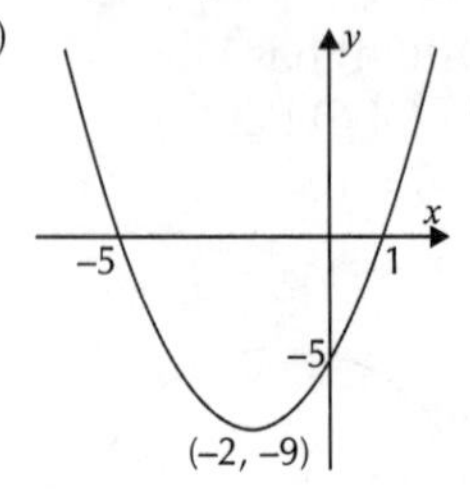

b)

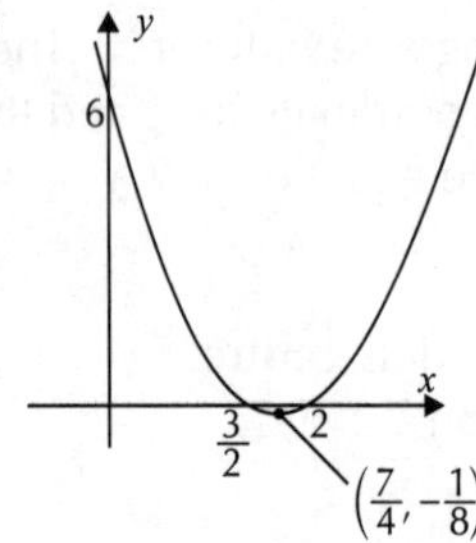

c)

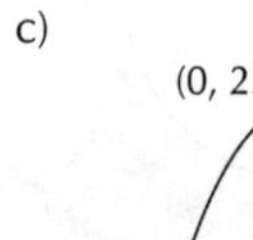
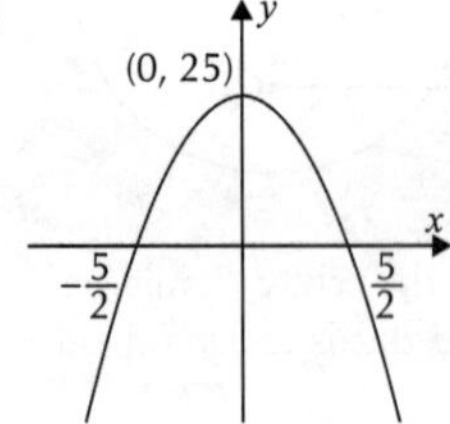

d)

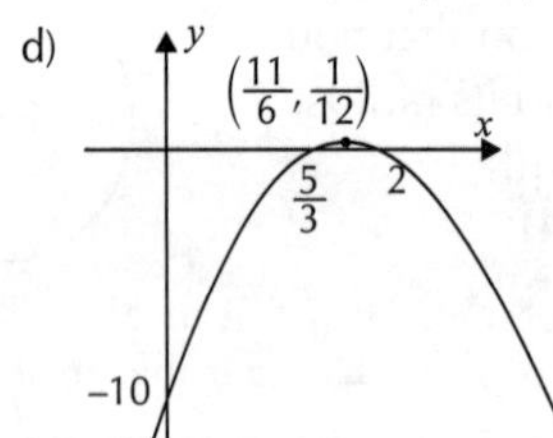

Exam Questions

1 a) $3x^2+2x-2=3\left(x^2+\frac{2}{3}x\right)-2=3\left(x+\frac{1}{3}\right)^2+d$ ***[1 mark]***
$3\left(x+\frac{1}{3}\right)^2+d=3x^2+2x-2$
$\Rightarrow 3x^2+2x+\frac{1}{3}+d=3x^2+2x-2$
$\Rightarrow d=-2-\frac{1}{3}=-\frac{7}{3}$ ***[1 mark]***
So $3x^2+2x-2=3\left(x+\frac{1}{3}\right)^2-\frac{7}{3}$ ***[1 mark]***

b) The minimum occurs when $\left(x+\frac{1}{3}\right)^2=0$, i.e. when $x=-\frac{1}{3}$.
Then $3\left(x+\frac{1}{3}\right)^2-\frac{7}{3}=3\times 0-\frac{7}{3}$,
so the coordinates are $\left(-\frac{1}{3},-\frac{7}{3}\right)$. ***[1 mark]***

2 $6x^2=1-3x \Rightarrow 6x^2+3x-1=0 \Rightarrow 6\left(x^2+\frac{1}{2}x\right)-1=0$ ***[1 mark]***
$6\left(x^2+\frac{1}{2}x\right)-1=6\left(x+\frac{1}{4}\right)^2+d \Rightarrow 6\left(x+\frac{1}{4}\right)^2+d=6x^2+3x-1$
$\Rightarrow 6x^2+3x+\frac{3}{8}+d=6x^2+3x-1$
$\Rightarrow d=-1-\frac{3}{8}=-\frac{11}{8}$ ***[1 mark]***
So $6\left(x+\frac{1}{4}\right)^2-\frac{11}{8}=0$. ***[1 mark]*** Now solve this to find x:
$6\left(x+\frac{1}{4}\right)^2=\frac{11}{8} \Rightarrow \left(x+\frac{1}{4}\right)^2=\frac{11}{48} \Rightarrow x=-\frac{1}{4}\pm\sqrt{\frac{11}{48}}=-\frac{1}{4}\pm\frac{\sqrt{33}}{12}$
So the exact solutions are $x=-\frac{1}{4}+\frac{\sqrt{33}}{12}$ or $-\frac{1}{4}-\frac{\sqrt{33}}{12}$ ***[1 mark]***

3 a) E.g. If $7+2\sqrt{6}$ is a root of $f(x)=0$, then $f(7+2\sqrt{6})=0$
$\Rightarrow (7+2\sqrt{6})^2-14(7+2\sqrt{6})+k=0$ ***[1 mark]***
$\Rightarrow 49+28\sqrt{6}+24-98-28\sqrt{6}+k=0$ ***[1 mark]***
$\Rightarrow -25+k=0 \Rightarrow k=25$ ***[1 mark]***
So $f(7-2\sqrt{6})=(7-2\sqrt{6})^2-14(7-2\sqrt{6})+25$
$=49-28\sqrt{6}+24-98+28\sqrt{6}+25=0$ ***[1 mark]***
so $7-2\sqrt{6}$ is the other root of $f(x)$.
You'd still get the marks if you used a different method here.

b)

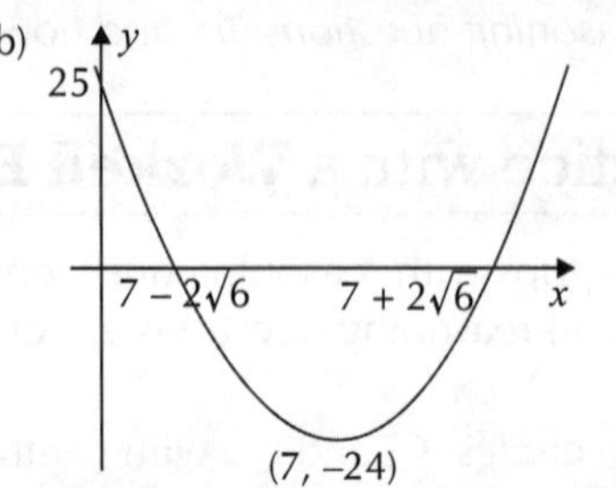

[3 marks available — 1 mark for a u-shaped curve, 1 mark for correct x- and y-intercepts, 1 mark for the correct coordinates of the minimum point]

4 a) The completed square is:
$(x-6)^2+d=x^2-12x+36+d$ ***[1 mark]***
Equating coefficients gives $15=36+d$,
so $d=15-36=-21$. ***[1 mark]***
The final expression is $(x-6)^2-21$.

b) The minimum occurs when the expression in brackets is equal to 0, so the minimum is -21. ***[1 mark]***
The expression in brackets is equal to 0 when $x=6$. ***[1 mark]***

Page 5 — The Quadratic Formula

Warm-Up Questions

1 a) (i) discriminant = 0, 1 repeated real root (ii) $x=-\frac{7}{2}$
b) (i) discriminant = –3, no real roots
c) (i) discriminant = 0, 1 repeated real root (ii) $x=\frac{\sqrt{2}}{3}$

2 The discriminant of the equation $px^2+3x+(3-p)=0$ is $3^2-4p(3-p)=9-12p+4p^2=(3-2p)^2$. Since $(3-2p)^2\geq 0$ for all values of p, the discriminant ≥ 0, so the roots are always real.

Exam Questions

1 For equal roots, $b^2-4ac=0$. $a=1$, $b=2k$ and $c=4k$, so:
$b^2-4ac=(2k)^2-(4\times 1\times 4k)$ ***[1 mark]***
$=4k^2-16k=4k(k-4)=0$ ***[1 mark]***
so $k=4$ (as k is non-zero) ***[1 mark]***

2 a) For distinct real roots, $b^2-4ac>0$ ***[1 mark]***
$a=p+1$, $b=p+1$ and $c=1$
so $b^2-4ac=(p+1)^2-4(p+1)(1)>0$ ***[1 mark]***
$\Rightarrow p^2+2p+1-4p-4>0 \Rightarrow p^2-2p-3>0$ ***[1 mark]***

b) The graph of $y=p^2-2p-3$ crosses the horizontal axis when $p^2-2p-3=(p+1)(p-3)=0$
So it crosses at $p=-1$ and $p=3$ ***[1 mark]***
The quadratic is u-shaped (since the coefficient of p^2 is positive) so $p^2-2p-3>0$ outside of these values: ***[1 mark]***
$p<-1$ or $p>3$ ***[1 mark]***

Page 7 — Quadratic Inequalities

Warm-Up Questions

1 a) $-10<x<10$ b) $x<-\sqrt{2}$ or $x>\sqrt{2}$ c) $x\leq -5$ or $x\geq 5$

2 a) $-\frac{1}{3}\leq x\leq 2$ b) $x<-2$ or $x>\frac{3}{2}$ c) $x\leq -3$ or $x\geq -2$

3 a) $x\leq -3$ or $x\geq 1$ b) $x<-\frac{1}{2}$ or $x>1$ c) $-3<x<2$

Answers

Exam Questions

1 a) $2x^2 + 2 \leq x^2 + 18 \Rightarrow x^2 \leq 16 \Rightarrow -4 \leq x \leq 4$ ***[1 mark]***

b) $20 - x - x^2 > 0 \Rightarrow (4 - x)(5 + x) > 0$
The graph crosses the x-axis at $x = 4$ and $x = -5$. ***[1 mark]***
The coefficient of x^2 is negative so the graph is n-shaped.
So $20 - x - x^2 > 0$ when $-5 < x < 4$. ***[1 mark]***

c) $-4 \leq x < 4$ ***[1 mark]***

2 $x^2 - 3x \geq 10$ ***[1 mark]*** $\Rightarrow x^2 - 3x - 10 \geq 0$
$\Rightarrow (x - 5)(x + 2) \geq 0 \Rightarrow x \leq -2$ or $x \geq 5$. ***[1 mark]***
$x > 0$ as it is a length which must be positive, so the possible range of values is $x \geq 5$. ***[1 mark]***

3 $(4x + 1) \times 2x < 1$ ***[1 mark]*** $\Rightarrow 8x^2 + 2x - 1 < 0$ ***[1 mark]***
$\Rightarrow (4x - 1)(2x + 1) < 0$ ***[1 mark]*** $\Rightarrow -0.5 < x < 0.25$
$x > 0$ as $2x$ is a length and length must be positive,
so 0 m $< x < 0.25$ m ***[1 mark]***

Page 10 — Factorising Cubics and Quartics

Warm-Up Questions

1 $a = 1$

2 a) $f(-1) = (-1)^3 - 7 \times (-1) - 6 = 0$
You could also divide by the factor $(x + 1)$ using synthetic or algebraic long division, and show that the remainder is 0.

b) $x^3 - 7x - 6 = (x + 1)(x + 2)(x - 3)$

3

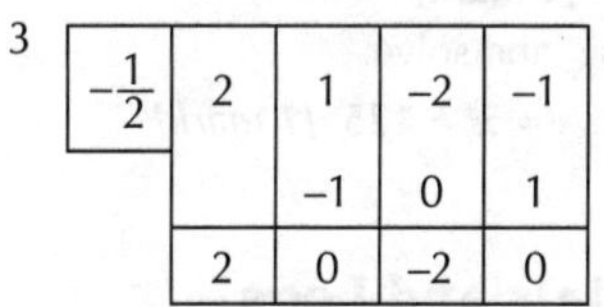

$-\frac{1}{2}$	2	1	-2	-1
		-1	0	1
	2	0	-2	0

$\Rightarrow 2x^3 + x^2 - 2x - 1 = (2x^2 - 2)(x + \frac{1}{2}) = 2(x^2 - 1)(x + \frac{1}{2})$
$= (x^2 - 1)(2x + 1)$

So the result of the division is $x^2 - 1$.
The divisor in the question is in the form $ax + b$, but you need to divide by $x + \frac{b}{a}$ for synthetic division to work. Then don't forget to adjust the quotient at the end to get the right answer.

Exam Questions

1 a) $f(1) = 1^3 - (3 \times 1^2) + (3 \times 1) - 1 = 0$ ***[1 mark]***
Since $f(1) = 0$, $(x - 1)$ is a factor of $f(x)$. ***[1 mark]***
The first mark would also be given for using algebraic long division or synthetic division to show that the remainder is zero.

b) $x^3 - 3x^2 + 3x - 1 = (x - 1)(x^2 - 2x + 1)$ ***[1 mark]***
$= (x - 1)^3$ ***[1 mark]***
The quadratic factor can be found by inspection, or by using the result of algebraic long division or synthetic division.

2 a) $f(1) = 1^4 - (6 \times 1^3) + (13 \times 1^2) - (12 \times 1) + 4 = 0$
$f(2) = 2^4 - (6 \times 2^3) + (13 \times 2^2) - (12 \times 2) + 4 = 0$ ***[1 mark]***
Since $f(1) = 0$ and $f(2) = 0$, $(x - 1)$ and $(x - 2)$ are factors of $f(x)$.
[1 mark]

b) One quadratic factor is $(x - 1)(x - 2) = x^2 - 3x + 2$.
$x^4 - 6x^3 + 13x^2 - 12x + 4 = (x^2 - 3x + 2)(x^2 - 3x + 2)$ ***[1 mark]***
$= (x - 1)^2(x - 2)^2$ ***[1 mark]***
So the solutions are $x = 1$ and $x = 2$. ***[1 mark]***

3 a) $f(-1) = 0$ as $(x + 1)$ is a factor ***[1 mark]***,
so $(a \times (-1)^3) - (3 \times (-1)^2) + (b \times (-1)) - 3 = 0$
$\Rightarrow a + b = -6$ ***[1 mark]***
$f(2) = -15$ as $(x - 2)$ leaves remainder -15 when dividing $f(x)$, so
$(a \times 2^3) - (3 \times 2^2) + (b \times 2) - 3 = -15 \Rightarrow 8a + 2b = 0$ ***[1 mark]***
$\Rightarrow 4a + b = 0$. Solving the equations for a and b simultaneously, you get $a = 2$ ***[1 mark]*** and $b = -8$ ***[1 mark]***.

b) $2x^3 - 3x^2 - 8x - 3 = (x + 1)(2x^2 - 5x - 3)$ ***[1 mark]***
$= (x + 1)(2x + 1)(x - 3)$ ***[1 mark]***
So $f(x) = 0$ when $x = -1$, $x = -\frac{1}{2}$ and $x = 3$. ***[1 mark]***

Page 12 — Cubic and Quartic Graphs

Warm-Up Questions

1 a)

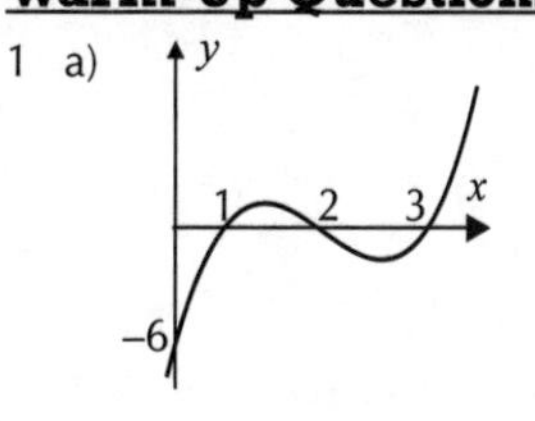

b)

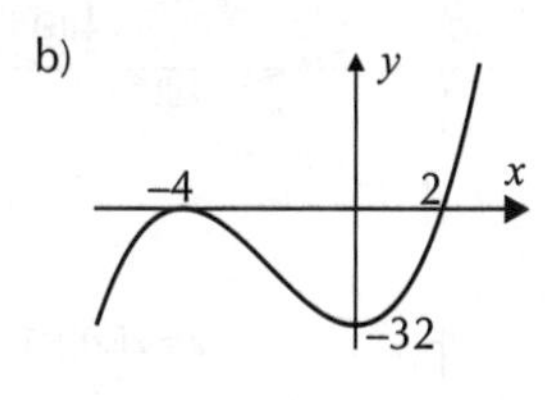

c)

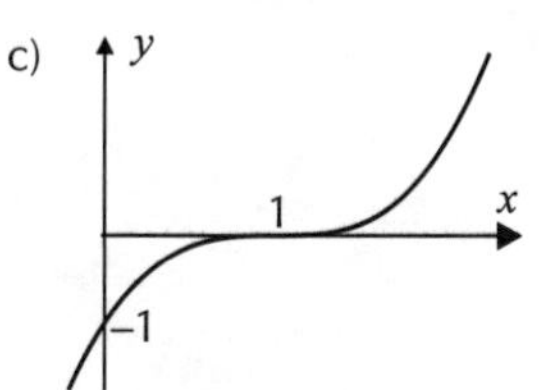

2 a)

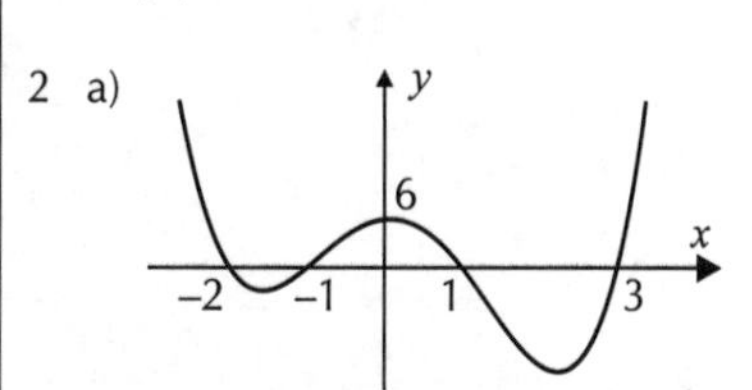

b)

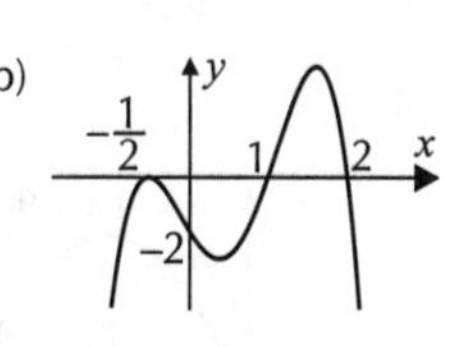

c)

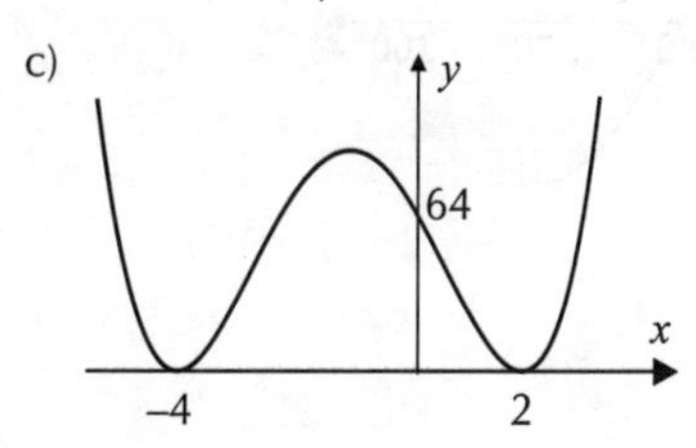

Exam Questions

1 $f(x)$ has roots at $x = 1$ and $x = 3$, so $a = 1$ and $b = 3$ ***[1 mark]***.
As $(2, 1)$ lies on the curve, $1 = f(2) = k(2 - 1)^2(2 - 3)^2 = k$
$\Rightarrow k = 1$ ***[1 mark]***
Alternatively, you could choose $a = 3$ and $b = 1$.

2 The curve just touches the x-axis at $x = -2$ and $(x - a)$ is a double root, so $a = -2$ ***[1 mark]***. The remaining roots are $x = 1$ and $x = 3$, so $b = 1$ and $c = 3$ ***[1 mark]***. As $(2, 4)$ lies on the curve,
$4 = f(2) = k(2 + 2)^2(2 - 1)(2 - 3) = -16k \Rightarrow k = -\frac{1}{4}$ ***[1 mark]***
Alternatively, you could choose $b = 3$ and $c = 1$.

Page 14 — Graph Transformations

Warm-Up Questions

1 a)

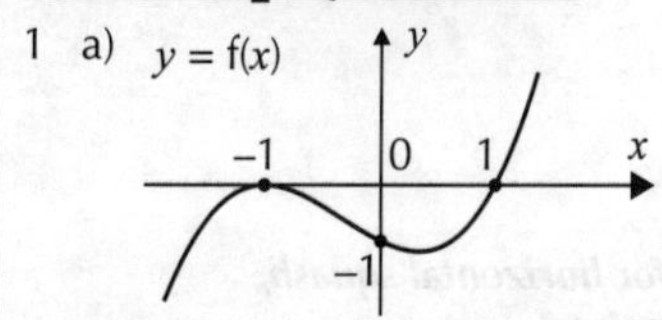

b) (i)

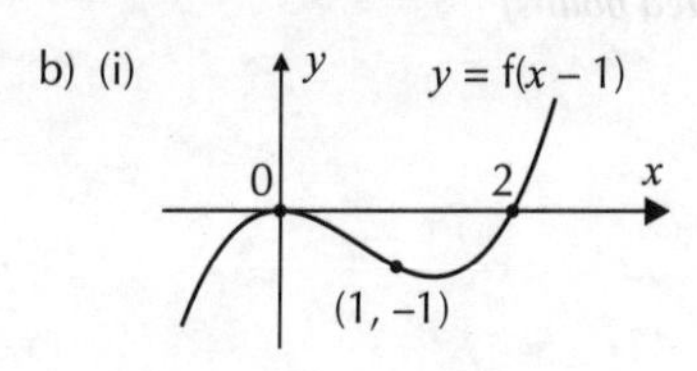

(ii)

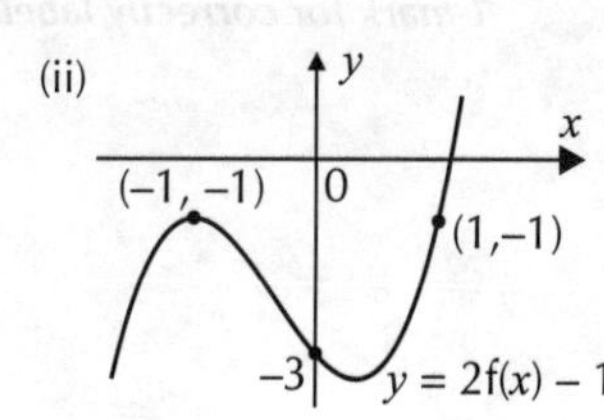

(iii)

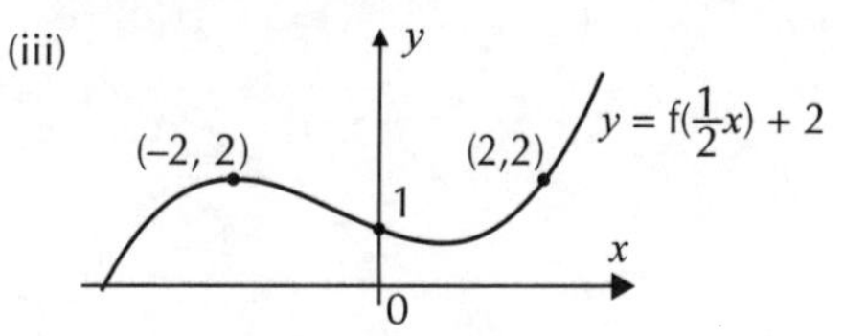

Answers

2 a) 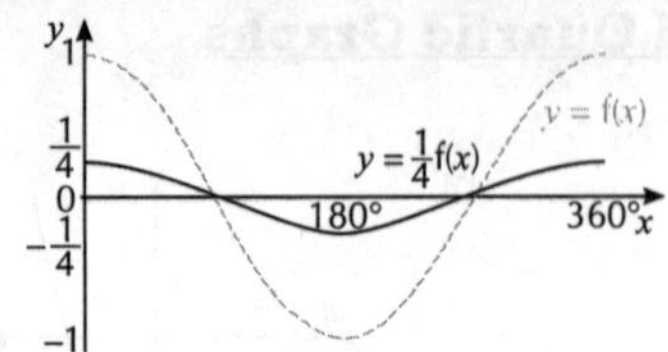

b) 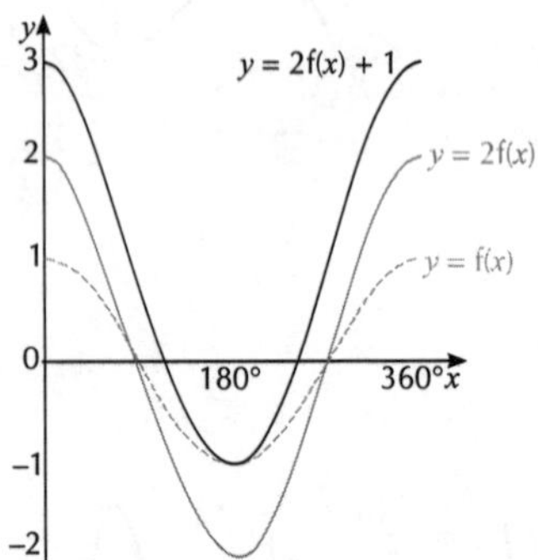

c) 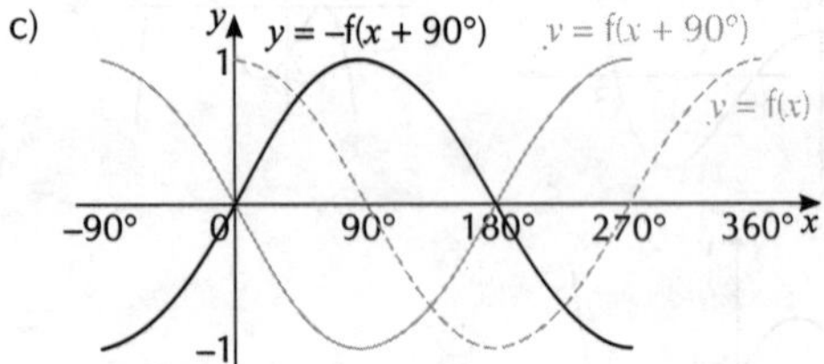

Exam Question

1 a) 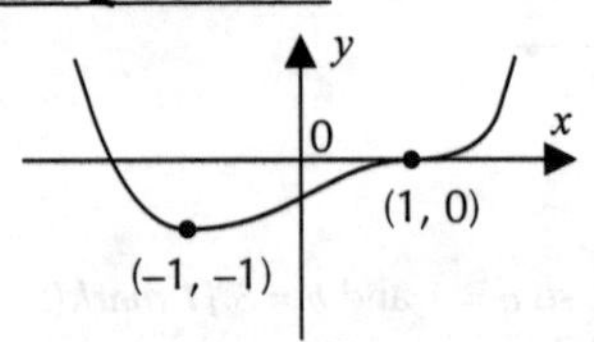

[2 marks available — 1 mark for vertical translation, 1 mark for correctly labelled points]

b) 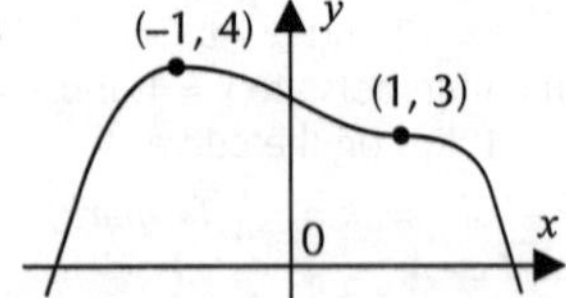

[3 marks available — 1 mark for reflection in x-axis, 1 mark for vertical translation, 1 mark for correctly labelled points]

c) 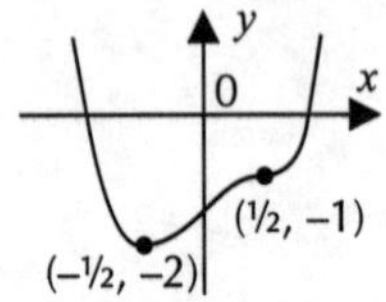

[2 marks available — 1 mark for horizontal squash, 1 mark for correctly labelled points]

Page 16 — Exponentials and Logs

Warm-Up Questions

1 a) 3 b) –3 c) 2

2 a) log 75 b) log 2 c) 0

3 a) 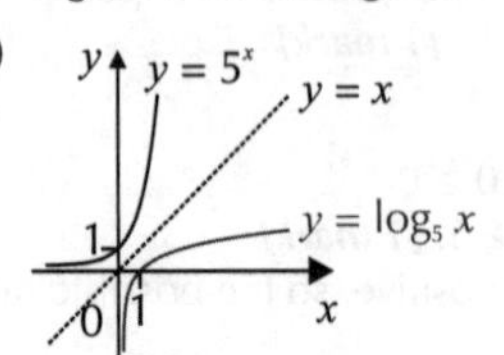

b) 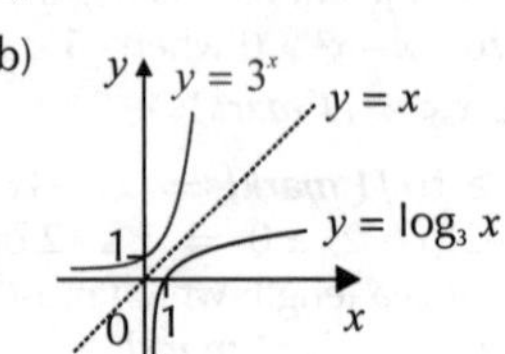

Exam Questions

1 $\log_7 (y + 3) + \log_7 (2y + 1) = 1$
$\Rightarrow \log_7 ((y + 3)(2y + 1)) = 1$ ***[1 mark]***
To remove the $\log_7$, do 7 to the power of each side:
$(y + 3)(2y + 1) = 7^1 = 7$ ***[1 mark]***
Multiply out, rearrange, and re-factorise:
$2y^2 + 7y + 3 = 7 \Rightarrow 2y^2 + 7y - 4 = 0$ ***[1 mark]***
$\Rightarrow (2y - 1)(y + 4) = 0$
$\Rightarrow y = \frac{1}{2}$ or $y = -4$,
but since $y > 0$, $y = \frac{1}{2}$ is the only solution. ***[1 mark]***

2 Use log laws to simplify the left-hand side:
$\log_n 45 - 2\log_n 3 = \log_n 45 - \log_n 3^2$ ***[1 mark]*** $= \log_n 45 - \log_n 9$
$= \log_n \frac{45}{9} = \log_n 5$ ***[1 mark]***
Use 'n to the power of' to remove $\log_n$ and solve:
$\log_n 5 = \frac{1}{3} \Rightarrow 5 = n^{\frac{1}{3}}$ ***[1 mark]*** $\Rightarrow n = 5^3 = 125$ ***[1 mark]***

Page 18 — Using Exponentials and Logs

Warm-Up Questions

1 $x = -0.258$ (3 s.f.)

2 $x = 2$

3 14.2 years (1 d.p.)

Exam Question

1 a) Make a table of values for t and $\log_{10} p$ (round values to 3 d.p.):

t	1	2	3	4	5
$\log_{10} p$	1	1.114	1.230	1.380	1.544

[1 mark for all values correct]

Plot the graph and draw the line of best fit:

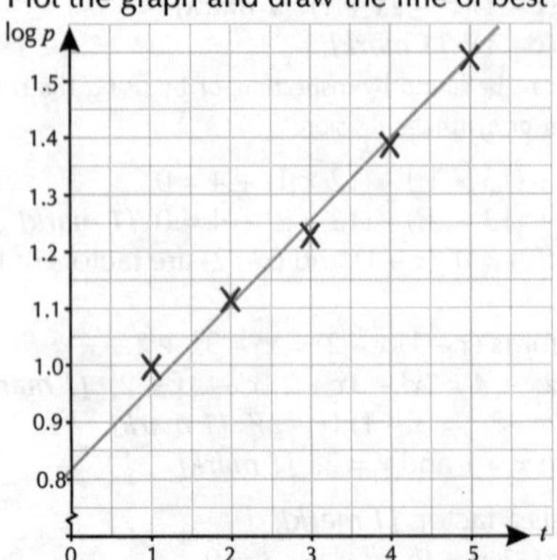

[1 mark for plotting points correctly and drawing a suitable line of best fit]

Answers

b) You are given the equation $p = ab^t$. Using the laws of logs, this rearranges to: $\log p = t\log b + \log a$
Comparing this to $y = mx + c$ shows that the gradient of the graph is equal to $\log b$ and the vertical-axis intercept is equal to $\log a$.
[1 mark for both correct]
Use gradient = $\frac{y_2 - y_1}{x_2 - x_1}$ with points (x_1, y_1) and (x_2, y_2) chosen from your line of best fit to find $\log b$.
e.g. taking the points (3, 1.25) and (4, 1.4) gives gradient $\frac{1.4 - 1.25}{4 - 3} = 0.15$ ***[1 mark]***
So $\log b = 0.15 \Rightarrow b = 1.41$ (2 d.p.) ***[1 mark for $0.9 \leq b \leq 1.9$]***
Now read off your vertical-axis intercept to find $\log a$:
$\log a = 0.82 \Rightarrow a = 6.61$ (2 d.p.) ***[1 mark for $6.5 \leq a \leq 7.5$]***
Don't worry if your values aren't exactly the same as in this solution. It will depend on the line of best fit you have drawn — everybody's will be slightly different. The examiners have a range of answers which are allowed, so as long as yours are within that range then you'll be fine. Look back at p.17-18 if you struggled with this question — it is quite tricky.

c) $t = 10 \Rightarrow p = 6.61(1.41)^{10} = 205.30$
So the author's income will be approximately £205 000.
[1 mark for answer between £150 000 and £250 000]

Page 20 — Modelling Using Exponentials and Logs

Warm-Up Questions

1 a) $x = e - 3$ b) $x = \frac{\ln 6}{2}$ c) $x = 6$ d) $x = \frac{1}{4}\left(1 - \ln\frac{5}{3}\right)$

2 $x = e^4$ or $x = e^6$

3 a) £7500 b) £1015 (nearest £) c) 13.5 years (1 d.p.)

Exam Questions

1 a) When $t = 0$ (i.e. when the mink were introduced to the habitat) $M = 74 \times e^0 = 74$, so there were 74 mink originally. ***[1 mark]***

b) After 3 years, $M = 74 \times e^{0.6 \times 3}$ ***[1 mark]*** = 447 mink. ***[1 mark]***
You can't round up here as there are only 447 whole mink.

c) For $M = 10\,000$:
$10\,000 = 74e^{0.6t} \Rightarrow e^{0.6t} = 10\,000 \div 74 = 135.1351$
$\Rightarrow 0.6t = \ln 135.1351 = 4.9063$ ***[1 mark]***
$\Rightarrow t = 4.9063 \div 0.6 = 8.2$ years
so it would take 9 complete years for the population to exceed 10 000. ***[1 mark]***

2 a) B is the value of A when $t = 0$.
From the table, $B = 50$. ***[1 mark]***

b) Substitute $t = 5$ and $A = 42$ into $A = 50e^{-kt}$:
$42 = 50e^{-5k} \Rightarrow e^{-5k} = \frac{42}{50} \Rightarrow e^{5k} = \frac{50}{42}$ ***[1 mark]***
$\Rightarrow 5k = \ln\left(\frac{50}{42}\right) = 0.17435...$
$\Rightarrow k = 0.17435... \div 5 = 0.03487... = 0.0349$ (3 s.f.) ***[1 mark]***

c) $A = 50e^{-0.03487...t}$ [using the values from parts a) and b)],
so when $t = 10$, $A = 50 \times e^{-0.03487... \times 10}$ ***[1 mark]***
= 35.28 = 35 to the nearest whole number. ***[1 mark]***

d) The half-life will be the value of t when A reaches half of the original value of 50, i.e. when $A = 25$.
$25 = 50e^{-0.03487...t} \Rightarrow \frac{25}{50} = e^{-0.03487...t} \Rightarrow \frac{50}{25} = e^{0.03487...t}$
$\Rightarrow e^{0.03487...t} = 2$ ***[1 mark]***
$\Rightarrow 0.03487...t = \ln 2$ ***[1 mark]***
So $t = \ln 2 \div 0.03487...$
= 19.877... = 20 days to the nearest day. ***[1 mark]***

Page 22 — Composite and Inverse Functions

Warm-Up Questions

1 a) (i) $fg(2) = \frac{3}{7}$, (ii) $gf(1) = 9$, (iii) $fg(x) = \frac{3}{2x + 3}$
b) (i) $fg(2) = 108$, (ii) $gf(1) = 7$, (iii) $fg(x) = 3(x + 4)^2$

2 a) domain: $x \in \mathbb{R}$, range: $-1 \leq x \leq 1$
b) domain: $x \in \mathbb{R}$, range: $-1 \leq x \leq 1$
c) domain: $x \in \mathbb{R}$ excluding all odd integer multiples of $\frac{\pi}{2}$, range: $x \in \mathbb{R}$
d) domain: $x \in \mathbb{R}$, range: $x > 0$
e) domain: $x > 0$, range: $x \in \mathbb{R}$

3 $f^{-1}(x) = \frac{x^2}{2} + 2$

Exam Questions

1 a) $h(x) = f(g(x)) = f(x - 2)$ ***[1 mark]***
$= \frac{1}{(x-2)^2 - 9} = \frac{1}{x^2 - 4x + 4 - 9}$
$= \frac{1}{x^2 - 4x - 5} = \frac{1}{(x-5)(x+1)}$ ***[1 mark]***

b) The denominator can't be 0, so $x - 5 \neq 0 \Rightarrow x \neq 5$ and $x + 1 \neq 0 \Rightarrow x \neq -1$. So the domain is $x \in \mathbb{R}, x \neq -1, 5$. ***[1 mark]***

2 a) $f(g(x)) = f(2\pi x)$ ***[1 mark]*** $= \cos 2\pi x$ ***[1 mark]***
b) $g(f(x)) = g(\cos x) = 2\pi \cos x$ ***[1 mark]***

3 a) Form the equation $y = e^{x+1}$. Rearrange to make x the subject: $y = e^{x+1} \Rightarrow \ln y = x + 1$ ***[1 mark]*** $\Rightarrow x = \ln y - 1$ ***[1 mark]***
Replace x with $f^{-1}(x)$ and y with x to get $f^{-1}(x) = \ln x - 1$ ***[1 mark]***

b) $\ln x$ is only defined for positive x, so any $x \leq 0$ cannot be in the domain of $f^{-1}(x)$. ***[1 mark]***

Page 24 — Recurrence Relations

Warm-Up Questions

1 a) $u_{n+1} = u_n + 2$, with $u_0 = 2$ b) $u_{n+1} = u_n + 4$, with $u_0 = 5$
c) $u_{n+1} = u_n - 1$, with $u_0 = 5$ d) $u_{n+1} = \frac{1}{3}u_n$, with $u_0 = 9$

2 a) $a_3 = 5$ b) $b_3 = 30$

3 a) $-\frac{10}{7}$ b) $\frac{50}{11}$

4 a) $u_0 = 2$, $u_1 = 3$, $u_2 = \frac{7}{2} = 3.5$, $u_3 = \frac{15}{4} = 3.75$
b) The recurrence relation has the form $u_{n+1} = au_n + b$ with $-1 < a < 1$.
c) 4

Exam Questions

1 a) Plug in the expression for u_1 given in the question:
$u_2 = au_1 - 5 = a(2a + 1) - 5 = 2a^2 + a - 5$ ***[1 mark]***

b) $u_2 + 4 = 0 \Rightarrow 2a^2 + a - 5 + 4 = 0$ from part a)
$\Rightarrow 2a^2 + a - 1 = 0$ ***[1 mark]*** $\Rightarrow (a + 1)(2a - 1) = 0$
Hence $a = -1$ or $a = \frac{1}{2}$ ***[1 mark]***. The sequence has a limit, so $-1 < a < 1$ and therefore $a = \frac{1}{2}$ ***[1 mark]***.

2 a) $a_{n+1} = -a_n \Rightarrow a_n = -a_{n+1} \Rightarrow a_{n-1} = -a_n$
So $a_1 = -a_2 = 1$ and $a_0 = -a_1 = -1$ ***[1 mark]***

b) The sequence gives $b_1 = 6$ and $b_2 = 13$. Use the recurrence relation to get two equations in p and q:
$6 = 27p + q$ and $13 = 6p + q$ ***[1 mark for both]***
Solve the equations simultaneously to find p and q.
$p = -\frac{1}{3}$ ***[1 mark]*** and $q = 15$ ***[1 mark]***

Answers

c) (i) The sequence is generated by a recurrence relation of the form $a_{n+1} = ra_n + s$ where $s = 0$ and $r = -1$. Since r does not lie in the range $-1 < r < 1$, the sequence does not have a limit. ***[1 mark]***

(ii) Use the limit formula: $\frac{15}{1-\left(-\frac{1}{3}\right)}$ ***[1 mark]*** $= 11.25$ ***[1 mark]***

3 Set up a recurrence relation to measure the climber's progress:
$u_{n+1} = \frac{2}{3}u_n + 10$ — where u_n is the amount of rope climbed immediately prior to the nth rest period, with $u_0 = 10$ ***[1 mark]***

(Losing $\frac{1}{3}$ of the progress is the same as keeping $\frac{2}{3}$ of the progress.)

As $-1 < \frac{2}{3} < 1$ the sequence has a limit: $\frac{10}{1-\frac{2}{3}} = 30$ ***[1 mark]***

The limit is greater than 25 (the length of the rope), so the climber will eventually reach the top ***[1 mark]***.

For the final 2 marks, you could also calculate terms up to $u_4 = 2110 \div 81 = 26.049...$ and then state that $u_4 > 25$.

Page 25 — Revision Summary

1 a) $f(x) = -2(x - 4)^2 + 5$ b) (4, 5)

2 $m < -3$ or $m > 3$

3 $k = 4 \pm 2\sqrt{3}$

4 a) $x < -7$ or $x > 7$ b) $-2\sqrt{2} \le x \le 2\sqrt{2}$ c) $x < -2$ or $x > \frac{1}{3}$

5 a) $a = 6$, $b = 3$ b) $f(x) = (3x - 1)(2x - 3)(x + 1)$

6 $x = -3$, $x = -2$, $x = \frac{1}{2}$, $x = 3$

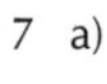
7 a)

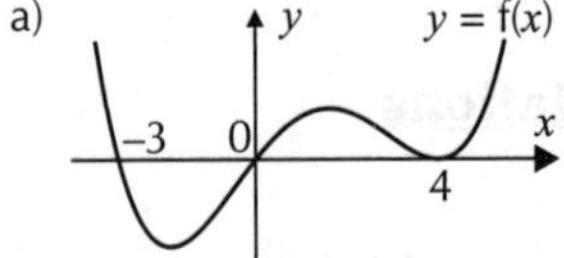

b) (i)

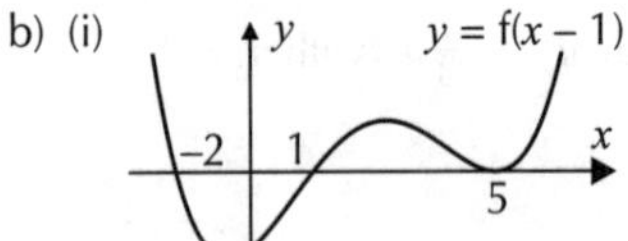

(ii)

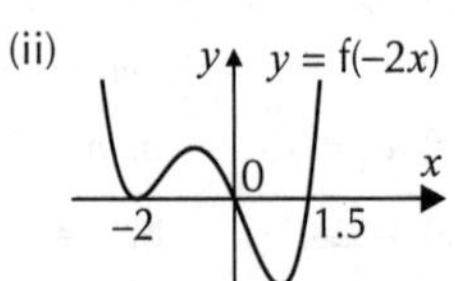

(iii)

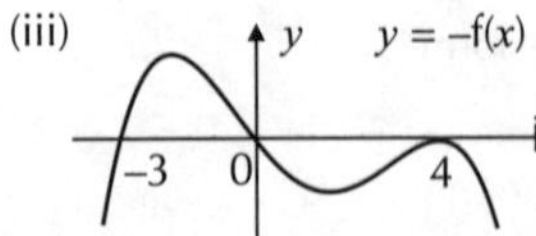

8 a) $\log_2 4$ b) $x = 16$

9 a) $p = 0.015$ (2 s.f.) b) $A = 48$

10 a) $h(x) = 2x^3 - 3$ b) $h^{-1}(x) = \sqrt[3]{\frac{1}{2}(x+3)}$

11 a) $p = -\frac{1}{2}$ b) $-\frac{4}{3}$

12 a) $5r^2 + rt + t$ b) $r = \pm\frac{1}{2}$

c) $r = -\frac{1}{2}$ fi $u_2 = \frac{1}{2}$

$r = \frac{1}{2} \Rightarrow u_2 = \frac{3}{2}$

Section Two — Trigonometric Skills

Page 29 — Trig Graphs and Transformations

Warm-Up Questions

1

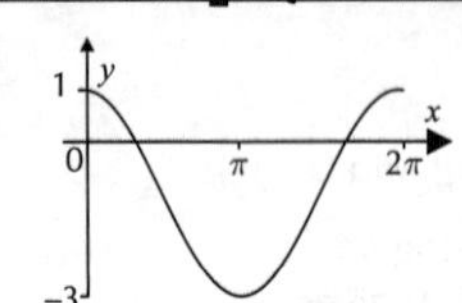

2 a)

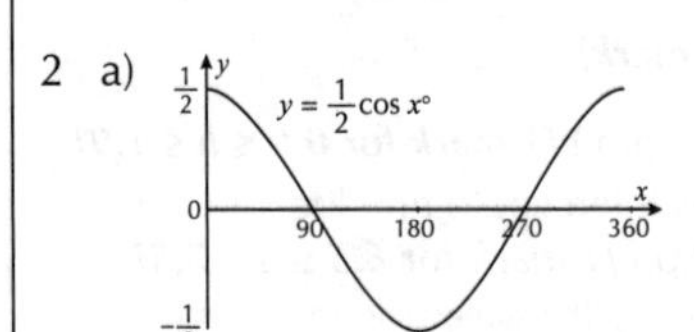

b)

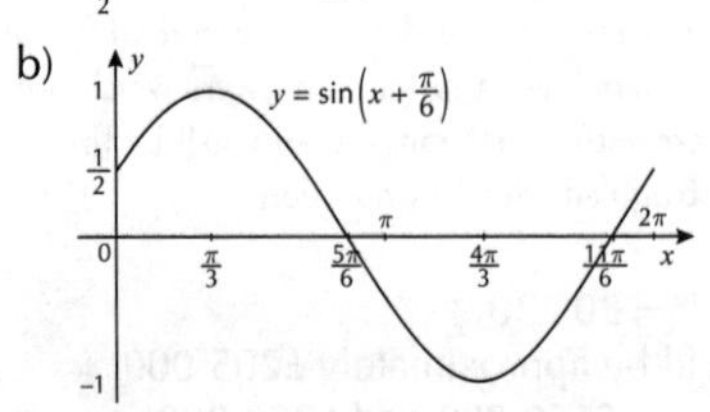

c)

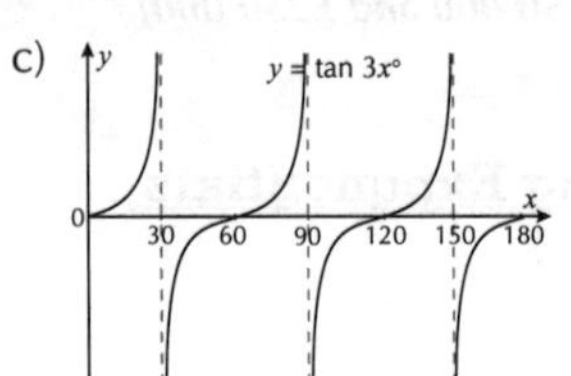

3 $p = 4$, $q = \frac{1}{4}$, $r = 3$

Exam Questions

1 a)

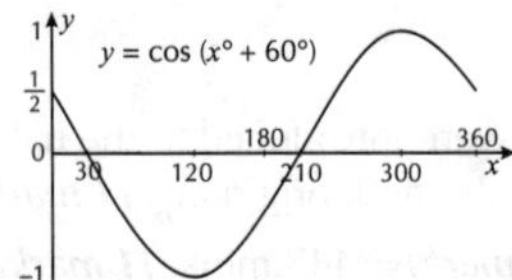

[2 marks — 1 mark for correct shape of cos x graph, 1 mark for shift of 60° to the left]

b) The graph of $y = \cos(x° + 60°)$ cuts the x-axis at 30 and 210, so for $0 \le x \le 360$, $\cos(x° + 60°) = 0$ when $x = 30$ ***[1 mark]*** and $x = 210$ ***[1 mark]***.

2

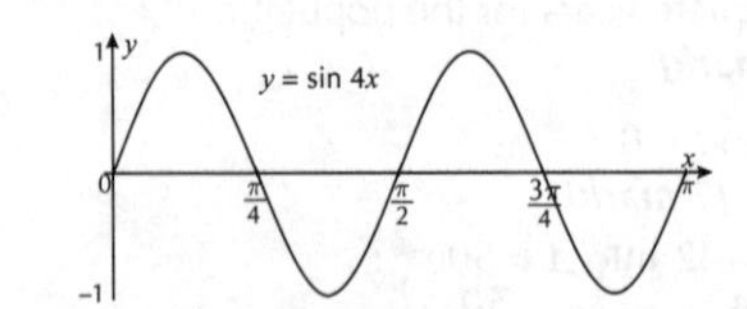

[2 marks — 1 mark for correct shape of sin x graph, 1 mark for two repetitions of sine wave between 0 and π]

Page 33 — Solving Trig Equations

Warm-Up Questions

1 a) (i) $x = \frac{\pi}{3}, \frac{2\pi}{3}$ (ii) $x = \frac{\pi}{4}, \frac{5\pi}{4}$ (iii) $x = \frac{3\pi}{4}, \frac{5\pi}{4}$

b) (i) $x = 33.0, 57.0, 123.0, 147.0, 213.0, 237.0, 303.0, 327.0$
(ii) $x = 127.5, 342.5$ (iii) $x = 179.8$

2 $x = 1.23$ (3 s.f.), $\frac{2\pi}{3}$, $\frac{4\pi}{3}$, 5.05 (3 s.f.)

3 $x = -30$

4 $(\sin y + \cos y)^2 + (\cos y - \sin y)^2 \equiv 2$

Answers

Exam Questions

1 a) Look for solutions in the range $-\frac{\pi}{4} \le x - \frac{\pi}{4} \le 2\pi - \frac{\pi}{4}$ $(= \frac{7\pi}{4})$.

$2\cos\left(x - \frac{\pi}{4}\right) = \sqrt{3} \Rightarrow \cos\left(x - \frac{\pi}{4}\right) = \frac{\sqrt{3}}{2}$ ***[1 mark]***

Solving this gives $x - \frac{\pi}{4} = \frac{\pi}{6}$, which is in the range — so it's a solution. From the symmetry of the cos graph there's another solution at $2\pi - \frac{\pi}{6} = \frac{11\pi}{6}$. But this is outside the range for $x - \frac{\pi}{4}$, so you can ignore it. Using symmetry again, there's also a solution at $-\frac{\pi}{6}$ — and this one is in your range. ***[1 mark]***

So solutions for $x - \frac{\pi}{4}$ are $-\frac{\pi}{6}$ and $\frac{\pi}{6} \Rightarrow x = \frac{\pi}{12}$ and $x = \frac{5\pi}{12}$

[1 mark for both correct]

You might find it useful to sketch a graph — or you could use the CAST diagram if you prefer.

b) $\sin 2x° = -\frac{1}{2}$, so look for solutions in the range $0 \le 2x \le 720$.

It's easier to see what's going on by drawing a graph for this one:

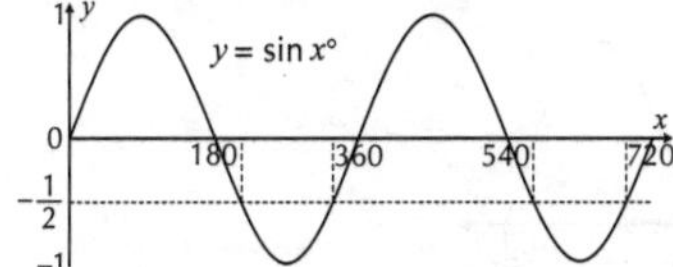

The graph shows there are four solutions between 0 and 720.

Putting $\sin 2x° = -\frac{1}{2}$ into your calculator gives you the solution $2x = -30$, but this is outside the range.

From the graph, you can see that the solutions within the range occur at $180 + 30$, $360 - 30$, $540 + 30$ and $720 - 30$ ***[1 mark]***, so $2x = 210, 330, 570$ and 690 ***[1 mark]***.

Dividing by 2 gives: $x = 105, 165, 285$ and 345

[1 mark for all four correct solutions]

2 a) $\sin^2 x = 1 - \cos^2 x$, so

$2(1 - \cos x) = 3\sin^2 x \Rightarrow 2(1 - \cos x) = 3(1 - \cos^2 x)$ ***[1 mark]***

$\Rightarrow 2 - 2\cos x = 3 - 3\cos^2 x$

$\Rightarrow 3\cos^2 x - 2\cos x - 1 = 0$ ***[1 mark]***

b) From part a), the equation can be written as:

$3\cos^2 x° - 2\cos x° - 1 = 0$

Now this looks suspiciously like a quadratic equation, so factorise:

$(3\cos x° + 1)(\cos x° - 1) = 0$

$\Rightarrow \cos x° = -\frac{1}{3}$ or $\cos x° = 1$ ***[1 mark for both]***

For $\cos x° = -\frac{1}{3}$, $x = 109.5$ (1 d.p.), ***[1 mark]***

and a second solution can be found from

$x = (360 - 109.5) = 250.5$. ***[1 mark]***

For $\cos x° = 1$, $x = 0$ ***[1 mark]*** and $x = 360$. ***[1 mark]***

3 Set the equations equal to each other: $3\cos^2 x = \sin^2 x$

$\cos^2 x + \sin^2 x = 1$, so $3\cos^2 x = 1 - \cos^2 x$ ***[1 mark]***

$\Rightarrow 4\cos^2 x = 1 \Rightarrow \cos^2 x = \frac{1}{4} \Rightarrow \cos x = \pm\frac{1}{2}$ ***[1 mark]***

For $\cos x = \frac{1}{2}$: $x = \frac{\pi}{3}$ ***[1 mark]*** and $x = \frac{5\pi}{3}$ ***[1 mark]***

For $\cos x = -\frac{1}{2}$: $x = \frac{2\pi}{3}$ ***[1 mark]*** and $x = \frac{4\pi}{3}$ ***[1 mark]***

Finding a point of intersection is the same as setting the two equations equal to each other and solving. Make sure you don't divide by cos2 x here, because it could be 0, and dividing by 0 is a very big no-no.

Page 35 — Addition and Double Angle Formulas

Warm-Up Questions

1 $\frac{\sqrt{2} + \sqrt{6}}{4}$

2 $x = 0, 150, 180, 210, 360$

3 a) $\sin\frac{x}{2}\cos\frac{x}{2} = \frac{1}{2}\sin x$ b) $6 - 12\sin^2 2a = 6\cos 4a$

Exam Questions

1 $\sin 3x \equiv \sin(2x + x) \equiv \sin 2x \cos x + \cos 2x \sin x$ ***[1 mark]***

$\equiv (2\sin x \cos x)\cos x + (1 - 2\sin^2 x)\sin x$ ***[1 mark]***

$\equiv 2\sin x\cos^2 x + \sin x - 2\sin^3 x$

$\equiv 2\sin x(1 - \sin^2 x) + \sin x - 2\sin^3 x$ ***[1 mark]***

$\equiv 2\sin x - 2\sin^3 x + \sin x - 2\sin^3 x$

$\equiv 3\sin x - 4\sin^3 x$ ***[1 mark]***

2 Using the double angle formula, $\cos 2x = \cos^2 x - \sin^2 x$ and so $\cos^2 x - \sin^2 x + \sin^2 x + 4\cos x + 3 = 0$

$\Rightarrow \cos^2 x + 4\cos x + 3 = 0$ ***[1 mark]***

This quadratic factorises to: $(\cos x + 3)(\cos x + 1) = 0$ ***[1 mark]***

$\cos x = -3$ gives no solutions and $\cos x = -1 \Rightarrow x = \pi$

So $x = \pi$ is the only solution in the range. ***[1 mark]***

3 $\sin 3x = \sin(2x + x)$ which by the addition formula for sin gives:

$\sin(2x + x) = \sin 2x \cos x + \cos 2x \sin x$ ***[1 mark]***

Use double angle formulas for $\sin 2x$ and $\cos 2x$ to get:

$\sin(2x + x) = 2\sin x\cos^2 x + (2\cos^2 x - 1)\sin x$ ***[1 mark]***

$= \sin x(2\cos^2 x + 2\cos^2 x - 1)$

$= \sin x(4\cos^2 x - 1)$

So $p = 4$ and $q = -1$. ***[1 mark]***

Page 37 — The Wave Function

Warm-Up Questions

1 $a\cos x + b\sin x \equiv k\cos(x - \alpha)$

$b\sin x + a\cos x \equiv k\sin(x + \alpha)$

2 $5\sin x° - 6\cos x° \equiv \sqrt{61}\sin(x° - 50.2°)$ (1 d.p.)

Exam Questions

1 a) $9\sin x + 12\cos x \equiv k\sin(x + \alpha)$. Using the sin addition formula, $9\sin x + 12\cos x \equiv k\sin x\cos\alpha + k\cos x\sin\alpha$.

Equating coefficients of $\sin x$ and $\cos x$ gives:

$k\cos\alpha = 9$ and $k\sin\alpha = 12$ ***[1 mark]***

$\frac{k\sin\alpha}{k\cos\alpha} = \tan\alpha$, so $\tan\alpha = \frac{12}{9} = \frac{4}{3}$

Solving this gives $\alpha = 0.9272...$ ***[1 mark]***

$k = \sqrt{9^2 + 12^2} = \sqrt{81 + 144} = \sqrt{225} = 15$ ***[1 mark]***

So $9\sin x + 12\cos x = 15\sin(x + 0.927)$ (3 s.f.)

b) If $9\sin x + 12\cos x = 3$, then from part a),

$15\sin(x + 0.9272...) = 3$, so $\sin(x + 0.9272...) = 0.2$.

The range for x is $0 \le x \le 2\pi$, which becomes $0.9272... \le x + 0.9272... \le 7.2104...$

Solving the equation gives $(x + 0.9272...) = 0.2013...$ ***[1 mark]***

As this is outside the range, use a sketch to find values that are in the range:

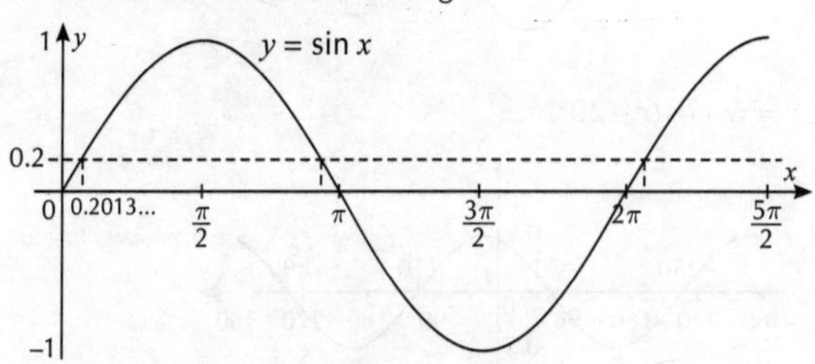

From the graph, it is clear that there are solutions at:

$\pi - 0.2013... = 2.940...$ ***[1 mark]***

and $2\pi + 0.2013... = 6.484...$ ***[1 mark]***

So $(x + 0.9272...) = 2.940...$ and $6.484...$

$\Rightarrow x = 2.01$ (3 s.f.) ***[1 mark]*** and $x = 5.56$ (3 s.f.) ***[1 mark]***

Be careful with the range — if you hadn't extended it to $2\pi + 0.927$, you would have missed one of the solutions.

c) $9\sin x + 12\cos x = 15\sin(x + 0.927)$, so the maximum and minimum values of $9\sin x + 12\cos x$ are ± 15. ***[1 mark]***

This means the maximum and minimum values of $f(x)$ are $10 + 15 = 25$ ***[1 mark]*** and $10 - 15 = -5$. ***[1 mark]***

Answers

2 a) $5\cos x^\circ + 12\sin x^\circ \equiv k\cos(x^\circ - \alpha^\circ)$. Using the cos addition formula, $5\cos x^\circ + 12\sin x^\circ \equiv k\cos x^\circ\cos\alpha^\circ + k\sin x^\circ\sin\alpha^\circ$.
Equating coefficients gives:
$k\cos\alpha^\circ = 5$ and $k\sin\alpha^\circ = 12$ ***[1 mark]***
$\frac{k\sin\alpha^\circ}{k\cos\alpha^\circ} = \tan\alpha^\circ$, so $\tan\alpha^\circ = \frac{12}{5}$
Solving this gives $\alpha = 67.3801... = 67.38$ (2 d.p.) ***[1 mark]***
$k = \sqrt{5^2 + 12^2} = \sqrt{25 + 144} = \sqrt{169} = 13$ ***[1 mark]***
So $5\cos x^\circ + 12\sin x^\circ = 13\cos(x^\circ - 67.38^\circ)$ (2 d.p.)

b) From part a), if $5\cos x^\circ + 12\sin x^\circ = 2$, then this means that $13\cos(x^\circ - 67.3801...^\circ) = 2$,
so $\cos(x^\circ - 67.3801...^\circ) = \frac{2}{13}$ ***[1 mark]***.
The range of x is $0 \le x \le 360$, which becomes $-67.3801... \le x - 67.3801... \le 292.6198...$ ***[1 mark]***.
Solving the equation gives:
$x - 67.3801... = 81.1501...$ and $278.8598...$ ***[1 mark]***
$\Rightarrow x = 148.53$ (2 d.p.) ***[1 mark]***, $x = 346.23$ (2 d.p.) ***[1 mark]***

c) The minimum points of the cos curve have a value of -1, so as $5\cos x^\circ + 12\sin x^\circ = 13\cos(x^\circ - 67.38^\circ)$, the minimum value of $5\cos x^\circ + 12\sin x^\circ$ is -13. ***[1 mark]***
Hence the minimum value of $(5\cos x^\circ + 12\sin x^\circ)^3$ is $(-13)^3 = -2197$. ***[1 mark]***

Page 38 — Revision Summary

1 Divide by 180, then multiply by π.

2 a) $\frac{\pi}{3}$ b) $\frac{3\pi}{2}$ c) $\frac{29\pi}{60}$

3 a) 45° b) 72° c) 320°

4 $\sin^2 x + \cos^2 x \equiv 1$

5 $\tan x \equiv \frac{\sin x}{\cos x}$

6 $\sin x \frac{\sin x}{\cos x}\cos x + \cos^2 x = \sin^2 x + \cos^2 x = 1$

7 a) 2π b) 360° c) π

8 A translation of 2 units to the left.

9

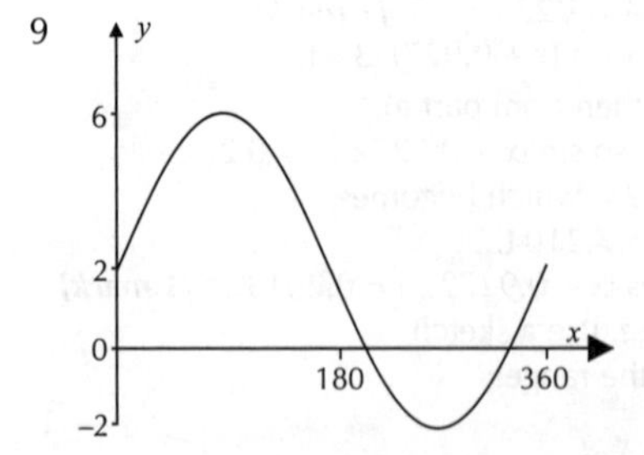

10 a) $y = \frac{1}{2}\cos(x - 20^\circ)$

b)

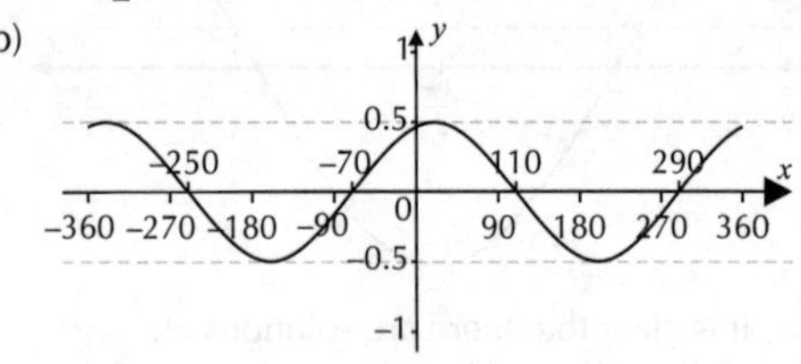

11

$\frac{\pi}{2}$ 90°
S A
π 180° 0
T C
270° $\frac{3\pi}{2}$

12 $x = 7.5$, 37.5, 97.5 and 127.5

13 a) $x = \frac{5\pi}{12}$ and $x = \frac{23\pi}{12}$

b) $x = 48.2$ and $x = 311.8$ (1 d.p.)

14 a)

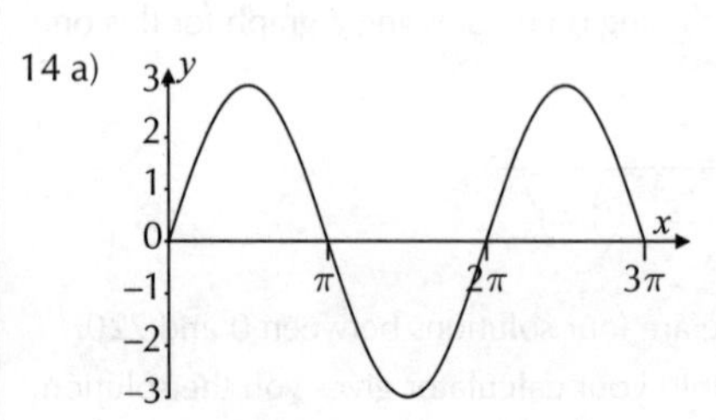

b)

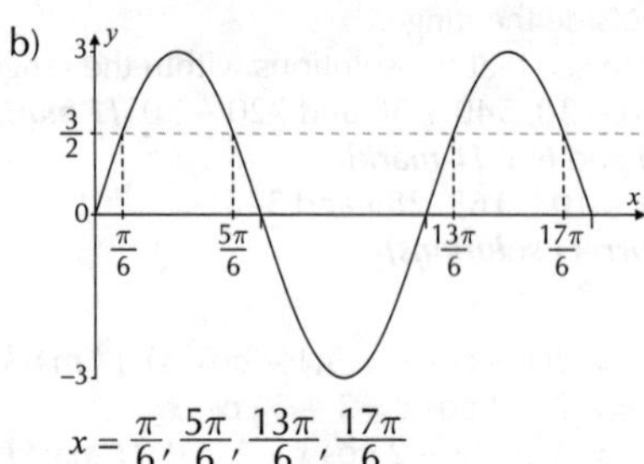

$x = \frac{\pi}{6}, \frac{5\pi}{6}, \frac{13\pi}{6}, \frac{17\pi}{6}$

15 a) $\cos x = \frac{\sqrt{161}}{15}$ b) $\tan x = \frac{8}{\sqrt{161}}$

16 a) $\sin 105^\circ = \sin(45^\circ + 60^\circ)$
Using the addition formula gives:
$\sin 105^\circ = \sin 45^\circ\cos 60^\circ + \cos 45^\circ\sin 60^\circ$
$= \frac{1}{\sqrt{2}} \times \frac{1}{2} + \frac{1}{\sqrt{2}} \times \frac{\sqrt{3}}{2} = \frac{1 + \sqrt{3}}{2\sqrt{2}}$

b) $\cos\frac{5\pi}{6} = \cos\left(\frac{\pi}{3} + \frac{\pi}{2}\right)$
Using the addition formula gives:
$\cos\frac{5\pi}{6} = \cos\frac{\pi}{3}\cos\frac{\pi}{2} - \sin\frac{\pi}{3}\sin\frac{\pi}{2}$
$= \frac{1}{2} \times 0 - \frac{\sqrt{3}}{2} \times 1 = -\frac{\sqrt{3}}{2}$

17 a) $\sin 2x = 2\sin x\cos x$
b) $\cos 2x = \cos^2 x - \sin^2 x$
(or $\cos 2x = 1 - \sin^2 x$ or $\cos 2x = 2\cos^2 x - 1$)

18 $2 - \frac{\cos^2 x}{1 - \sin^2 x} + \frac{\sin 2x}{\cos^2 x} = 2 - \frac{\cos^2 x}{\cos^2 x} + \frac{2\sin x\cos x}{\cos^2 x} = 1 + 2\tan x$

19 $x = \frac{3\pi}{2}$

20 $a\sin x + b\cos x \equiv k\sin(x + \alpha)$
$a\sin x - b\cos x \equiv k\sin(x - \alpha)$
$a\cos x + b\sin x \equiv k\cos(x - \alpha)$
$a\cos x - b\sin x \equiv k\cos(x + \alpha)$

21 a) $17\cos(x + 0.489...)$
b) $x = 0.84$, 4.46 (2 d.p.)
c) Minimum $= -17$, maximum $= 17$

Answers

Section Three — Geometry Skills

Page 41 — Linear Coordinate Geometry

Warm-Up Questions

1 $y = \frac{3}{2}x - 4$

2 a) $y = -\frac{1}{2}x + 4$

b) 2.68 radians (3 s.f.)

Your calculator will give you –0.4636... radians, but you want the angle measured anti-clockwise from the positive x-axis, so you need to add π.

Exam Questions

1 a) $3y = 15 - 4x \Rightarrow y = -\frac{4}{3}x + 5$

so the gradient of the line PQ is $m = -\frac{4}{3}$ ***[1 mark]***.

Gradient of line L = $-1 \div -\frac{4}{3} = \frac{3}{4}$ ***[1 mark]***, so $y = \frac{3}{4}x + c$

Now use the x- and y-coordinates of R to find c:

$1 = \frac{3}{4}(3) + c \Rightarrow 1 = \frac{9}{4} + c \Rightarrow c = -\frac{5}{4} \Rightarrow y = \frac{3}{4}x - \frac{5}{4}$

[1 mark]

This can also be written as $3x - 4y - 5 = 0$.

b) $m = \tan\theta \Rightarrow \theta = \tan^{-1}\left(\frac{3}{4}\right)$ ***[1 mark]***

$= 0.644$ radians (3 s.f.) ***[1 mark]***

2 a) The median from A goes through A and the midpoint of BC.

Midpoint of BC = $\left(\frac{2+3}{2}, \frac{3+(-1)}{2}\right) = \left(\frac{5}{2}, 1\right)$ ***[1 mark]***

The line from A (1, 2) to $\left(\frac{5}{2}, 1\right)$ has gradient:

$m = \frac{2-1}{1-\frac{5}{2}} = \frac{1}{\left(-\frac{3}{2}\right)} = -\frac{2}{3}$ ***[1 mark]***

so the equation of the median from A is:

$y - 2 = -\frac{2}{3}(x - 1) \Rightarrow y = -\frac{2}{3}x + \frac{8}{3}$ ***[1 mark]***

This can also be written as $2x + 3y - 8 = 0$.

b) The perpendicular bisector of BC is perpendicular to BC and goes through its midpoint $\left(\frac{5}{2}, 1\right)$.

The gradient of BC, $m_{BC} = \frac{3-(-1)}{2-3} = -4$ ***[1 mark]***

so the gradient of the perpendicular bisector is $\frac{1}{4}$ ***[1 mark]***.

The equation of the perpendicular bisector of BC is:

$y - 1 = \frac{1}{4}(x - \frac{5}{2}) \Rightarrow y = \frac{1}{4}x + \frac{3}{8}$ ***[1 mark]***

This can also be written as $2x - 8y + 3 = 0$.

c) Median: $2x + 3y - 8 = 0 \Rightarrow 2x = -3y + 8$

Perpendicular bisector: $2x - 8y + 3 = 0 \Rightarrow 2x = 8y - 3$

Set the two lines equal to each other and solve:

$-3y + 8 = 8y - 3 \Rightarrow 11y = 11 \Rightarrow y = 1$

$2x = (8 \times 1) - 3 = 5 \Rightarrow x = \frac{5}{2}$

so the point of intersection is $\left(\frac{5}{2}, 1\right)$.

[3 marks available — 1 mark for eliminating one variable, 1 mark for finding one coordinate, 1 mark for complete correct answer]

You can also start from the $y = mx + c$ form of the equations.

Page 44 — Circle Geometry

Warm-Up Questions

1 $(x - 3)^2 + (y + 1)^2 = 49$ and $x^2 + y^2 - 6x + 2y - 39 = 0$

2 a) radius 3, centre (0, 0) b) radius 2, centre (2, –4)

c) radius 5, centre (–3, 4)

3 $y = 6x - 12$

4 $(x - 5)^2 + (y + 4)^2 = 16$

Exam Questions

1 From the equation, the centre of the circle is at (2, –5) ***[1 mark]***.

The gradient of the tangent is perpendicular to the gradient of the radius: $m_{rad} = \frac{-5-(-8)}{2-1} = 3$ ***[1 mark]***

so the gradient of the tangent is $-\frac{1}{3}$ ***[1 mark]***

The equation of the tangent at (1, –8) is:

$y - (-8) = -\frac{1}{3}(x - 1) \Rightarrow y = -\frac{1}{3}x - \frac{23}{3}$ ***[1 mark]***

This can also be written as $x + 3y + 23 = 0$.

2 JK is a diameter so the centre is the midpoint of JK:

Midpoint of JK = $\left(\frac{2+8}{2}, \frac{3+(-7)}{2}\right) = (5, -2)$ ***[1 mark]***

The radius is the distance from the centre to either J or K:

Radius = $\sqrt{(5-2)^2 + (-2-3)^2} = \sqrt{9+25} = \sqrt{34}$ ***[1 mark]***

So the equation of the circle is: $(x - 5)^2 + (y + 2)^2 = 34$ ***[1 mark]***

This is calculated with point J — using K will give you different values in the square root, but you'll get the same radius.

3 a) The radius of circle A is 10 and the radius of circle B is 5.

[1 mark for both values correct]

Find the distance between the two centres (–2, 9) and (10, 0):

$\sqrt{(-2-10)^2 + (9-0)^2} = \sqrt{225} = 15$ ***[1 mark]***

So the ratio in which P divides the line is 2:1

[1 mark — also accept 1:2]

b) P is $\frac{2}{3}$ along the line l from the centre of A. The difference in x-coordinates of the centres of A and B is 10 – (–2) = 12, and the difference in y-coordinates is 0 – 9 = –9. ***[1 mark]***

$\frac{2}{3}$ of each distance is 8 (x-coordinates) and –6 (y-coordinates) so add these to the coordinates of the centre of A:

(–2 + 8, 9 + (–6)) = (6, 3) ***[1 mark]***

You can also work out this point using vectors.

c) For A and B to touch C internally, the diameter of C must be the sum of the diameters of A and B — so its radius is the sum of the radii of A and B, 10 + 5 = 15.

The centres of A, B and C are collinear, so the centre of C is on the line l. Since the radius of C is 15, and the radius of A is 10, the centre of C is 5 units along the line l (towards B) from the centre of A, i.e. half way between the centre of A and point P (see diagram).

(–2, 9) C A P B (10, 0)

Midpoint of AP = $\left(\frac{-2+6}{2}, \frac{9+3}{2}\right) = (2, 6)$

So the equation of the circle C is: $(x - 2)^2 + (y - 6)^2 = 15^2 = 225$

[4 marks available — 1 mark for finding the radius of C, 1 mark for identifying the centre of C as the midpoint of AP, 1 mark for finding the centre of C, 1 mark for the final equation]

Page 46 — Solving Geometrical Problems

Warm-Up Questions

1 a) (–1, –5) and (5, 19) b) (3, –4) and (6, 2)

2 a) (3, –7) and (5, 1) b) (–8, 1) and (–4, 7)

3 Substituting $x = -2y$ into the circle equation and solving gives: $5(y - 2)^2 = 0 \Rightarrow y = 2$ is the only solution. This means the line and circle only meet once, so the line is a tangent.

At $y = 2$, $x = -4$, so the line is tangent at (–4, 2).

Answers

Exam Questions

1 Set the two equations equal to each other:
$4 - 3x = 16 + 10x - x^3 \Rightarrow x^3 - 13x - 12 = 0$ ***[1 mark]***
$\Rightarrow (x + 1)(x^2 - x - 12) = 0$
$\Rightarrow (x + 1)(x - 4)(x + 3) = 0$ ***[1 mark]***
So the x-coordinates of the points of intersection are $x = -1$ and $x = -3$ and $x = 4$ ***[1 mark for all three points]***. The corresponding y-coordinates are $y = 7$, $y = 13$ and $y = -8$. ***[1 mark]***
So the points of intersection are (–1, 7), (–3, 13) and (4, –8).
[1 mark for correct intersection points]

2 Substitute $y = 2x + 13$ into the circle equation:
$(x + 1)^2 + ((2x + 13) - 6)^2 = 5$
$\Rightarrow (x + 1)^2 + (2x + 7)^2 = 5$
$\Rightarrow x^2 + 2x + 1 + 4x^2 + 28x + 49 = 5$
$\Rightarrow 5x^2 + 30x + 45 = 0$
$\Rightarrow 5(x + 3)(x + 3) = 0$
$x = -3$ is the only solution so there is only one point of intersection, so $y = 2x + 13$ is a tangent to the circle.
At $x = -3$, $y = 7$, so they touch at the point (–3, 7).
[5 marks available — 1 mark for correctly substituting the line equation into the circle equation, 1 mark for factorising the resulting equation, 1 mark for identifying the x-coordinate, 1 mark for showing the line y = 2x + 13 is a tangent to the circle, 1 mark for the coordinates of the point of intersection]

3 Substitute $y = 1 - 3x$ into the circle equation:
$x^2 + (1 - 3x)^2 - 8x + 12(1 - 3x) + 27 = 0$ ***[1 mark]***
$\Rightarrow x^2 + 1 - 6x + 9x^2 - 8x + 12 - 36x + 27 = 0$
$\Rightarrow 10x^2 - 50x + 40 = 0$
$\Rightarrow 10(x - 4)(x - 1) = 0$ ***[1 mark]***
The x-coordinates of the intersection points are $x = 1$ and $x = 4$ ***[1 mark]***, and the corresponding y-coordinates are $y = -2$ and $y = -11$, so the points of intersection are (1, –2) ***[1 mark]*** and (4, –11) ***[1 mark]***.

Page 49 — Vectors

Warm-Up Questions

1 a) $\mathbf{b} - \mathbf{a}$ b) $\mathbf{a} - \mathbf{b}$ c) $\mathbf{b} - \mathbf{c}$ d) $\mathbf{c} - \mathbf{a}$

2 a) $2\mathbf{i} - 4\mathbf{j}$ b) $-\mathbf{i} + 4\mathbf{j} - 2\mathbf{k}$ c) $-\mathbf{j}$

3 a) $\begin{pmatrix} 13 \\ -10 \end{pmatrix}$ b) 16.40 (2 d.p.)

4 a) $\sqrt{6}$ b) $\sqrt{14}$ c) $\sqrt{14}$

Exam Questions

1 $\overrightarrow{BC} = \overrightarrow{AC} - \overrightarrow{AB} = \begin{pmatrix} -2 \\ 4 \end{pmatrix} - \begin{pmatrix} -5 \\ 2 \end{pmatrix} = \begin{pmatrix} 3 \\ 2 \end{pmatrix}$ ***[1 mark]***

$\overrightarrow{BM} = \frac{1}{2}\overrightarrow{BC} = \frac{1}{2}\begin{pmatrix} 3 \\ 2 \end{pmatrix}$

$\overrightarrow{AM} = \overrightarrow{AB} + \overrightarrow{BM} = \begin{pmatrix} -5 \\ 2 \end{pmatrix} + \frac{1}{2}\begin{pmatrix} 3 \\ 2 \end{pmatrix} = \begin{pmatrix} -\frac{7}{2} \\ 3 \end{pmatrix}$ ***[1 mark]***

So, $|\overrightarrow{AM}| = \sqrt{\left(-\frac{7}{2}\right)^2 + 3^2} = \frac{\sqrt{85}}{2}$ ***[1 mark]***

2 a) $\mathbf{a} - \mathbf{b} = (\mathbf{i} + 3\mathbf{j} - 4\mathbf{k}) - (p\mathbf{i} + 2\mathbf{j} + \sqrt{12}\mathbf{k})$
$= (1 - p)\mathbf{i} + \mathbf{j} + (-4 - \sqrt{12})\mathbf{k}$
Substituting $p = 1$ gives $\mathbf{a} - \mathbf{b} = \mathbf{j} + (-4 - \sqrt{12})\mathbf{k}$

As a column vector, this is $\begin{pmatrix} 0 \\ 1 \\ -4-\sqrt{12} \end{pmatrix}$ ***[1 mark]***

b) $|\mathbf{b}| = \sqrt{p^2 + 2^2 + (\sqrt{12})^2}$ ***[1 mark]*** $= \sqrt{p^2 + 16}$
$|\mathbf{b}| = 5 \Rightarrow \sqrt{p^2 + 16} = 5 \Rightarrow p^2 + 16 = 25$ ***[1 mark]***
$\Rightarrow p^2 = 9 \Rightarrow p = -3$ or $p = 3$ ***[1 mark]***

3 a) $\overrightarrow{PR} = \overrightarrow{PQ} + \overrightarrow{QR}$ ***[1 mark]*** $= (6\mathbf{i} + 2\mathbf{j} - 2\mathbf{k}) + (-4\mathbf{i} + \mathbf{j} + 8\mathbf{k})$
$= (6 - 4)\mathbf{i} + (2 + 1)\mathbf{j} + (-2 + 8)\mathbf{k} = 2\mathbf{i} + 3\mathbf{j} + 6\mathbf{k}$ ***[1 mark]***

b) $\overrightarrow{RP} = -\overrightarrow{PR} = -2\mathbf{i} - 3\mathbf{j} - 6\mathbf{k}$
$|\overrightarrow{RP}| = \sqrt{(-2)^2 + (-3)^2 + (-6)^2} = \sqrt{49} = 7$ ***[1 mark]***
So the unit vector in the direction of $\overrightarrow{RP}$ is:

$\frac{1}{7}\overrightarrow{RP} = -\frac{2}{7}\mathbf{i} - \frac{3}{7}\mathbf{j} - \frac{6}{7}\mathbf{k}$ or $\begin{pmatrix} -\frac{2}{7} \\ -\frac{3}{7} \\ -\frac{6}{7} \end{pmatrix}$ as a column vector. ***[1 mark]***

Page 51 — More Vectors

Warm-Up Questions

1 $2\mathbf{i}$ and $-7\mathbf{i}$, $10\mathbf{j} + 12\mathbf{k}$ and $5\mathbf{j} + 6\mathbf{k}$, $-3\mathbf{i} + 2\mathbf{j} - 4\mathbf{k}$ and $3\mathbf{i} - 2\mathbf{j} + 4\mathbf{k}$

2 a) 1 : 4 b) (13, 25, –3)

3 $a = -7$, $b = -2$, $c = -2$

4 a) $b = 4$ b) B(5, 0, –1), C(–5, –4, 7)

Exam Questions

1 $\overrightarrow{AB} = (1 - 3)\mathbf{i} + (-4 - (-5))\mathbf{j} + (4 - 7)\mathbf{k} = -2\mathbf{i} + \mathbf{j} - 3\mathbf{k}$
$\overrightarrow{BC} = (-5 - 1)\mathbf{i} + (-1 - (-4))\mathbf{j} + (-5 - 4)\mathbf{k} = -6\mathbf{i} + 3\mathbf{j} - 9\mathbf{k}$
So $\overrightarrow{BC} = 3\overrightarrow{AB}$ and so $\overrightarrow{AB}$ is parallel to $\overrightarrow{BC}$. Also $\overrightarrow{AB}$ and $\overrightarrow{BC}$ have a point in common (B). So A, B and C are collinear.
[3 marks available — 1 mark for finding two vectors between the points A, B and C, 1 mark for showing that the two vectors are parallel, 1 mark for observing they have a point in common and drawing the correct conclusion]

2 a) The change in x-coordinate from K to L is $1 - (-7) = 8$ and from L to M is $-7 - (-19) = 12$ ***[1 mark]***, so the ratio in which L divides KM is 8 : 12 = 2 : 3 ***[1 mark]***.
b) Look at the change in z-coordinate: $q - 7 = 5 \Rightarrow q = 12$ ***[1 mark]***
c) KL : LM = 2 : 3, so KL = $\frac{2}{5}$KM ***[1 mark]***.
Now look at the change in y-coordinates:
$p - (-5) = \frac{2}{5}(5 - (-5)) \Rightarrow p = 4 - 5 = -1$ ***[1 mark]***

3 $\overrightarrow{PQ} = -\overrightarrow{OP} + \overrightarrow{OQ} = -\begin{pmatrix} 1 \\ 0 \\ 3 \end{pmatrix} + \begin{pmatrix} 11 \\ 5 \\ 18 \end{pmatrix} = \begin{pmatrix} 10 \\ 5 \\ 15 \end{pmatrix}$ ***[1 mark]***

$\overrightarrow{PR} = \frac{4}{5}\overrightarrow{PQ} = \frac{4}{5}\begin{pmatrix} 10 \\ 5 \\ 15 \end{pmatrix} = \begin{pmatrix} 8 \\ 4 \\ 12 \end{pmatrix}$ ***[1 mark]***

$\overrightarrow{OR} = \overrightarrow{OP} + \overrightarrow{PR} = \begin{pmatrix} 1 \\ 0 \\ 3 \end{pmatrix} + \begin{pmatrix} 8 \\ 4 \\ 12 \end{pmatrix} = \begin{pmatrix} 9 \\ 4 \\ 15 \end{pmatrix}$ ***[1 mark]***

4 The resultant vector is $\mathbf{r} = \mathbf{d} + \mathbf{f} + \mathbf{w} = (a + 1)\mathbf{i} + b\mathbf{j} + (c - 2)\mathbf{k}$ ***[1 mark]***. $\mathbf{r}$ is parallel to $\mathbf{i} + \mathbf{j} + \mathbf{k}$, so $\mathbf{r} = p(\mathbf{i} + \mathbf{j} + \mathbf{k})$ for a scalar p. This implies that $a + 1 = p$, $b = p$ and $c - 2 = p$ ***[1 mark]***.
$|\mathbf{r}| = \sqrt{(a + 1)^2 + b^2 + (c - 2)^2} = \sqrt{p^2 + p^2 + p^2} = \sqrt{3p^2}$ ***[1 mark]***
$\Rightarrow \sqrt{3p^2} = \sqrt{12} \Rightarrow 3p^2 = 12 \Rightarrow p^2 = 4 \Rightarrow p = 2$ or -2 ***[1 mark]***
The question says that $b = p > 0$, so $p = 2$ only.
This gives $a = p - 1 = 1$, $b = p = 2$, and $c = p + 2 = 4$. ***[1 mark]***

Answers

Page 53 — The Scalar Product

Warm-Up Questions

1 a) -5 b) 1

2 112.6° (1 d.p.)

3 $t = 2$

4 $|\mathbf{u}| = 3\sqrt{2}$

Exam Questions

1 $\overrightarrow{AB} = (6 - 1)\mathbf{i} + (-1 - 0)\mathbf{j} + (3 - 5)\mathbf{k} = 5\mathbf{i} - \mathbf{j} - 2\mathbf{k}$
$\overrightarrow{CD} = (2 - t)\mathbf{i} + (1 - 6)\mathbf{j} + (-2 - 3)\mathbf{k} = (2 - t)\mathbf{i} - 5\mathbf{j} - 5\mathbf{k}$
[1 mark for both correct]
$\overrightarrow{AB}.\overrightarrow{CD} = 0$ as $\overrightarrow{AB}$ is perpendicular to $\overrightarrow{CD}$ ***[1 mark]***
$\Rightarrow (5 \times (2 - t)) + (-1 \times -5) + (-2 \times -5) = 0$ ***[1 mark]***
$\Rightarrow 10 - 5t + 5 + 10 = 0 \Rightarrow 5t = 25 \Rightarrow t = 5$ ***[1 mark]***

2 The question gives $\theta = 120°$ and $|\mathbf{w}| = 6$.
Calculate $|\mathbf{u}| = \sqrt{(-5)^2 + (\sqrt{8})^2 + 4^2} = \sqrt{49} = 7$ ***[1 mark]***
Use the scalar product formula:
$\mathbf{u}.\mathbf{w} = \cos\theta\,|\mathbf{u}|\,|\mathbf{w}| = \cos(120°) \times 7 \times 6$ ***[1 mark]***
$= -\frac{1}{2} \times 42 = -21$ ***[1 mark]***

3 a) $\overrightarrow{SQ} = -\overrightarrow{PS} + \overrightarrow{PQ} = -(3\mathbf{i} - 4\mathbf{j} + \mathbf{k}) + (\mathbf{i} + 2\mathbf{j} - 4\mathbf{k})$
$= -2\mathbf{i} + 6\mathbf{j} - 5\mathbf{k}$ ***[1 mark]***

b) $\overrightarrow{SR}$ is parallel to $\overrightarrow{PQ}$ so $\overrightarrow{SR} = p(\mathbf{i} + 2\mathbf{j} - 4\mathbf{k})$ for some scalar p.
$|\overrightarrow{SQ}| = \sqrt{(-2)^2 + 6^2 + (-5)^2} = \sqrt{65}$ ***[1 mark]***
$|\overrightarrow{SR}| = \sqrt{p^2(1^2 + 2^2 + (-4)^2)} = p\sqrt{21}$ ***[1 mark]***
$\overrightarrow{SQ}.\overrightarrow{SR} = p[(-2 \times 1) + (6 \times 2) + (-5 \times -4)] = 30p$ ***[1 mark]***
Use the formula to calculate the angle QSR:
$\cos^{-1}\left(\frac{\overrightarrow{SQ}.\overrightarrow{SR}}{|\overrightarrow{SQ}||\overrightarrow{SR}|}\right) = \cos^{-1}\left(\frac{30p}{p\sqrt{65}\sqrt{21}}\right)$ ***[1 mark]***
$= \cos^{-1}\left(\frac{30}{\sqrt{65}\sqrt{21}}\right) = 35.7$ (1 d.p.) ***[1 mark]***

4 $\mathbf{p}.(\mathbf{q} + \mathbf{r}) = \mathbf{p}.\mathbf{q} + \mathbf{p}.\mathbf{r}$ by the distributive law.
$\mathbf{p}$ and $\mathbf{r}$ are perpendicular, so $\mathbf{p}.\mathbf{r} = 0$ ***[1 mark]***.
$\mathbf{p}.\mathbf{q} = \cos\theta\,|\mathbf{p}|\,|\mathbf{q}| = 0.5 \times 1 \times 1 = 0.5$ ***[1 mark]***
$\Rightarrow \mathbf{p}.(\mathbf{q} + \mathbf{r}) = \mathbf{p}.\mathbf{q} + \mathbf{p}.\mathbf{r} = 0.5 + 0 = 0.5$ ***[1 mark]***

Page 54 — Revision Summary

1 a) (i) $y = 4x + 31$ (ii) $4x - y + 31 = 0$
b) (i) $y = -6x + \frac{39}{2}$ (ii) $12x + 2y - 39 = 0$
c) (i) $y = -\frac{1}{2}x + \frac{29}{8}$ (ii) $4x + 8y - 29 = 0$

2 $y = 7x - 2$

3 $m_{AB} = \frac{-7-(-3)}{1-(-2)} = -\frac{4}{3}$, $m_{BC} = \frac{-3-1}{-2-(-5)} = -\frac{4}{3}$. AB and BC have the same gradient and both go through B, so A, B and C are collinear.

4 a) $y = \frac{1}{5}x - 3$ or $x - 5y - 15 = 0$
b) $\theta = 0.197$ (3 s.f.)

5 a) Altitude — a line from a vertex of a triangle that is perpendicular to the opposite side
b) Median — a line from a vertex of a triangle that intersects the opposite side at its midpoint
c) Perpendicular bisector — a line perpendicular to the midpoint of a side of a triangle

6 a) $x^2 + y^2 - 2x + 6y - 7 = 0$, radius $= \sqrt{17}$ and centre $(1, -3)$
b) $(x - 3)^2 + (y + 5)^2 = 12$, radius $= \sqrt{12} = 2\sqrt{3}$ and centre $(3, -5)$

7 $y = 2x + 19$

8 $(x + 3)^2 + (y - 1)^2 = 100$

9 $(x + 2)^2 + (y - 1)^2 = 16$

10 (0, –3), (1, 0) and (5, 12)

11 (3, –5) and (4, –2)

12 The line is a tangent to the circle.

13 Substituting $y = 8 - x$ into the circle equation and simplifying gives:
$2x^2 + 4x + 2 = 0 \Rightarrow 2(x + 1)(x + 1) = 0$
So $x = -1$ is the only solution. This means the line and circle intersect at only one point, so $y = 8 - x$ is a tangent.

14 $\overrightarrow{BC} = \overrightarrow{BA} + \overrightarrow{AE} + \overrightarrow{ED} + \overrightarrow{DC} = -\mathbf{s} + \mathbf{t} + \mathbf{u} - \mathbf{v}$

15 a) $\begin{pmatrix} 2 \\ 6 \\ -3 \end{pmatrix}$ b) (10, 8, –7)
c) $14\mathbf{i} + 9\mathbf{j} - 9\mathbf{k}$ d) $\sqrt{21}$

16 The vectors are parallel because $\mathbf{u}$ is a scalar multiple of $\mathbf{v}$ ($\mathbf{u} = -3\mathbf{v}$).

17 $\frac{2}{11}\mathbf{i} + \frac{6}{11}\mathbf{j} + \frac{9}{11}\mathbf{k}$

18 a) $p = 2$
b) 14.97 (2 d.p.)

19 10

20 $t = 0$

21 a) (i) 0° (ii) 180° (iii) 90° (iv) 90°
b) 163.4°

Answers

Section Four — Calculus Skills

Page 56 — Differentiation

Warm-Up Questions

1 a) $\frac{dy}{dx} = 2x$ b) $\frac{dy}{dx} = 4x^3 + \frac{1}{2\sqrt{x}}$

c) $\frac{dy}{dx} = -\frac{14}{x^3} + \frac{3}{2\sqrt{x^3}} + 36x^2$

2 $\frac{dy}{dx} = -16$

3 $y = 3x - 42$

Exam Questions

1 Rewrite the expression as $x^{-1} + 2x^{\frac{3}{2}}$ ***[1 mark]***

Differentiate to get $\frac{dy}{dx} = -x^{-2} + 3x^{\frac{1}{2}}$ ***[1 mark for each correct term]***

Putting $x = 4$ into the derivative gives:

$\frac{dy}{dx} = -4^{-2} + 3(4)^{\frac{1}{2}} = -\frac{1}{16} + 6 = \frac{95}{16}$ ***[1 mark]***

2 Simplify the fraction first: $y = 2x^3 - 5$

Find the y-coordinate at $x = 2$: $y = 2(2)^3 - 5 = 11$ ***[1 mark]***

Differentiate the equation to get $\frac{dy}{dx} = 6x^2$ ***[1 mark]***

Put $x = 2$ into the derivative to find gradient: $6 \times 2^2 = 24$ ***[1 mark]***

Use $y - b = m(x - a)$ to find the equation of the tangent:

$y - 11 = 24(x - 2) \Rightarrow y = 24x - 37$ ***[1 mark]***

3 a) Find the y-coordinate at $x = -1$:

$y = (-1)^3 - (4 \times -1) + 2 = 5$ ***[1 mark]***

Differentiate the equation to get $\frac{dy}{dx} = 3x^2 - 4$ ***[1 mark]***

Find the gradient at $x = -1$: $\frac{dy}{dx} = 3(-1)^2 - 4 = -1$ ***[1 mark]***

Use $y - b = m(x - a)$ to find the equation of the tangent:

$y - 5 = -1(x - (-1)) \Rightarrow y = 4 - x$ ***[1 mark]***

b) Set the equation of the tangent equal to the equation of the curve and rearrange:

$x^3 - 4x + 2 = 4 - x \Rightarrow x^3 - 3x - 2 = 0$ ***[1 mark]***

Factorise the equation: $(x + 1)$ is a factor since $x = -1$ is a solution. Then use this to find the rest of the factorisation:

$(x + 1)^2(x - 2) = 0$ ***[1 mark]***

Other point is at $x = 2$ ***[1 mark]*** so find y at this point:

$y = 4 - 2 = 2$, so B is (2, 2) ***[1 mark]***.

Page 59 — Stationary Points

Warm-Up Questions

1 $x = 3$ — minimum, $x = -\frac{5}{3}$ — maximum

2 a) Increasing when $x > 0.5$, decreasing when $x < 0.5$

b) Increasing when $x < -\frac{4}{3}$ and $x > 0$, decreasing when $-\frac{4}{3} < x < 0$

3

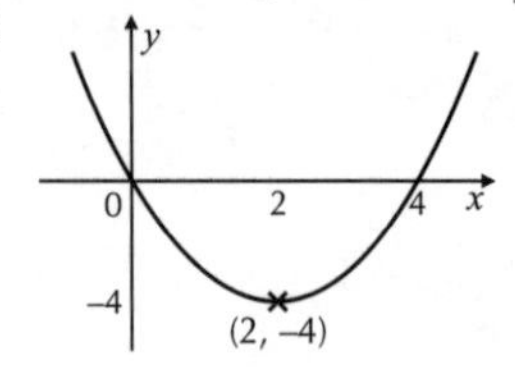

Exam Questions

1 Differentiate f(x): $f'(x) = -7 - 6x^2$ ***[1 mark for both correct terms]***

Since $x^2 > 0$ for all x, $-6x^2$ is always negative, so $f'(x) = -7 - 6x^2 < 0$ for all x ***[1 mark]***. If the gradient is negative for all x, the function is strictly decreasing ***[1 mark]***.

2 a) Differentiate f(x) and set equal to zero:

$f'(x) = 3x^2 + 8x - 3 = 0$ ***[2 marks for fully correct derivative, otherwise 1 mark for one or two terms correct]***

Factorise the derivative: $(x + 3)(3x - 1) = 0$ ***[1 mark]***

So there are stationary points at $x = -3$ and $x = \frac{1}{3}$. ***[1 mark]***

$f(-3) = 20$ and $f\left(\frac{1}{3}\right) = \frac{40}{27}$ so the stationary points are $(-3, 20)$ and $\left(\frac{1}{3}, \frac{40}{27}\right)$. ***[1 mark]***

b) E.g. use a nature table:

x	–4	–3	0	$\frac{1}{3}$	1
$f'(x)$	13	0	–3	0	8
slope	/	—	\	—	/

[1 mark]

From this, you can state that $x = -3$ is a maximum ***[1 mark]*** and $x = \frac{1}{3}$ is a minimum. ***[1 mark]***

Alternatively, you can differentiate again and look at the second derivative.

c) The curve of $f'(x)$ crosses the x-axis at the stationary points of $f(x)$, i.e. at $x = -3$ and $x = \frac{1}{3}$. $f'(x)$ is positive when $x < -3$ and $x > \frac{1}{3}$, and is negative when $-3 < x < \frac{1}{3}$.

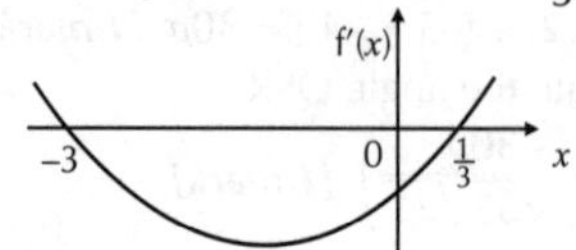

[2 marks available — 2 marks for a fully correct graph with both x-intercepts marked, otherwise 1 mark for any curve that crosses the x-axis at –3 and $\frac{1}{3}$ only]

Page 60 — Chain Rule

Warm-Up Question

1 a) $\frac{dy}{dx} = 36(3x - 7)^{11}$ b) $\frac{dy}{dx} = \frac{2x}{\sqrt{2x^2 + 6}}$

c) $\frac{dy}{dx} = \frac{2 - 9x^2}{2(3x^3 - 2x)^{\frac{3}{2}}}$

Exam Questions

1 a) Write y in terms of powers of x: $y = (x^2 - 8x)^{\frac{1}{2}}$

Now set $u = x^2 - 8x$, so $\frac{du}{dx} = 2x - 8$, and $y = u^{\frac{1}{2}}$ so $\frac{dy}{du} = \frac{1}{2}u^{-\frac{1}{2}}$

Using the chain rule: $\frac{dy}{dx} = \frac{dy}{du} \times \frac{du}{dx}$

$= \frac{1}{2}(x^2 - 8x)^{-\frac{1}{2}} \times (2x - 8) = \frac{x - 4}{\sqrt{x^2 - 8x}}$

[3 marks available — 1 mark for writing y in a differentiable form, 1 mark for attempting to use the chain rule with $u = x^2 - 8x$, 1 mark for the correct answer]

b) Put $x = -1$ into the derivative to find the gradient at this point:

$\frac{dy}{dx} = \frac{(-1) - 4}{\sqrt{(-1)^2 - 8(-1)}} = -\frac{5}{3}$ ***[1 mark]***

Use $y - b = m(x - a)$ to find the equation of the tangent:

$y - 3 = -\frac{5}{3}(x - (-1)) \Rightarrow y = \frac{4 - 5x}{3}$ ***[1 mark]***

Answers

2 Rewrite the equation as $f(x) = 2(x^3 - 5x)^{-\frac{1}{2}}$

Set $u = x^3 - 5x$, so $\frac{du}{dx} = 3x^2 - 5$, and $y = 2u^{-\frac{1}{2}}$, so $\frac{dy}{du} = -u^{-\frac{3}{2}}$

Apply the chain rule: $= \frac{dy}{dx} = \frac{dy}{du} \times \frac{du}{dx}$

$= -(x^3 - 5x)^{-\frac{3}{2}} \times (3x^2 - 5) = \frac{(5 - 3x^2)}{(x^3 - 5x)^{\frac{3}{2}}}$

Evaluate $f'(x)$ at $x = -1$: $f'(-1) = \frac{(5 - 3(-1)^2)}{((-1)^3 - 5(-1))^{\frac{3}{2}}} = \frac{2}{8} = \frac{1}{4}$

[4 marks available — 1 mark for writing y in a differentiable form, 1 mark for attempting to use the chain rule with u = $x^3 - 5x$, 1 mark for a fully correct expression for the derivative, 1 mark for correctly evaluating at x = –1]

Page 61 — Differentiating sin and cos

Warm-Up Question

1 a) $8 \cos 4x$ b) $-6 \sin 3x$ c) $-3x^2 \sin x^3$

Exam Question

1 a) Use the sin double angle formula to rewrite the left-hand side as $\frac{2 \sin x \cos x}{2 \sin x} - \cos x \sin^2 x$. ***[1 mark]***

Cancel the 2 sin *x* from the fraction, and factorise out cos *x*: $\cos x\,(1 - \sin^2 x)$. ***[1 mark]***

Then use the trig identity $\cos^2 x + \sin^2 x \equiv 1$ to get $\cos x\,(\cos^2 x) \equiv \cos^3 x$. ***[1 mark]***

b) From part a), $\frac{d}{dx}\left(\frac{\sin 2x}{2 \sin x} - \cos x \sin^2 x\right) = \frac{d}{dx}(\cos^3 x)$.

Differentiate $\cos^3 x$ using the chain rule:

$u = \cos x$ so $\frac{du}{dx} = -\sin x$, and $y = u^3$ so $\frac{dy}{du} = 3u^2$.

$\frac{dy}{dx} = \frac{dy}{du} \times \frac{du}{dx} = 3(\cos x)^2 \times -\sin x = -3 \cos^2 x \sin x$

[3 marks available — 1 mark for identifying u, 1 mark for using the chain rule, 1 mark for the correct answer]

Page 63 — Using Differentiation

Warm-Up Questions

1 Greatest value is $\frac{1}{9}$ and least value is –36.

2 $m = 53.3$ g (3 s.f.), $h_{max} = 94.8$ m (3 s.f.)

Exam Questions

1 a) Expand the brackets to get the function in a differentiable form: $y = 2x^3 + 5x^2 - 4x - 3$ ***[1 mark]***

Differentiate each term to get $\frac{dy}{dx} = 6x^2 + 10x - 4$

[1 mark for differentiating the first term, 1 mark for differentiating the rest]

b) Find the stationary points of *y*:

$6x^2 + 10x - 4 = 0 \Rightarrow 2(3x - 1)(x + 2) = 0$

$\Rightarrow$ stationary points are at $x = -2$ and $x = \frac{1}{3}$ ***[1 mark]***

$x = \frac{1}{3}$ is outside the interval, so just find value of *y* at $x = -2$:

$y = (2 \times -2 + 1) \times (-2 + 3) \times (-2 - 1) = -3 \times 1 \times -3 = 9$ ***[1 mark]***

Find the value of *y* at the ends of the interval:

At $x = -1$, $y = (2 \times -1 + 1) \times (-1 + 3) \times (-1 - 1) = -1 \times 2 \times -2 = 4$.

At $x = -3$, $y = 0$. ***[1 mark for both correct y-values]***

The greatest value on the interval is 9 and the least is 0. ***[1 mark]***

2 a) Find the value of *x* that gives the minimum value of *y*, i.e. the stationary point of curve *y*, by differentiating and solving $\frac{dy}{dx} = 0$: $\frac{dy}{dx} = \frac{1}{\sqrt{x}} - \frac{27}{x^2}$ ***[1 mark]***

$\frac{dy}{dx} = 0 \Rightarrow \frac{1}{\sqrt{x}} - \frac{27}{x^2} = 0 \Rightarrow \frac{1}{\sqrt{x}} = \frac{27}{x^2} \Rightarrow x^{\frac{3}{2}} = 27$ ***[1 mark]***

$\Rightarrow x = 9$ is a stationary point ***[1 mark]***

Use a nature table to show $x = 9$ is the minimum:

x	8	9	10
$\frac{dy}{dx}$	–0.0683...	0	0.0462...
slope	\	—	/

[1 mark for a correct method, 1 mark for showing the point is a minimum]

So $x = 9$ is a minimum, so the speed that gives the minimum coal consumption is 9 mph.

You could also find the second derivative at x = 9 and show it is positive.

b) $y = 2\sqrt{9} + \frac{27}{9} = 9$ units of coal ***[1 mark]***

3 a) Surface area $= 2(d \times x) + 2\left(d \times \frac{x}{2}\right) + \left(x \times \frac{x}{2}\right)$

$= 2dx + dx + \frac{x^2}{2} = 3dx + \frac{x^2}{2}$ ***[1 mark]***

Surface area $= 72 \Rightarrow 3dx + \frac{x^2}{2} = 72$

$\Rightarrow x^2 + 6dx = 144$ ***[1 mark]*** $\Rightarrow d = \frac{144 - x^2}{6x}$ ***[1 mark]***

Volume = width × height × depth $= \frac{x}{2} \times x \times d$

$V = \frac{x^2}{2} \times \frac{144 - x^2}{6x} = \frac{144x^2 - x^4}{12x} = 12x - \frac{x^3}{12}$ as required ***[1 mark]***

b) Differentiate *V* and then solve $\frac{dV}{dx} = 0$: $\frac{dV}{dx} = 12 - \frac{x^2}{4}$ ***[1 mark]***

$12 - \frac{x^2}{4} = 0 \Rightarrow \frac{x^2}{4} = 12 \Rightarrow x^2 = 48$ ***[1 mark]***

$\Rightarrow x = \sqrt{48} = 4\sqrt{3}$ ***[1 mark]***

c) $4\sqrt{3} = 6.928...$, so using a nature table:

x	6	$4\sqrt{3}$	7
$\frac{dV}{dx}$	3	0	–0.25
slope	/	—	\

$x = 4\sqrt{3}$ at V_{max}, so $V_{max} = (12 \times 4\sqrt{3}) - \frac{(4\sqrt{3})^3}{12}$

$V_{max} = 55.4$ m³ (3 s.f.)

[3 marks available — 1 mark for a correct method, 1 mark for showing that the stationary point is a maximum, 1 mark for calculating V_{max}]

Again, you could have found the second derivative here.

Page 65 — Integrating f(x) = x^n

Warm-Up Questions

1 a) $2x^5 + C$ b) $\frac{3x^2}{2} + \frac{5x^3}{3} + C$ c) $\frac{3}{2}x^2 + \frac{7}{x} + C$

2 $y = 3x^2 - 11x + 8$

3 $f(x) = \frac{3x^4}{4} + 2x - \frac{11}{4}$

Exam Questions

1 a) Multiply out the brackets and simplify the terms:

$(5 + 2\sqrt{x})^2 = (5 + 2\sqrt{x})(5 + 2\sqrt{x})$

$= 25 + 10\sqrt{x} + 10\sqrt{x} + 4x = 25 + 20\sqrt{x} + 4x$

So $a = 25$, $b = 20$ and $c = 4$

[3 marks available — 1 mark for each constant]

b) Integrate your answer from a), treating each term separately:

$\int (25 + 20\sqrt{x} + 4x)\,dx = 25x + \left(20x^{\frac{3}{2}} \div \frac{3}{2}\right) + \left(\frac{4x^2}{2}\right) + C$

$= 25x + \frac{40\sqrt{x^3}}{3} + 2x^2 + C$

[3 marks available — 1 mark for each term involving x. Lose 1 mark if C missing or answers not simplified (surds not necessary)]

Don't forget to add C, don't forget to add C, don't forget to add C. Once, twice, thrice I beg of you, because it's very important.

2 a) The tangent at (1, 2) has the same gradient as the curve at that point, so use $f'(x)$ to calculate the gradient: ***[1 mark]***

$f'(1) = \frac{1^5 - 2}{1} = -1$ ***[1 mark]***

Put this into the straight-line equation $y - b = m(x - a)$ ***[1 mark]***

$y - 2 = -1(x - 1) \Rightarrow y = -x + 1 + 2 = -x + 3$ ***[1 mark]***

b) Rewrite $f'(x)$ as $x^3 - \frac{2}{x^2}$ so you can integrate:

$f(x) = \int \left(x^3 - \frac{2}{x^2}\right) dx = \int (x^3 - 2x^{-2})\,dx$ ***[1 mark]***

$= \frac{x^4}{4} - 2\frac{x^{-1}}{-1} + C = \frac{x^4}{4} + 2x^{-1} + C = \frac{x^4}{4} + \frac{2}{x} + C$

[1 mark for increasing power by one and dividing for each term, 1 mark for simplifying fractions]

Now use the coordinates (1, 2) to find the value of C: ***[1 mark]***

$2 = \frac{1^4}{4} + \frac{2}{1} + C \Rightarrow 2 - \frac{1}{4} - 2 = C \Rightarrow C = -\frac{1}{4}$

So $f(x) = \frac{x^4}{4} + \frac{2}{x} - \frac{1}{4}$ ***[1 mark]***

Page 66 — Integrating f(x) = (x + q)ⁿ and (px + q)ⁿ

Warm-Up Questions

1 a) $\frac{1}{5}(x+8)^5 + C$ b) $-\frac{1}{6}(3x-2)^{-2} + C$ c) $-\frac{2}{7}(12-7x)^{\frac{1}{2}} + C$

2 $y = -\frac{1}{10}(7-2x)^5 + C$

Exam Questions

1 Rewrite the function in an integrable form: $\int (4x+3)^{-\frac{1}{3}}\,dx$ ***[1 mark]***

Integrate the function: $\frac{1}{4\times\frac{2}{3}}(4x+3)^{\frac{2}{3}} + C = \frac{1}{\left(\frac{8}{3}\right)}(4x+3)^{\frac{2}{3}} + C$

[1 mark for starting to integrate by increasing power and dividing by new power, 1 mark for completing integration]

Simplify to get: $\frac{3}{8}(4x+3)^{\frac{2}{3}} + C$ ***[1 mark]***

2 Integrate $\frac{dy}{dx}$ to find an expression for y: $y = \frac{1}{4\times -5}(2-5x)^4 + C$

Put the given coordinate (1, –6) into this equation:

$-6 = -\frac{1}{20}(2-5)^4 + C = -\frac{81}{20} + C \Rightarrow C = -\frac{39}{20}$

so $y = -\frac{1}{20}(2-5x)^4 - \frac{39}{20}$

[4 marks available — 1 mark for starting to integrate by increasing power and dividing by new power, 1 mark for completing integration, 1 mark for using the coordinates to find C, 1 mark for the correct answer]

Page 68 — Integrating sin and cos

Warm-Up Questions

1 a) $2\sin 3x + C$ b) $-\frac{3}{2}\cos(2x + 1) + C$

c) $\frac{2}{3}\sin 6x + \frac{2}{3}\cos(3x + 4) + C$

2 $-\frac{3}{4}\cos 2x + \frac{1}{10}\sin 5x + \frac{x}{2} + C$

Exam Questions

1 Integrate the function:

$\frac{-7}{3} \times \cos(3x-4) = -\frac{7}{3}\cos(3x-4) + C$

[1 mark for integrating the trig function, 1 mark for dividing by the coefficient of x]

2 a) Use the sin double angle formula and $\cos^2 x + \sin^2 x \equiv 1$ to write: $1 - \cos^2 2x \equiv \sin^2 2x \equiv 4\sin^2 x\cos^2 x$ ***[1 mark]***

Substitute $\cos^2 x \equiv 1 - \sin^2 x$ to get $4\sin^2 x\,(1 - \sin^2 x)$ ***[1 mark]***

Expanding gives $1 - \cos^2 2x \equiv 4\sin^2 x - 4\sin^4 x$ ***[1 mark]***

You could also use the sin version of the cos double angle formula here.

b) Using part a), you can see that:

$\int 8\sin^4 x - 8\sin^2 x\,dx \equiv -2\int 1 - \cos^2 2x\,dx$ ***[1 mark]***

To integrate this, use the identity $\cos^2 x \equiv \frac{1}{2}(\cos 2x + 1)$ to write $\cos^2 2x \equiv \frac{1}{2}(\cos 4x + 1)$. ***[1 mark]***

So the integral is $-2\int 1 - \cos^2 2x\,dx = -2\int 1 - \frac{1}{2}(\cos 4x + 1)\,dx$

$= -2\left(x - \frac{1}{2}\left(\frac{1}{4}\sin 4x + x\right)\right) = -x + \frac{1}{4}\sin 4x + C$

[1 mark for integrating the trig function, 1 mark for dividing by the coefficient of x]

3 Integrate the gradient to find $y = -6 \times \frac{1}{4}\cos 4x + C$

$= -\frac{3}{2}\cos 4x + C$

[1 mark for integrating the trig function, 1 mark for dividing by the coefficient of x]

Use the point $(\frac{\pi}{4}, -2)$ to find the constant of integration:

$-2 = -\frac{3}{2}\cos(\pi) + C \Rightarrow -2 = \frac{3}{2} + C \Rightarrow C = -\frac{7}{2}$ ***[1 mark]***

So the equation of the curve is $y = -\frac{3}{2}\cos(4x) - \frac{7}{2}$ ***[1 mark]***

Page 71 — Definite Integrals

Warm-Up Questions

1 a) 4 b) $6\sqrt{2} - \frac{33}{8}$ c) 3

2 36

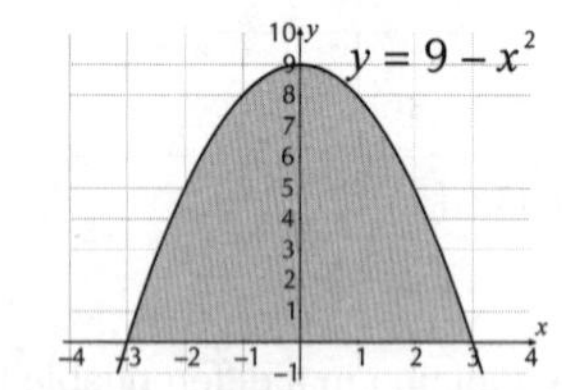

Exam Questions

1 $\int_{\frac{\pi}{2}}^{\pi} 5\cos\left(\frac{1}{2}x + \frac{\pi}{4}\right) dx = 10\left[\sin\left(\frac{1}{2}x + \frac{\pi}{4}\right)\right]_{\frac{\pi}{2}}^{\pi}$

$= 10\left(\sin\frac{3\pi}{4} - \sin\frac{\pi}{2}\right)$

$= 10\left(\frac{\sqrt{2}}{2} - 1\right) = 5(\sqrt{2} - 2)$

[4 marks available — 1 mark for integrating cos x to sin x, 1 mark for dividing by the coefficient of x, 1 mark for substituting limits correctly, 1 mark for final answer]

Answers

2 The limits are the x-values when $y = 0$, so first solve:
$(x - 3)^2(x + 1) = 0$ ***[1 mark]***
$x = 3$ and $x = -1$ ***[1 mark for both values correct]***
Hence, to find the area, calculate:
$\int_{-1}^{3}(x - 3)^2(x + 1)\,dx$ ***[1 mark]*** $= \int_{-1}^{3}(x^3 - 5x^2 + 3x + 9)\,dx$
$= \left[\frac{x^4}{4} - \frac{5}{3}x^3 + \frac{3}{2}x^2 + 9x\right]_{-1}^{3}$ ***[1 mark]***
$= \left(\frac{3^4}{4} - \frac{5}{3}3^3 + \frac{3}{2}3^2 + (9 \times 3)\right) - \left(\frac{(-1)^4}{4} - \left(\frac{5}{3} \times (-1)^3\right) + \left(\frac{3}{2} \times (-1)^2\right) + (9 \times (-1))\right)$ ***[1 mark]***
$= 15\frac{3}{4} - \left(-5\frac{7}{12}\right) = 21\frac{1}{3}$ units^2 ***[1 mark]***

3 a) $m = \frac{y_2 - y_1}{x_2 - x_1} = \frac{0 - (-5)}{(-1) - 4} = -1$ ***[1 mark]***
$y - b = m(x - a)$
$y - (-5) = -1(x - 4) \Rightarrow y + 5 = 4 - x \Rightarrow y = -x - 1$ ***[1 mark]***

b) The shaded area lies between the curve and the line, so first expand the brackets to get the equation for the curve and subtract the equation of the line:
$(x^2 - 4x - 5) - (-x - 1) = x^2 - 3x - 4$ ***[1 mark]***
Now integrate this between the limits to find the shaded area:
$\int_{-1}^{4} x^2 - 3x - 4\,dx = \left[\frac{1}{3}x^3 - \frac{3}{2}x^2 - 4x\right]_{-1}^{4}$
$= \left(\frac{64}{3} - 24 - 16\right) - \left(-\frac{1}{3} - \frac{3}{2} + 4\right) = -\frac{125}{6}$
So the shaded area is $\frac{125}{6}$ units^2.
[5 marks available — 1 mark for subtracting the equations, 1 mark for attempting to integrate with the correct limits, 1 mark for a correct integration, 1 mark for substituting limits, 1 mark for the correct area]

Page 73 — Rates of Change

Warm-Up Questions

1 $\frac{dy}{dx} = -5\sin x - 9\cos(3x - 1)$

2 $v = t^3 - \frac{8}{3}t^{\frac{3}{2}} + 2t + 6$

Exam Questions

1 Call $y = f(x)$.
Then using the chain rule with $u = \cos 2x \Rightarrow \frac{du}{dx} = -2\sin 2x$
$y = 4u^2 \Rightarrow \frac{dy}{du} = 8u$
$\frac{dy}{dx} = \frac{dy}{du} \times \frac{du}{dx} = 8\cos 2x \times -2\sin 2x = -16\sin 2x\cos 2x$
Evaluating at $x = \frac{\pi}{8}$ gives:
$-16\sin\frac{2\pi}{8}\cos\frac{2\pi}{8} = -16 \times \frac{1}{\sqrt{2}} \times \frac{1}{\sqrt{2}} = -8$
[3 marks available —1 mark for attempting to use the chain rule with u = cos 2x, 1 mark for the correct derivative, 1 mark for evaluating correctly]

2 Find a general expression for P by integrating:
$P = \frac{a}{2}t^2 - 6t^{\frac{1}{2}} + C$
[1 mark for integrating either term correctly, 1 mark for completely correct integration]
When $t = 0$, $P = \frac{a}{2} \times 0 - 6 \times 0 + C = 500 \Rightarrow C = 500$ ***[1 mark]***
When $t = 9$, $P = 158$:
$158 = \frac{a}{2}(81) - 6(3) + 500 \Rightarrow \frac{a}{2}(81) = -324 \Rightarrow a = -8$ ***[1 mark]***
So $P = -4t^2 - 6t^{\frac{1}{2}} + 500$ ***[1 mark]***

3 a) Integrate the expression for acceleration: $v = 8t - t^2 + C$
[1 mark for integrating either term correctly, 1 mark for completely correct integration]

b) $v = 4$ when $t = 1$, so:
$4 = 8 \times 1 - 1^2 + C \Rightarrow 4 = 7 + C \Rightarrow C = -3$ ***[1 mark]***
Now you can use $v = 8t - t^2 - 3$ to find v when $t = 6$:
$v(6) = (8 \times 6) - 6^2 - 3 = 9$ m/s ***[1 mark]***

c) (i) Integrate the equation for velocity to get an equation for displacement, s: $s(t) = 4t^2 - \frac{1}{3}t^3 - 3t + K$
[1 mark for integrating either term correctly, 1 mark for completely correct integration]

(ii) You want to find the displacement from the initial position, so at time $t = 0$, displacement $s = 0 \Rightarrow K = 0$ ***[1 mark]***
$s(3) = (4 \times 3^2) - (\frac{1}{3} \times 3^3) - (3 \times 3)$
$= 36 - 9 - 9 = 18$ m ***[1 mark]***

Pages 74-75 — Revision Summary

1 a) $2x - 7$ b) $4 + \frac{9}{2x^{\frac{5}{2}}}$

2 The gradient of the tangent to a curve at a given point is equal to the gradient of the curve at that point — for a curve y, the gradient is equal to $\frac{dy}{dx}$ evaluated at the given point.

3 $y = 20x - 10$

4 a) A stationary point is a point on a curve where the gradient is zero.
b) A stationary point can be a maximum, a minimum or a point of inflexion.
c) You can use a nature table — evaluate the gradient of the function at two points either side of (but close to) the stationary point, then use their slopes to determine if the stationary point is a maximum, a minimum or a point of inflexion.
You could also find the second derivative of the curve and show that it is either negative (maximum) or positive (minimum) at the stationary point.

5 a) (1, −1)
b) Minimum

6 E.g.

x	1	$\sqrt{3}$	2
$\frac{dy}{dx}$	−8	0	8
slope	\	—	/

The gradient is negative to the left of the stationary point and positive to the right, so $\sqrt{3}$ is a minimum.
You might have used other values either side of $\sqrt{3}$ to show it's a minimum, but they should be close to $\sqrt{3}$ since y has other stationary points.

7 a) Increasing when $x < -3$ or $x > \frac{5}{3}$, decreasing when $-3 < x < \frac{5}{3}$
b)
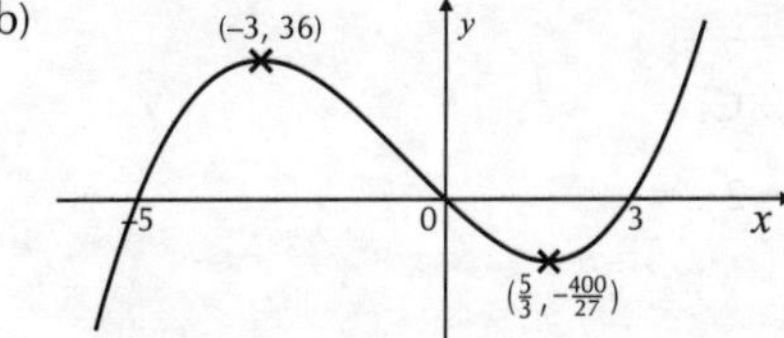

8
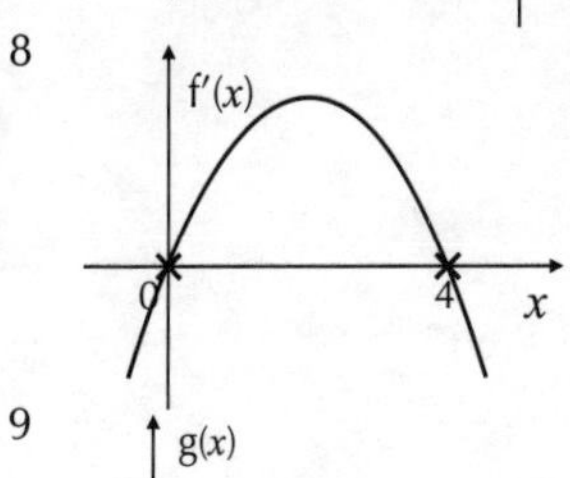

9
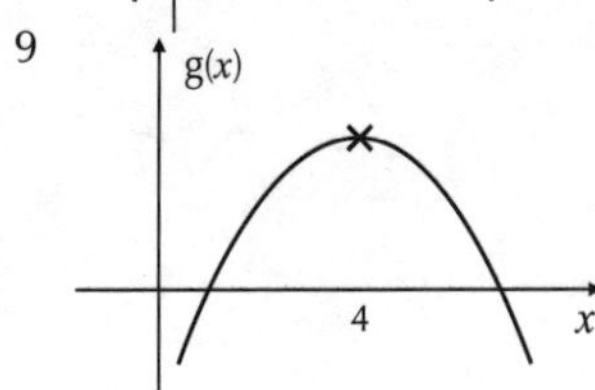

Answers

10 a) $20(5x + 2)^3$ b) $-48(7 - 4x)^{11}$

11 a) $-24 \sin 6x$ b) $-\cos \frac{1}{2}x$

12 −1

13 $\frac{dy}{dx} = \cos 2x$

14 Least value is 4, greatest value is 24

15 $x = y = \sqrt{18} = 3\sqrt{2}$

Since x = y, the shape with the smallest perimeter is actually a square.

16 a) Surface area A = $(2 \times x \times \frac{x}{4}) + (2 \times x \times d) + (2 \times d \times \frac{x}{4})$

Volume = $250 = \frac{x}{4} \times x \times d \Rightarrow x^2 d = 1000 \Rightarrow d = \frac{1000}{x^2}$

So the surface area A is

$$\frac{x^2}{2} + 2x\left(\frac{1000}{x^2}\right) + \frac{x}{2}\left(\frac{1000}{x^2}\right) = \frac{x^2}{2} + \frac{2000}{x} + \frac{500}{x} = \frac{x^2}{2} + \frac{2500}{x}$$

b) $x = \sqrt[3]{2500} = 13.6$ cm (3 s.f.)

17 There's more than one right answer when you integrate a function — you need the constant of integration to allow for the infinitely many possible solutions.

When you differentiate to get back to the original function, the constant disappears because the derivative of a constant is 0.

18 a) $2x^3 + 4x + C$ b) $-\frac{1}{x} - \frac{3}{2}x^2 + C$ c) $-\frac{1}{8}(4x - 2)^{-2} + C$

19 $y = x^3 - 2x + 4$

20 a) $\frac{2}{3} \sin \frac{3}{2}x + C$ b) $-\frac{3}{4} \cos 4x + C$ c) $-\frac{5}{2} \sin (1 - 2x) + C$

21 $y = \sin (3x - \frac{\pi}{2}) + 3 \cos 2x - 4$

22 a) $\frac{1}{2} \sin 2x + C$ b) $\frac{x}{2} - \frac{1}{12} \sin 6x + C$

23 A definite integral has limits but an indefinite integral doesn't.

24 Geometrically, the integral $\int_a^b f(x)\,dx$ represents the area under the curve f(x) between the limits $x = a$ and $x = b$.

25 a) $\frac{1}{4}$ b) $\frac{103}{6}$

26 a) 2 b) $\pi - 12$

27 $\frac{45}{8}$

28 $\frac{1}{6}$

29 $\frac{56}{3}$

30 $-\frac{2}{t^{\frac{5}{2}}}$

31 0

32 a) $x = 2t^{\frac{5}{2}} - \frac{4}{3}t^{\frac{3}{2}} + 2t^{\frac{1}{2}} + C$

b) $x = 2t^{\frac{5}{2}} - \frac{4}{3}t^{\frac{3}{2}} + 2t^{\frac{1}{2}} - 2$

33 $A = t^4 - 7t + 4$

34 a) 8

b) $s(t) = t^3 - 2t^2 + 3t + 3$

35 30

Section Five — Reasoning Skills

Page 77 — Reasoning Skills

Exam Questions

1 The car is driving uphill when its height above sea level (given by y) is increasing. This is the case when the derivative is greater than 0:

$\frac{dy}{dx} = -12x^2 + 20x - 7 > 0$

$-12x^2 + 20x - 7 = 0 \Rightarrow x = \frac{-20 \pm \sqrt{20^2 - 4 \times -12 \times -7}}{2 \times -12} = \frac{1}{2}$ or $\frac{7}{6}$

The coefficient of x^2 is negative, so the graph of the quadratic is n-shaped. This means the quadratic is positive for $\frac{1}{2} < x < \frac{7}{6}$.

So the car is travelling uphill when it has travelled between $\frac{1}{2}$ mile and $\frac{7}{6}$ miles, i.e. for $\frac{7}{6} - \frac{1}{2} = \frac{2}{3}$ of a mile.

[5 marks available — 1 mark for differentiating one term correctly, 1 mark for the fully correct derivative, 1 mark for finding both roots of the derivative, 1 mark for determining the range of x-values for y is increasing, 1 mark for the correct final answer]

2 Two segments have equal area if the chord that separates them is a diameter. This means that if the line $y = mx + 2$ passes through the centre of the circle, then $A_1 = A_2$. The coordinates of the centre, O, of the circle are (1, 1) (since $g = f = -1$ in the standard notation of the equation of the circle), so the line passes through the centre if $1 = m \times 1 + 2 \Rightarrow m = -1$. This is shown below.

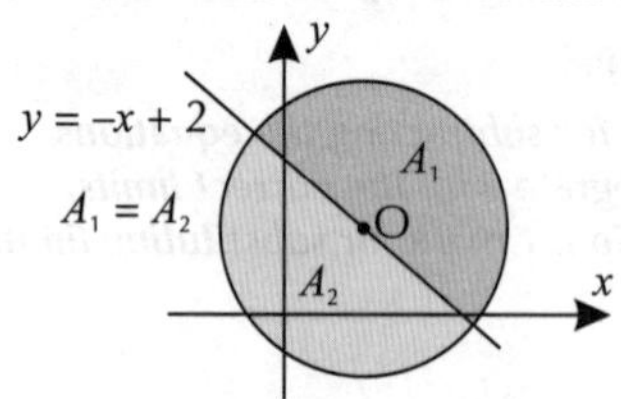

For $A_1 > A_2$, the area A_1 must include O, so the line must pass below O. Its intercept is fixed at $y = 2$, so the only way for this to happen is for it to have a steeper negative gradient, i.e. $m < -1$.

[4 marks available — 1 mark for using the correct centre of the circle, 1 mark for attempting to find m such that the line passes through the centre, 1 mark for attempting to adjust the equation of the line so that $A_1 > A_2$, 1 mark for stating that the required range is $m < -1$]

Index

Formula Sheet

Revising for your Higher exams is tricky enough, without having to worry about learning more formulas than you absolutely need to. Luckily, this page shows you all the ones that you'll be given at the front of your exam papers. Make sure you know what each of them means and how to use them.

Circles

$x^2 + y^2 + 2gx + 2fy + c = 0$ represents a circle with centre $(-g, -f)$ and radius $\sqrt{g^2 + f^2 - c}$

$(x - a)^2 + (y - b)^2 = r^2$ represents a circle with centre (a, b) and radius r

The Scalar Product

$\mathbf{a}.\mathbf{b} = |\mathbf{a}|\,|\mathbf{b}| \cos\theta$, where θ is the angle between vectors **a** and **b**

or $\mathbf{a}.\mathbf{b} = a_1b_1 + a_2b_2 + a_3b_3$, where $\mathbf{a} = \begin{pmatrix} a_1 \\ a_2 \\ a_3 \end{pmatrix}$ and $\mathbf{b} = \begin{pmatrix} b_1 \\ b_2 \\ b_3 \end{pmatrix}$

Trig Formulas

$\sin(A \pm B) = \sin A \cos B \pm \cos A \sin B$

$\cos(A \pm B) = \cos A \cos B \mp \sin A \sin B$

$\sin 2A = 2 \sin A \cos A$

$\cos 2A = \cos^2 A - \sin^2 A$
$= 2\cos^2 A - 1$
$= 1 - 2\sin^2 A$

Standard Trig Derivatives

$f(x)$	$f'(x)$
$\sin ax$	$a \cos ax$
$\cos ax$	$-a \sin ax$

Standard Trig Integrals

$f(x)$	$\int f(x)\,dx$
$\sin ax$	$-\frac{1}{a}\cos ax + C$
$\cos ax$	$\frac{1}{a}\sin ax + C$

MZR51